STRUCTURE AND FUNCTION
OF
ELASTIN AND COLLAGEN

STRUCTURE AND FUNCTION
OF
ELASTIN AND COLLAGEN

by

ILONA BANGA D. Sc. (Biol.)

Associate Professor at the First Institute of Pathological Anatomy and Experimental Cancer Research, Medical University, Budapest

AKADÉMIAI KIADÓ · BUDAPEST 1966

Manuscript revised by

GY. ROMHÁNYI M.D.
Professor of Pathological Anatomy
Medical University, Pécs

and

M. NÉMETH-CSÓKA M.D.
Reader at the First Surgical Clinic
Medical University, Pécs

Translated by

E. FARKAS M.D.

Foreword

THE PATHOLOGIST encounters several problems of medical science in his daily work. They may be solved by investigations through light- or electron microscopy, by the study of aetiological factors and by animal experiments.

In every human generation some branch of science reaches a higher level than others and this has an immediate effect upon other fields of knowledge.

I, personally, was convinced even at the very beginning of my career that the cultivation of pathological anatomy on a purely morphological basis can bring about only partial results. In view of the great results in biochemistry I foresaw that the conjunction of morphological investigations with chemical research afforded great perspectives. Through histochemistry chemical information is obtained with regard to the structure of tissues and this has already led to numerous valuable achievements. However, one person is hardly able to master several domains of science. Therefore, in the interest of the development of our biological and medical science the most appropriate method is the collaboration of people of different professional training. These considerations led me to instal a sub-department of chemistry in the institute under my direction. At my former working place, the Department of Pathological Anatomy of the University of Szeged, I equipped a chemical laboratory 30 years ago, but the research work carried out in common with a high-ranking biochemist could only be realized in 1946, when in my Department in Budapest Dr. Ilona Banga took over the duties of chief of the Sub-department of Biochemistry.

This book contains the results obtained together with Dr. Banga at our Department. In obtaining these valuable results the exceptional talent and invention, great professional skill and untiring perseverance of Dr. Banga were factors which cannot be too highly valued and appreciated.

Budapest, 1965

Prof. J. Baló

Director of the First Institute of
Pathological Anatomy and Cancer
Research, Medical University,
Budapest

PREFACE

THE OBJECT of this book is to throw light on the interrelations among the molecular-chemical and macromolecular-submicroscopic structure and the biological functions of elastin and collagen, the two scleroproteins which build up the wall of animal blood vessels. The reticular fibres are not dealt with, for these are still indistinguishable from the collagen fibres on the grounds of the above character-istics. Furthermore, in this work an attempt is made to synthesize the classic and modern morphological observations with the results of biochemical analyses and the properties of the fibre as a physical unit. The full accomplishment of this programme, however, conflicted with our other intention, viz. in this book we wished to summarize the research on connective tissue that has been proceeding in our Institute (First Institute of Pathological Anatomy and Experimental Can-cer Research, Medical University, Budapest) since 1947. The research was first focused on the elastase, subsequently on the elastolytic enzyme system and has eventually opened the way to clarify the complex nature of elastic and collagen fibres as functional units.

The discovery of elastase is to the credit of Prof. J. Baló who, during his intense studies on arteriosclerosis, postulated the existence of an elastin-specific enzyme. The isolation and separation techniques of modern biochemistry enabled us to prove that not a single enzyme, but an enzyme system is responsible for synthesizing and decomposing connective-tissue fibres. These investigations required a many-sided research programme. Chemical substances being important factors in the complex construction of fibres but released in minute amounts during classical enzymological studies had to be analysed. It was also important to study the mechanism of action of the different elastolytic enzymes. In addition, new methods had to be evolved by which submicroscopic structure, function and chemical processes could be studied as a whole. The relationships between physical changes and enzyme action had to be examined to make the biological changes and the pathology of the vascular wall comprehensible. The review of these investigations and of the corresponding literature reflects the efforts to understand the inter-relations. In fact, this book does not aim at completeness; it can only serve as a compass in facilitating the comprehension of the physiological and pathological conditions of the vascular system for all those who are interested in this problem.

The discovery of elastase compelled us to undertake heavy tasks in order to elucidate the exact biological function of this enzyme. Most of these problems, including the biochemical significance of the elastase enzyme and inhibitor systems, are still unsolved, although schools abroad (Hall, Tunbridge and co-workers in Leeds; Lansing and co-workers in Pittsburgh; Loeven in Leiden; Butturini in Parma and Alexeeva in Moscow, etc.) and we ourselves have uncovered many details. But even the unsolved problem which is closely related to the chemical structure and biological function of elastic and collagen fibres gives a reason for summing up the results and the interrelations in this book.

I should like to express my thanks and gratitude primarily to the Director of this Institute, Prof. J. Baló, who has been my collaborator in this work. Without his wide knowledge, steady work and wise instructions and criticism we should not have succeeded in this field of research. All that I have established as fact has resulted from our mutual work.

As regards the collagen studies, it is to the credit of Dr. D. Szabó that the submicroscopic alterations produced in the structure by chemical and enzymatic effects have been discovered and, also, demonstrated by convincing coloured microphotographs. His indefatigable and precise work has substantially contributed to the material of this book. We are grateful to Prof. G. Romhányi, for his enthusiastic work which soon resulted in new and modern methods for the histochemical study of elastase. His theory on the fine structure of the elastic fibre points the way for further investigation in this field. I am also greatly indebted to Dr. D. Schuller and Dr. J. László for their work and collaboration.

In the large-scale isolation of elastase the assistance of Dr. D. Bagdy deserves gratitude and thanks. His collaboration eliminated certain obstacles to our work. We are also grateful to other collaborators of the Research Institute for Pharmaceutical Industry (Budapest), namely to Dr. J. Borsy and Dr. P. Tolnay who have dealt with the pharmacology of elastase.

In the technical editorship, typing and revision of the manuscript the assistance of my laboratory co-workers has been invaluable.

Budapest, 1965   *Ilona Banga*

Contents

PART TWO

Macromolecular structure of the collagen fibre; submicroscopical, chemical, histochemical and physical evidence of their complex structure

XII

PART ONE

Macromolecular Structure of the Elastic Fibre;
Verification of its Complex Structure
by Histological, Submicroscopical, Histochemical
and Chemical Methods

CHAPTER I

MORPHOLOGICAL AND CHEMICAL INVESTIGATIONS

THEORIES ON THE FORMATION OF ELASTIC FIBRES

THE QUESTION of the formation and destruction of elastic fibres is still under discussion. In this chapter only a few of the corresponding theories are discussed. It is generally assumed that both collagen and elastic fibres are formed by fibroblasts. According to Krompecher's (1928, 1930) experiments, carried out in embryonic tissues, specific cells, elastoblasts, participate in the production of elastic fibres. The elastoblasts secrete an elastic substance in a granular form on their surface. Subsequently the granules become arranged in fibre form and, finally, the elastoblasts are destroyed. Theories suggesting the intercellular formation of the elastic substance have been opposed to this cellular theory. According to the former the mesenchymal network is impregnated by elastin. Hueck (1920) suggested that impregnation with elastin results in the formation of elastic fibres, whereas collagen impregnation of the same network gives rise to collagen fibres. According to Huzella's (1941) theory cells do take part in the production of the fibrous network, but the argyrophile fibres arise from the intercellular substance under the influence of certain lines of force.

Krompecher (1928, 1930) attributed a significance to mechanical factors as soon as he observed the formation of elastic fibres on the surface of elastoblasts in sheep embryo carotids. According to his description the elastic elements formed a circular membrane on the effect of the vascular tension, and the membrane became stronger and stronger at every systole. On the other hand, elastic fibres arose also from primitive pericellular membranes by thickening at the sites of the lines of force, as a result of contraction. Subsequently Krompecher (1940) gave a more exact description of the conditions required for the formation of elastic fibres: "Bei der Arterie scheint die pulsierende Wirkung, eine intermittierende Kraft die auslösende Ursache zu sein, wodurch die wandbildenden Mesenchymzellen — zuerst zirkulär angeordnet — ihrer Längsachse entsprechend gedehnt und nachher etwa auf die ursprüngliche Länge nachgelassen werden. Dieses Zerren, Anziehen scheint hier für die Elasticabildung der spezifische Reiz zu sein." He drew this conclusion from a comparative histogenetical examination of the vascular wall. Krompecher's co-workers, Lelkes and Karmazsin (1955) confirmed the above statements by experimental studies. They examined the *de novo* formed elastic elements in chick embryo heart and aorta-tissue cultures. New elastic elements were demonstrated in every pulsating heart culture irrespective of the embryo's age, whereas in none of the non-pulsating cultures. Formation of elastic elements could not be detected in aorta cultures, except in those having grown together with pulsating heart cultures. In the others, instead of the formation of new elastic elements, disintegration of the pre-existing ones was observed. It is of interest that Lelkes and Karmazsin found the embryonic heart extract described by Törő (1939) necessary for the formation of elastic fibres. This extract contains a special factor, called Corhormone, which activates the growth, and promotes *de novo* formation of cardiac fibroblasts.

MORPHOLOGICAL APPEARANCE

Studies on the elastic tissue have shown that at different sites of the body the elastic fibres differ both chemically and morphologically. Elastic fibres are present in the greatest quantities in elastic arteries (aorta and carotids), in the skin, in the loose connective tissue and in the ligamentum flavum. Among the elastic tissues the nuchal ligament (lig. nuchae) of cattle has been examined most intensively. This tissue contains 84% elastin.

The anatomical appearance of elastins in different tissues is not uniform. Figure 1a and b illustrate the elastic structure of the vascular wall, while Fig. 1c shows the elastic fibres of the lig. nuchae; Fig. 1a is Dees' (1923) drawing showing the structure of elastic lamellae of the vascular wall. In the longitudinal section the elastic elements occur in the form of densely-packed lamellae each containing a dense network of elastic fibres. The lamellae show gaps and windows (lamina fenestrata). The elastic lamellae are composed of two or even three kinds of elastic elements. The first element is a coarse network, in which the thick fibres show branchings. The diameter of the fibres ranges from 2 to 3 μ to the limit of microscopic visibility. The second element appears as a network consisting of very fine fibrils. Both the coarse and the fine fibres are embedded in a special substance termed matrix or cement material. In longitudinal sections of the aorta the membraneous formation of the elastin-containing substance is demonstrable by resorcin stain. The membranes lie over one another, but in appropriate sections their coherency is recognizable (Fig. 1b). Figure 1c shows the structure of elastic fibres in the lig. nuchae. Here the elastic fibres form compact, mat-like fascicles almost uniform in diameter (4 to 5 μ). These fibres, being rich in anastomoses, have no definite length and imitate the picture of heart muscles. Occasionally also branchings occur.

In the skin elastic fibres appear in forms different from the above formations. Coarse fibres resembling those common in the loose connective tissue show free branchings, while other fibres form networks. The latter are very fine fibres, being near to the limit of microscopic visibility (about 0·2 μ dia.).

The fibres in the loose connective tissue vary in diameter (from 1 to 0·2 μ) and show free branching. These cannot be mistaken for the compact, much thicker elastic fibres of the lig. nuchae.

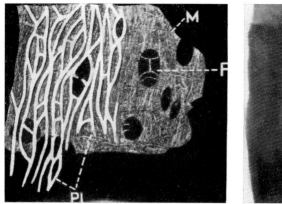

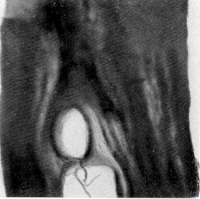

a   b

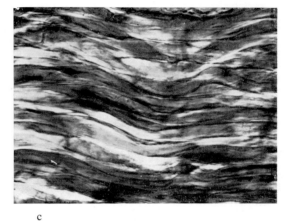

Fig. 1. Elastic structure of the vascular wall (a); (according to Dees' drawing); carotid wall, longitudinal section (b); elastic fibres of the lig. nuchae (c)

c

HISTOLOGICAL STAINING

The morphological diversity of the elastic fibres is also manifested in the histological staining. The elastic fibres give specific reactions with orcein and resorcin-fuchsin, but the shade and intensity of the resulting colour vary in different tissues. It should be noted that even the ground substance of the cartilage shows some affinity to orcein. The differences in staining according to our own experience and the data in the literature are summarized in Table 1.

Dempsey et al. (1952) thoroughly studied the type of the bond between elastic fibres and orcein. The reaction was not influenced by pH, and the authors were able to exclude both ionic and covalent bonds. They attribute the selective staining to weaker forces generating between elastic fibre and the ring structure of the dye molecule.

TABLE 1

Histological reactions of the elastic fibres characteristic of different tissues

Origin of elastic fibres	Histological reactions		
	Orcein or Resorcin-fuchsin	Cresyl violet	After phosphotungstic-acid oxydation with Schiff reagent
Aorta	Dark blue +++	Blue +	Pink +
Lig. nuchae	Purplish-blue ++	Purplish-blue +	Red ++
Loose connective tissue	Blue +	Bluish ±	Pink +
Skin	Blue +	Blue +	Red ++

Note: Crosses indicate the intensity of colour

The variability of the morphological appearance and histological staining makes it reasonable to suppose that the macromolecular components of the elastic tissue may be present in different proportions and/or the chemical structure of some components may be different, in different tissues. Naturally, an influence of age should not be neglected, though it is certainly not the only factor.

ELASTIC FIBRES IN DIFFERENT ANIMALS

The elastic fibres in different animals differ in their anatomical, histological and physicochemical properties. Hass (1939) noticed that elastic fibres were seen even in molluscs (invertebrates). These show the anatomical characteristics of elastic fibres, but do not stain with the dyes of elastic fibres (orcein and resorcin-fuchsin). Similar fibres occur in other invertebrates, and also in mammals during the first three months of foetal life. The characteristic staining of mammalian fibres appears in a later stage of foetal life.

TABLE 2

Characteristics of elastic fibres in different animal species

Method of examination	Elastic fibres			
	Invertebrates	Lophius	Teleost	Vertebrates
Anatomical appearance	Normal	Normal	Atypical	Normal
Histological staining	Lacking	Normal	Normal	Normal
In 0·1 N NaOH	?	Soluble	Soluble	Insoluble
In water and dilute acid	?	Insoluble	Insoluble	Insoluble

6

Lansing (1959) found an atypical form of elastic fibres in the conus arteriosus of the teleost *(Lophius piscatorius)*. These fibres covered the criteria of the elastic type of fibres as regards their anatomical, histological, elastic and other characteristics, except that the fibres were made soluble by boiling in 0·1 N NaOH within 15 minutes. The same procedure leaves the mammalian elastic fibres insoluble. Furthermore, the conus arteriosus of the elasmobranches is vascularized, contractile and rich in striated muscles and is considered to contain elastic fibres. According to these observations the variability of the elastic fibres in various animals is summarized in Table 2.

It can be concluded that fibres which anatomically resemble elastic fibres, but show no affinity to elastin-specific dyes, are present in various animals. In addition, there exist fibres acceptable as elastic fibres even as regards their staining properties, yet being atypical physicochemically. Finally, mammals have fibres which comply with all the criteria of elastic fibres, including anatomical, staining and physicochemical ones.

ISOLATION AND AMINO-ACID COMPOSITION OF ELASTIN

Studies on the chemical nature of elastin started at the middle of the last century. Attempts were made to separate elastin from soluble tissue elements. These studies were reviewed by Richards and Gies (1902). Abderhalden and Schittenhelm (1904) were the first to apply Emil Fischer's complete hydrolysis method for the analysis of elastin as protein. According to the analysis published by them only 61·1% of the elastin is synthesized of amino acids. The early research of the German investigators Kossel and Kutscher (1898) on the chemistry of elastin should also be mentioned. Subsequently, however, no data were published on this subject for more than 30 years. Then Stein and Miller (1938) developed a precise method for the isolation of elastin. The method was as follows. Fresh lig. nuchae obtained from the slaughterhouse was minced, first by a coarse mincing machine, then by a series of finer ones to a fine pulp. This was frozen in solid CO_2 and the powder so obtained was ground to an even finer powder. The latter (400 g) was submitted to consecutive extractions at low temperature with 5% NaCl solution, water and 0·25 M phosphate buffer of pH 8. Extraction with each solvent was repeated until the last two extracts failed to give the biuret test. The removal of the mucoid with the buffer was checked by the Mollisch test as well. As all soluble protein had been removed by this method, collagen was extracted with boiling water until two successive extracts remained biuret-negative. The extraction of collagen required 10 to 14 days. The fat was removed by washing 10 to 11 times with 1 litre hot alcohol. The residue so obtained was washed twice with an alcohol-ether mixture and dried in a vacuum exsiccator; 153 g elastin was obtained from 400 g of ligament (38%). The elementary analysis of the product showed 52·4% C, 7·2% H, 17·1% N, 0·17% S and 0·22% ash. The amino-acid content was 85%. The method was modified by Partridge et al. (1955). Recently this modified method has been used most widely for isolation of elastin.

Numerous investigators have carried out amino-acid analysis in elastin. Neumann (1949) employed a microbiological technique, Bowes and Kenten (1948, 1949) used the column chromatography whereas Gotte et al. (1963) chose the method developed by Moore et al. (1958). The data presented in Table 3 reflect the averages calculated from these analyses. Only scarce information is available on the amino-acid sequence of elastin. Kärkelä and Kulonen (1957) investigated the peptides in the acid-hydrolysate of elastin and found glycyl, glutamyl, proline, alanine and valine terminal residues. According to Moret and Gotte (1956) alkali hydrolysis results in smaller peptide molecules. The large molecule of α-elastin and the small molecule of β-elastin, both prepared by Partridge and Davis (1955), possessed the same amino-acid composition. The authors assume that β-elastin is a repeating unit in the elastin macromolecule. The fluorescent yellow substance, from which two components, *viz.* desmosin and isodesmosin, were separated by Partridge et al. (1963) and also by Thomas et al. (1963), appears to play an important role in the cross-linkages of elastin. Nevertheless, the information available at present seems to be too scanty to serve as a basis for a hypothetical structure for elastin.

TABLE 3

Amino-acid composition of the isolated elastin (averages from several data in the literature)

Amino acid	G amino acid/100 g protein	Amino acid	G amino acid/100 g protein
Glycine	25	Tyrosine	2
Alanine	22	Methionine	Traces
Leucine	8	Tryptophan	Traces
Isoleucine	4	Histidine	Traces
Valine	16	Arginine	1
Serine	1	Lysine	1
Threonine	1	Aspartic acid	1
Proline	13	Glutamic acid	3
Phenylalanine	6	Hydroxyproline	2

COMPARATIVE STUDIES ON ELASTIC AND OTHER FIBRES OF THE CONNECTIVE TISSUE

Table 4 provides comparative data on the properties of elastic fibres and those of collagen and reticular fibres. In the morphological properties microscopic, polarization-microscopic and electron-microscopic characteristics are included. As histological characteristics the staining properties are given. The X-ray diffraction method clarifies the differences in the internal structure between white and yellow fibres.

Comparative data for connective-tissue fibres

Fibre	Morphological characteristics			Histological staining	X-ray diffraction
	Microscope	Polarization microscope	Electron microscope		
Collagen fibre	Thick compact	Highly an-isotropic ++	Cross-striation with a periodicity of 640 Å	Picro-fuchsin Mallory	Reflections
Reticulin fibre	Thin branching	Anisotropic ++	Cross-striation with a period-icity of 640 Å	Schiff-positive	Reflections
Elastic fibre	Fine branching	Slightly birefracting	Filamentary structure	Orcein	Amorphous

Note: Crosses indicate the intensity of double refraction

Both elastic fibres and isolated elastin are highly resistant to heat, acid, alkali, other chemicals and enzymes. Their great resistance allows their separation from the white fibres of the connective tissue and soluble proteins and proteinoids. Based on this high resistance attempts were made in the middle of the last century to free the protein that builds up elastic fibres, now called elastin, from other tissue elements (Tilamus 1844; Horbaczewski 1882; Richards and Gies 1902). Abderhalden and Schittenhelm (1904) first proved the protein nature of elastin by means of Emil Fischer's acid-hydrolysis method.

T<small>ABLE</small> 5

Comparison of the physicochemical and chemical characteristics of elastin, collagen and reticulin

Scleroprotein	Boiling in			Carbohydrate content (%)	Digestibility by proteolitic enzymes
	Water	Acetic acid	Alkali		
Elastin	Stable	Stable	Stable	0·2—0·4	Elastase
Collagen	Gelatin formation			0·6—1·0	Collagenase and CMPase
Reticulin	Gelatin formation			4·0	Collagenase and CMPase

The physicochemical properties of elastin are substantially different from those of collagen and reticulin as shown in Table 5. In addition, elasticity is an important property distinguishing elastic fibres from inextensible, stable white fibres.

In his book written on the submicroscopic morphology of the protoplasm Frey-Wissling (1953) devotes only a few lines to the submicroscopic structure of elastin; this is because elastic fibres show scarcely any double refraction, i.e. they appear to be isotropic (Fig. 2a) in tissue; they become birefractile only in an extended state, in the presence of water (Fig. 2b). We have observed that in fluids of high refraction index, e.g. toluol, xylol and oil the dried fascicles of lig. nuchae (Fig. 2c) show a double refraction, irrespective of extension (Fig. 2d).

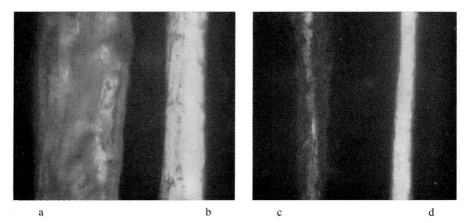

a   b   c   d

FIG. 2. Elastic fibre fascicle in the lig. nuchae; (a) in a wet state without extension; (b) the same when extended; (c) the same in a dry state; (d) the same when placed in toluol. Polarization micrographs

It has long been assumed that elastic fibres, having a fibrillar core, show a complex structure. Naturally, simple histological investigations failed to provide direct evidence for the complex structure. This was proved later by Romhányi (1955) who used his own technique based on the aniline reaction combined with polarization optics. The aniline reaction, being relatively specific for elastic fibres, had the great advantage that the disturbing effects of collagen and reticular fibres could be neglected in the course of the systematic evolvement of the method. The method is based on the oriented arrangement of aniline molecules on the fibres which eliminates the weak positive double refraction and gives rise to a definite negative double refraction. Romhányi (1955) showed that, under appropriate experimental conditions, collagen and reticular fibres fail to react with aniline, while muscle fibres show positive double refraction. Thus, aniline reaction is suitable for studying the submicroscopic structure of elastic fibres. Figure 3 shows the elastic fibres of the aorta of a new-born and an adult, for a comparison. This magnification reveals no isotropic line between the two anisotropic stripes. The isotropic line becomes visible only by higher magnification. In Fig. 4 the

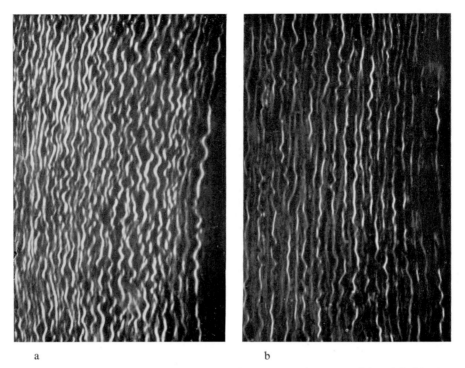

a   b

FIG. 3. Aniline reaction of the elastic fib res of the new-born (a); those of the adult (b). Note the wavy and straight course of the negatively birefringent fibres in (a) and (b); × 100 (after Romhányi 1955)

aorta of a new-born is magnified 250 and 450 times. The aniline reaction makes the characteristic structure of the elastic fibre well visible, especially in the latter case. In the aorta of an adult the same magnification fails to reveal any similar structure, presumably because the fine structure of the fibres had changed in adult age.

The pictures obtained by the aniline reaction in the aorta of a new-born and in the lig. nuchae suggest that elastic fibres have a spiral internal structure. In the new-born a single isotropic stripe which runs along the axis of the elastic fibre appears as a result of aniline reaction, whereas in the lig. nuchae two such stripes divide each fibre into three parts. These optical phenomena were regularly recognizable in every fibre, i.e. their appearance cannot be explained by any disturbing factor. An analysis of the phenomenon has shown (Romhányi 1955, 1962) that the compensation stripes which originate in those of the spiral structure of fibres are due to real isotropy. The central compensation stripe shows a 45° slope in new-borns and children, whereas in the lig. nuchae the optical effect is 20 to 25° (Fig. 5). The double refraction so obtained results from an oriented association of aniline molecules. A combination of the aniline reaction with elastica staining has shown that the structure elements reacting with aniline are smaller and narrower

11

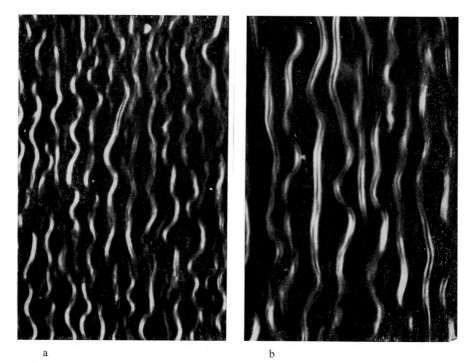

FIG. 4. Aniline reaction of elastic fibres in the aorta of the new-born; (a) × 250; (b) × 450 (photographs supplied by Prof. Romhányi)

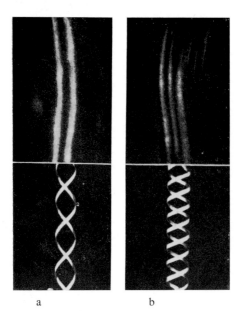

a   b

FIG. 5. Aniline reaction of elastic fibres in the aorta of the new-born (a); in the lig. nuchae (b). Top row: pictures observed by polarization microscopy. Bottom row: the corresponding helical structure (after Romhányi 1962)

than the stained structure, suggesting that aniline reacts only with a part of the elastic fibre, i.e. with the embedded fibrils. Romhányi (1955) assumed that resorcin-fuchsin and orcein react with the cementing substance or matrix, in which the fibrils are embedded. In the following chapters we will provide exact evidence of the chemical distinctness of the oriented spiral structure from the matrix or cementing substance (Banga, Loeven and Romhányi 1965).

These submicroscopic investigations have proved in a direct way that elastic fibres are complex in nature and consist of at least two, possibly three components. In the next chapter, while discussing the tensibility of elastic fibres, we will point out that the functional unit includes also the spiral-running collagen fibres enclosing the elastic fibres which are bound to the former by the aid of a mucoid.

ELECTRON-MICROSCOPIC STRUCTURE

Wolpers (1944) and, subsequently, Gross (1949) were the first to examine elastic fibres by electron microscopy. It was demonstrated that collagen fibres show a characteristic cross-striation of 640 Å periodicity (Schmitt et al. 1942; Wolpers 1944), whereas elastic fibres show very low electron density and no internal structure.

Dettmer (1952) based his electron-microscopic studies on the supposition that the great resemblance between elastin and collagen must manifest itself in the fine structure as well. He followed the principles of the digestion experiments of Ewald (1890) who was the first to suppose the existence of a so-called stroma inside the elastin. However, Ewald was unable to confirm this supposition because, according to his explanation, the fibrils were masked by being embedded in a substance impenetrable to light. Furthermore, his studies were hindered by the fact that these fibrils are too small to be detectable by light microscopy. Consequently, they can only be examined by electron microscopy. The difficulties in preparing collagen-free elastic tissue in a native state pose the most serious problem in these studies. Although collagen is removable by boiling in acetic acid or alkali, it is questionable whether or not the fine structure of the elastic tissues remains intact even if the elasticity of the tissue is unaltered. The removal of the extraordinarily resistant, amorphous elastin substance in order to make the embedded fibrils demonstrable by electron microscopy represents another problem.

Dettmer (1952), omitting extraction and boiling, employed only ultrasonic irradiation in preparing elastic fibrils from the pigeon's wing ligament (Flügelband der Taube) which consists of elastic fibres exclusively. The fibrils so obtained had cross-striation showing a periodicity almost identical with that of collagen. The diameter of the fibres ranged from 600 to 800 Å. As a result of these experiments Dettmer concluded that the elastic tissue of the pigeon's wing ligament consists of two components, amorphous matrix and fibrils. The former could not be transluminated except through its thinnest sites; it stained with osmium, but not with silver. The fibrils embedded in the amorphous matrix showed a cross-striation corresponding to that seen both in collagen and reticulin. D and H components were recognizable here, too, though the D component gave less contrast here than in the collagen. The silver-treated fibrils representing an impregnation type similar to that of reticulin were easily distinguishable from collagen. These findings make Dettmer's (1952) hypothesis reasonable that the elastic tissue is related to the collagen and reticulin tissue also morphologically as shown by the similar fibrillar basic structures and almost identical periodicity of cross-striation. According to Dettmer's conception there is no difference between elastic tissue and the other two types of tissue, except in the quantity and in the special properties of the matrix.

In addition, Dettmer carried out experiments with trypsin digestion. His trypsin preparation dissolved the amorphous matrix, but did not digest the embedded fibrils. The preparation was a crude pancreas powder (Dettmer's personal communication) which, as established later, contained elastase, too. The digestion of the matrix may thus be attributed to this enzyme. The undigestibility of the fibres suggests that these are different from the cement material of elastin in their morphological or chemical structure.

In contrast to this, Hall et al. (1952) came to another conclusion as a result of their electron-microscopic studies. These authors also supposed that elastin consists of two components, i.e. fibrils are embedded in a matrix containing sulphate and polysaccharides. The fibrils resemble the matrix except for their molecular structure. The fact that both the matrix and the fibrils are digestible by elastase can be explained, according to these authors, by the essentially identical chemical structure of the two components. The light-microscopic investigations of Lansing et al. (1952) led to similar results. These investigators also found elementary fibrils in the matrix and demonstrated that elastase digested both the elementary fibrils and the matrix. In their micrographs the fibrils appear to aggregate by twisting and by formation of fascicles. Dettmer's (1952) observation was confirmed by Schwarz and Dettmer (1953) in cremolan-embedded sections of human aortae. The same authors extended their investigations to the elastase preparation isolated by Banga (1952). The fibrillar component of the elastic fibrils remained intact after elastase treatment, i.e. it proved to be resistant. The authors state that the specific elastolytic effect is limited to the electron-optically homogeneous matrix and fails to alter the fibrillar component. Examining resorcin-fuchsin-stained preparations under the electron microscope the authors made observations suggesting that the cementing substance which is stainable with resorcin-fuchsin was digested by elastase, while the fibrillar component remained intact. The contradiction between the experimental findings of Hall et al. (1952) and Lansing et al. (1952), and those of Dettmer (1952) were explained by Banga's (1952) observations, viz. short heat treatment made collagen fibres digestible by elastase, whereas native collagen is resistant to the enzyme. Since both Hall et al. (1952) and Lansing et al. (1952) used isolated elastin in their elastolysis-combined electron-microscopic experiments, the elastin-matrix-embedded fibrils, even if they consisted of a collagen-like substance, must have been digested by elastase during their

14

isolation procedure which included boiling in acetic acid or alkali, i.e. a treatment that made the collagen-like substance sensitive to elastase. Dettmer (1952) and Schwarz and Dettmer (1953), on the other hand, used native elastic tissues which had not been exposed to any boiling or other heat effect. Consequently, if the fibrils embedded in the elastic matrix behaved like collagen, they might have been detectable by electron microscopy even after the matrix had disappeared. Hall et al. (1953) supposed that elastic fibres cannot be freed from collagen fibres by the procedure employed by Dettmer. They suggested that the cross-striated fibrils seen by the latter investigator were collagen fibrils. In fact, the silver-impregnated preparations published by Dettmer look different from those obtainable from collagen tissues. It is, nevertheless, uncertain where the filaments showing collagen-like ultrastructure inside the elastic matrix belong; they may belong to the elastin as well as to the collagen tissue. On the other hand, our own experiments published in the following chapters have clearly distinguished the matrix and the embedded fibrils from each other both morphologically and chemically and have shown that two different enzymes account for their digestion.

Later, based on electron-microscopic examination of the lig. nuchae, Dettmer (1956) withdrew his statement on the periodical cross-striation of the matrix-embedded filaments, but insisted on the reality of his observation that filaments are embedded in the matrix.

Keech (1960) examined ultrathin sections of the elastase-digested rat aorta and found a residual, lead-stainable reticular network. These experiments confirmed the double nature of elastin which had been supposed on the basis of the above-mentioned chemical and enzymatic investigations of the morphology of elastin-containing tissues.

Yokota (1957), who examined longitudinal sections of elastase-digested lig. nuchae by electron microscopy, observed a soft reticulum consisting of fine threads variable in thickness. The reticulum was mingled with collagen fibrils originating in the surrounding network. He confirmed the findings of the above investigators and those published earlier by Franchi and Robertis (1951) and Bahr (1951) who had not applied enzymatic digestion. In Kawase's laboratory Usuku (1958) found a reticulum of beaded fibrils in elastase-treated and potassium-permanganate-fixed ultrathin sections of the lig. nuchae. Subsequently the same author demonstrated the presence of such fibrils in unfixed, frozen sections as well (Usuku 1959). Similar, punctiform units lying 200 Å from one another in the mucopolysaccharide matrix were described by Pease (1961).

Cox and Little (1961) examined the electron-microscopic structure of elastic fibres in various elastic tissues. In contrast to the above authors, these investigators could not confirm the existence of a double-component system of elementary fibrils. Their failure might have been due to the use of high-concentration chemicals during the isolation of the elastic tissue. The fibrils might have disintegrated either during the 90-hour treatment in 45% solution of peracetic acid (Peressigsäure) or in the 10% potassium hydroxide applied over 30 to 40 hours in the course of preparation. The former has a strong oxidizing power, whereas the latter might have extracted mucopolysaccharides. According to our submicroscopic investigations the matrix-embedded fibrils are detectable when stained with toluidine blue. Consequently, acid mucopolysaccharides must play a part in their construction. Briefly, the detection of morphological units by electron microscopy cannot be expected if the molecular construction of the units has been altered by the procedures employed during the isolation of the elastic substance. It should thus be concluded that the results of Cox and Little (1961) are unacceptable because of the inadequacy of their preparation technique.

X-RAY DIFFRACTION STUDIES

For X-ray diffraction studies fibres consisting of almost pure collagen can be obtained from the tail of rodents. Thus, the regularly arranged structure of collagen can readily be studied, and the results undoubtedly refer to collagen. However, no kind of tissue contains collagen-free elastin. Even the approximately 16% collagen present in lig. nuchae prevents the crystalline, i.e. regulated, structure of elastin from being elucidated by the X-ray diffraction technique. The initial studies of Kolpak (1935) as well as the subsequent detailed investigations of Astbury (1938, 1940) suggested that the X-ray diagram of the unextended lig. nuchae shows a diffuse ring with an unoriented structure, whereas extension results in meridional and equatorial rings corresponding to the typical structure of collagen. Astbury (1938, 1940) attributed this phenomenon to the little amount of collagen present in lig. nuchae. Later Ramachandran and Santhanam (1957) studied the structure of the elastin of lig. nuchae extensively. In some of their experiments elastin was autoclaved to be freed from collagen which transforms into water-soluble gelatin during this procedure. After such a pretreatment elastin showed an X-ray diffraction pattern resembling that of thermally-shrunk collagen, except that two layer lines characteristic of collagen, viz. the 11 Å to 12 Å equatorial and the 2·86 Å meridional ones, were lacking. Instead of these, two wide reflections appeared at 2·2 Å and 4·4 Å, respectively. Of these the latter had already been observed by Astbury, whereas the former was first described by Ramachandran and Santhanam (1957). In addition, a central halo with a weak maximum about 9 to 10 Å appeared. All these are also present in the X-ray patterns of gelatin and of contracted collagen. The above authors suggest that autoclaving leaves the essential helical triplex structure intact, while it destroys the regularly arranged lattice structure of these. In the case of thermally-shrunk collagen the transformation of the structure is reversible as shown by the fact that normal conditions can be restituted by extending the fibres at room temperature. Based on the finding that the diffraction pattern of collagen-free elastin is similar to that of thermally-shrunk collagen, the authors have accepted that elastin, too, has a triple-chain helical basic structure which, however, shows no cross-linkages. The lack of cross-linkages may be attributed to the fact that elastin is poor in polar side groups and especially poor in hydroxyproline, the latter being the most important factor in the formation of

16

cross-linkages. On the basis of a theoretical consideration and their own experiments the authors suppose that collagen and elastin are analogous proteins both being constructed according to the triple arrangement suggested by Ramachandran and Kartha (1955) and Ramachandran (1956). The amino-acid composition of elastin agrees with that of collagen in two important respects: first, slightly more than one third of its amino-acid content is represented by glycine; second, the proline content of the two substances is almost identical. Triple-helix structure would be impossible if less than one third of the amino-acid residues were glycine, for in such a structure at least every third alpha-carbon atom must be free of any side-group. The five-atomic ring of proline also fits well in this structure. It is of interest that both of the synthetic polypeptides, polyglycine and polyproline, take up triple-chain configuration (Rich and Crick 1955; Cowan and McGavin 1955). Thus, a close relation between elastin and collagen can be assumed even without any direct evidence of every third alpha-C atom belonging to a glycine residue or of an identical relative position of glycine and proline residues in collagen and elastin. In spite of the close resemblance, the number of amino-acid residues per turn (being approximately $3^{1}/_{2}$ in the smaller helix) may be different for the two scleroproteins.

As regards its X-ray diffraction pattern collagen can be rendered similar to elastin by chemical treatments, too. Ramachandran and Santhanam (1957) produced contracted collagen by treating collagen with nickel nitrate or calcium chloride at room temperature. It was found that regardless of the reagent used first the structure was disintegrated, and subsequently the 2·86 Å layer line and the equatorial layer lines at 11 to 12 Å simultaneously disappeared. The pattern so obtained resembled that of normal elastin to such an extent that it could easily be mistaken for the latter. It is of special interest that the reflections appearing in the pattern of the treated collagen are identical with those shown by elastin. Thus, collagen if contracted by chemicals shows the physical properties characteristic of elastin. Of these properties elasticity is the most characteristic.

The fact that the structure of the chemically-treated collagen can be restored by washing the added salts proves, according to the above authors, that the modification produced by the chemicals is very slight. The great resemblance of elastin and the appropriately treated collagen both in physical characteristics and X-ray pattern suggests that elastin is closely related to collagen.

As a result of further treatment with nickel nitrate even the central halo surrounding the central point disappears and the patterns so obtained show only a diffuse ring at 4·4 Å, with very little intensity inside. This is identical with the pattern of the drastically shrunk rat-tail tendon, recorded by Astbury (1940), and that of gelatin sol, recorded by Katz et al. (1931) at a high temperature. When elastin is treated with concentrated nickel nitrate solution, the resulting pattern is also similar to those of the thermally-shrunk collagen and of the gelatin sol. Drastic heating produces in elastin modifications resembling those shown by collagen

17

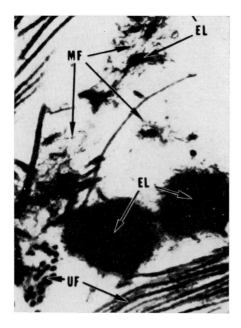

FIG. 6. UF = ultrafibril (collagen); EL = elastic fibre; MF = microfibril (after Low 1962)

after the same treatment. If elastin is autoclaved and its X-ray pattern is recorded immediately, the patterns will be identical with those given by the thermally-shrunk collagen, i.e. a single ring is seen at 4·5 Å, and the central regions appear to be clear. Similarly, when the X-ray pattern of wet elastin was recorded, the resulting patterns were very similar to those of wet gelatin. Thus, not only collagen can be transformed into an elastin-like substance, but both elastin and collagen can produce almost identical structures if they have undergone the same treatment. All these observations clearly show that elastin belongs to the collagen family of proteins and, like collagen, is synthesized at the molecular level of amino-acid residues according to the triple-chain arrangement.

FINE FILAMENTOUS MICROFIBRILS OF THE INTERCELLULAR SUBSTANCE

Jakus (1954) was the first to observe fine extracellular filaments in sections of the connective tissue. In tissues embedded in Vestopal-W polyester, according to the technique developed by Ryter and Kellenberger (1958), these filaments became well distinguishable from other fibrils (Low 1961a). The filaments, termed micro-fibrils (Low 1961b), are different both from collagen and elastic fibres. Their thickness rarely attains 100 Å, whereas the reticular fibres are, on average, 250 Å in thickness. Low (1962) has excellently demonstrated the three kinds of fibre in the intracellular substance of the heart (Fig. 6). He calls these fibres collagen-fibre units (Ultrafibrils = UF), elastic fibres (EL) and microfibrils (MF), respectively.

CHAPTER II

The Relationship between Macromolecular Structure and Function in Elastic Fibres

Conceptions Concerning the Elasticity of the Elastic Fibre

THE IMPORTANCE and function of the elastic fibres both in the arteries and lig. nuchae lie in their extensibility to 1·5 to 2 times of their original length. Their function should be similar to that of a strip of rubber or a rubber balloon. It was the simplest supposition that elastic fibres were also built up like an elastic ribbon. However, several authors have demonstrated that the elasticity of elastic fibres cannot be compared with that of an elastic rubber band. Ranke (1925) based his theory on the physical characteristics of the elastic substance. Accordingly, its elasticity can be compared with that of a steel spring (Biegungselastizität) (Meyer and Ferri 1936; Wöhlisch et al. 1943). The experiments of Redenz (1927) and Wöhlisch and Rochemont (1927) also spoke against a structure like that of a rubber band. These investigators have demonstrated that elasticity is a basic property of the elastic substance. In lig. nuchae very weak forces result in maximum extension. Further elongation cannot be achieved by increasing the force. Instead, at a certain tension the ligament breaks. Accordingly, the intensity of the force is not in direct relation to the elongation. The reaction is similar to the zero-type enzyme reaction showing maximum effect at a low substrate concentration, i.e. no increase in activity results from any increase in the substrate concentration. Consequently, the elasticity of lig. nuchae is not identical with that of the rubber, but, as pointed out by Redenz (1927) as regards extension, the elastic fibre is more similar to vulcanized caoutchouc than to rubber. The experiments published in the following appear to support the conception accepted also by Romhányi (1955), i.e. the elasticity of elastin results from both the physical arrangement and a peculiar chemical structure of this substance. The qualitative difference in elasticity between the rubber and the elastic fibre is explainable by the fact that the latter is complex in its structure.

The Role of Collagen and Collagenmucoid$_1$ in the Function of Elastic Fibres

The Close Association between Elastin and Collagen

According to our investigations elastic fibres are held together by collagen and the associated collagenmucoid, both in the aorta and lig. nuchae. We call this substance collagenmucoid$_1$ to distinguish it from mucoid$_2$ which is digestible by

FIG. 7. Aorta section. Phenol reaction. Straight, birefringent elastic fibres are surrounded by a spiral ring of birefringent collagen fibres

collagenmucoproteinase. This collagenmucoid$_1$ (in the following, mucoid$_1$) is the substance readily disintegratable, and soluble in water at 67 to 70 °C or in dilute acids (Banga 1953). The elastic fibres are surrounded by collagen and mucoid$_1$ in a spiral construction as evidenced morphologically in Fig. 7 (Banga, Loeven and Romhányi 1965). According to our studies the collagen present in lig. nuchae is firmly bound to the elastic fibres by the aid of mucoid$_1$, making the physicochemical properties of the former different from those of native collagen. Separation either by enzymatic reaction or chemical extraction will restitute, thus make demonstrable, the well-known physicochemical characteristics of collagen. The fact that the collagen in lig. nuchae shows the same characteristics as shown, e.g. in the tendon of Achilles and that only the association to the elastic fibres prevents their demonstrability can be proved by the following experiment. The collagen in the lig. nuchae, unlike native collagen, fails to show the thermocontraction phenomenon, i.e. its fibres show no contraction when heated. In addition, these fibres show neither the neutral nor the acid swelling. Removal of the elastic fibres from the native lig. nuchae by elastase does not alter the histological demonstrability of any of the collagen fibres (Banga 1955). These elastin-free collagen fibres show heat contraction in water at 67 °C, in general at the temperature characteristic of the heat contraction of the mammalian collagen. The same fibres show the swelling characteristic of collagen both in water and in 0·5 to 0·1 % acetic acid. Consequently, the lack of the physicochemical properties of collagen fibres in the native lig. nuchae proves that collagen fibres are firmly associated to elastic fibres in the native state. The collagen fibres of the aorta behave similarly, whereas those of the carotids and the arteria iliaca show contraction and swelling in acetic acid, even in tissue sections.

The questions arise, 1. what is the physiological importance of the presence of collagen and mucoid$_1$ among elastic fibres, and of the former being wound around the latter in spiral configuration (Fig. 7); 2. why a relatively strong association has developed between collagen and elastin in these two kinds of tissue. The

20

questions may be explained by the structure of elastic fibre which needs water molecules to fulfil its function, i.e. it must be in the hydrated state. In a dry state neither the aorta nor the lig. nuchae is elastic and will not become elastic even in liquids other than water or physiological buffer solutions, although, e.g. any one of toluol, phenol or aniline changes the double refraction of the fibres, i.e. penetrates the lig. nuchae intermicellarily. On the other hand, it is known that in contrast to collagen fibres, elastic fibres, obtained either from the aorta or from the lig. nuchae, swell only to a small extent in water or in dilute acid or alkaline solutions. The chemical explanation of this difference can be given by the fact that 80% of elastin is built up of apolar amino acids unable to fix water molecules, whereas collagen contains polar amino acids in a high percentage. If, therefore, the elastic fibre needs water molecules for its function but, owing to its chemical construction, cannot fix them, it must be assumed that the closely associated water molecules play an important role in the function of the elastic fibre.

According to our observation, in the aorta and lig. nuchae the elastic fibres are bound to collagen to such an extent that the water molecules present in the swollen collagen and mucoid$_1$ are accessible for the elastin. For this reason it is possible that collagen and mucoid$_1$ serve as a water reservoir, namely in a peculiar physical system, in which during the extension of the elastic fibres only the collagen molecules (micelles) are compressed and so express the water to be taken up by the elastic fibres.

THE FUNCTIONAL ROLE OF THE SPIRAL STRUCTURE OF THE COLLAGEN FIBRE

The spiral structure of collagen at the macromolecular level (Fig. 7) can be evidenced by the following experiment as well. If a fascicle of lig. nuchae 2 cm in length is extended to 4 cm and in this state placed in elastase solution, all the elastic fibres will have been dissolved within 24 to 48 hours, as controllable by histological staining.

The resulting fascicle will not tear and, in contrast to the reaction of the starting material, ceasing of the extension will not result in contraction. (The degree of contraction is inversely proportional to the extent of solubilization of the elastic fibres. In the case of 50% solubilization the elasticity is reduced by 50%; as solubilization has attained 100%, the fibres cease to be elastic. The elastase-insoluble substance is pure collagen.) Histological staining shows the collagen fibres to be continuous. These fibres being non-elastic their continuity can only be explained by assuming that in an extended state the collagen spiral surrounding elastic fibres is straightened, i.e. its length changes parallel to that of the elastic fibres. The contraction of elastic fibres is accompanied by the contraction of the surrounding collagen spiral. However, after the elastic fibres have been removed, the spiral, being non-elastic in itself, will remain extended. Only the chemical bonds fixing the spirals to the elastic fibres make the former able to spring together. Functionally it is of great importance that the collagen fibre, instead of being in an extended state, appears to be folded up. Only its fixedness to elastic fibres is significant, viz. in supplying the water essential for the elasticity of elastic fibres. To the increased compactness of the contracted spiral an increased number of polar groups and hydrophilic mucopolysaccharide molecules are associated, both being significant in water fixation.

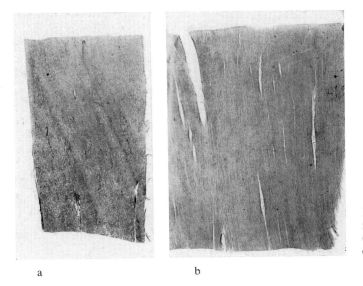

FIG. 8. Heated lig. nuchae; (a) control; (b) after 10 minutes elastolysis

a   b

Another experiment has shown that collagen and an intercellular mucoid play a part in keeping elastic fibres together. Lig. nuchae consists of 80 to 84% elastic and 16 to 20% collagen fibres. Its whole mucopolysaccharide (MPS) content amounts to about 1%. If fibres of lig. nuchae are submitted to a heat effect at 67 to 70 °C, its collagen shows no contraction, yet the bond between collagen and elastin will loosen. In elastase solution the sections so obtained will stretch and extend, growing to 2 to 3 times their original volume (Fig. 8); some fibres even disintegrate. In Fig. 8 the left section is the control, whereas the right section had been treated, both stained with resorcin-fuchsin. The preceding experiments have shown that enzymatic dissolution of the elastic fibres fails to disintegrate the fibre fascicles; the structure of the latter remains intact. Unlike this, in the present experiment heat-treatment rendered a substance sensitive to elastase. Thus, enzymatic treatment resulted, by removing this substance, in disintegration of the preheated elastic fibres. This experiment has proved that elastic fibres are kept together by a substance, termed mucoid$_1$, located between collagen and elastin. Beside the peculiar structure of the elastic substance itself, mucoid$_1$ may be a significant factor of elasticity.

22

Lig. nuchae is the best model for studying the elasticity of elastic fibres. It consists of 84% elastin, 1 to 2% mucopolysaccharide (MPS), and the remainder is collagen. Wood (1954) examined the influence of the removal of the last two substances on the elasticity of the lig. nuchae. He extracted the collagen partly by water, partly by boiling with acetic acid; MPS were extracted by hyaluronidase, $CaCl_2$, potassium periodate and periodic acid. Wood prepared load-extension curves of single strips and calculated the tensible properties as in the change in the work (W) necessary to stretch the material to a given extension. He used the equation

$$R = \frac{W_2 - W_1}{W_1}$$

where R indicates the change in elasticity brought about by the treatment, whereas W_1 and W_2 represent the work the fibre was able to perform before and after treatment. The equation is valid only for strips of equal cross-sectional areas. Negative R values indicate an increased elasticity due to the loosening of cross-linkages. In such cases the same work can be performed by reduced loading. Positive R values, on the other hand, indicate that new cross-linkages have developed. Wood obtained negative R values, i.e. weakened cross-linkages after collagen had been removed. Extraction of the hyaluronidase-sensitive MPS led to similar results. Potassium-periodate or periodic-acid treatment, on the other hand, greatly stabilized the cross-linkages. Supposedly, periodic acid gave rise to aldehydes by splitting and oxidizing sugar molecules, and the aldehydes produced the new cross-linkages that stabilized the macromolecules. Heating for five minutes at 70 °C also stabilized the fibres.

All these experiments have proved that in the function of elastic fibres, besides the two components of elastin (see Fig. 23), the collagen and the collagen-fixed mucoid₁ also take part. Hyaluronidase-sensitive MPS also play a role, but it is uncertain whether these belong to the cementing substance of the elastin or that of the collagen.

ALTERATION IN THE ELASTICITY OF THE VASCULAR WALL IN RELATION TO AGE AND ARTERIO- (ATHERO-) SCLEROSIS

The elastic tensibility of the human vascular wall has been examined by numerous investigators for a long period of time. Various methods having been employed, several authors established, as early as the end of the last century, that the elastic tensibility of the elastic arteries (aorta, carotids, coronaries) decreases with age and as a result of arterio- (athero-) sclerosis. This is demonstrated in Fig. 9 showing the elastic tensibility of the carotids of three persons of different ages. Methods of measuring the elasticity have been reviewed in Reuterwall's work: "Über die

Elastizität der Gefässwände und die Methoden ihrer näheren Prüfung" (1921). As the most reproducible method, measurement of the elastic tensibility of vascular strips has been accepted most generally. Tensibility is expressed in the so-called elasticity module (E. mod.), i.e. the load needed by a strip of known cross-section to be extended by a given percentage. Banga and Baló (1961a) used a modified method in their experiments. Considering the sensitivity of the apparatus constructed by themselves, they made efforts to establish appropriate experimental conditions

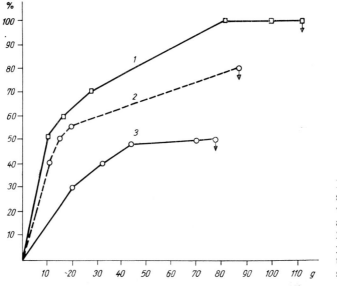

FIG. 9. Percentage tensibility of the carotid wall as a function of age; 1 = 35 years; 2 = 47, and 3 = 75 years of age. Preparation No. 3 is arteriosclerotic

to distinguish the effect of age from that of arteriosclerosis, on the basis of the E. mod. The estimation of the extent of vascular lesion was based on the percentage involvement of the aorta intima in atheromatous plaques. Examining carotid strips free of macroscopic lesions Banga and Baló have confirmed the well-known fact that elastic tensibility is a function of age. Strips originating from young persons could be extended by 110 to 120%, while those obtained from old persons broke at 70 to 80% extension (Fig. 9). The value of E. mod. was found to depend on the degree of extension from which it was calculated.

A comparison of the E. mod. values calculated from 40% and 70% extension of the same strip resulted in an interesting relationship to age as well as to the severity of atherosclerosis. Tables 6 and 7 present the E. mod. values for the carotids of persons of different ages and degree of atherosclerosis. The two tables refer to the same cases in the identical distribution: groups 1 and 2 comprise cases free of atherosclerosis and those showing a low degree of atherosclerosis (about 20%) regardless of age; group 3 refers to old persons and those having suffered from severe atherosclerosis. A comparison of the E. mod. values in

24

Table 6 with those of Table 7 resulted in interesting conclusions. The E. mod. as calculated from 40% extension showed no correlation to age, provided the vascular wall was free of atherosclerosis. In group 2 the E. mod. increased with age; in group 3 the rise of the E. mod. was not in direct relation to the severity of the lesions.

TABLE 6

Elasticity module in relation to age and atherosclerosis in the case of 40% extension

Carotid No.	Group	Age (years)	Wet weight (mg)	Cross-section (mm^2)	Load (g)	E.mod$_1$ (g/mm^2)	Degree of athero-sclerosis (%)
56		14	24	1·80	5	2·76	0
67		17	23	1·72	5	2·90	0
74	1	21	23	1·72	5	2·90	0
73		39	24	1·80	5	2·76	0
71		47	24	1·80	5	2·76	0
77		28	26	1·95	6	3·1	20
52		30	27	2·0	8	4·0	25
75	2	43	27	2·0	8	4·0	20
72		61	24	1·80	10	5·5	20
81		61	26	1·98	12	6·1	75
66		70	27	2·0	14	7·0	75
60	3	80	26	1·95	14	7·2	85
63		82	26	1·95	15	7·6	90

The E. mod. values calculated on the basis of 70% extension showed different relations (Table 7). Here the correlation between age and E. mod. was pronounced even in group 1. As compared with the young cases, in those from 39 to 47 years of age, E. mod. displayed a 40 to 110% increase. The age factor was conspicuous in group 2, too, i.e. the appearance of atherosclerosis did not influence the value of E. mod. which was proportional to age. For group 3 the correlations based on 70% extension were approximately the same as those based on 40% extension, i.e. E. mod. was not proportional to the severity of atherosclerosis, yet higher values corresponding to age were predominant.

It can thus be concluded that, in order to demonstrate the influence of age on the elasticity of the carotid wall, vascular strips should be submitted to strong tensible effects (e.g. 70% extension). Under such experimental conditions the carotids of old persons appear to be significantly less elastic than those obtained from young ones. An initial stage of atherosclerosis, however, is easier demonstrable

TABLE 7

Elasticity module in relation to age and atherosclerosis in the case of 70% extension

Carotid No.	Group	Age (years)	Wet weight (mg)	Cross-section (mm²)	Load (g)	E.mod$_1$ (g/mm²)	Degree of athero-sclerosis (%)
56		14	24	1·80	20	11·6	0
67		17	23	1·72	20	11.6	0
74	1	21	23	1.72	20	11·7	0
73		39	24	1·80	30	16·5	0
71		47	24	1·80	45	25·0	0
77		28	26	1·95	20	10·3	20
52		30	27	2·0	20	10·0	25
75	2	43	27	2·0	35	17·5	20
72		61	24	1·80	40	22·0	20
81		61	26	1·95	45	23·0	75
66		70	27	2·0	48	24·0	75
60	3	80	26	1·95	50	25·5	85
63		82	27	2·0	60	30·0	90

by applying 40% extension. Finally, an advanced stage of atherosclerosis is accompanied by no rise in the E. mod., irrespective of the degree of extension.

Banga and Baló (1961a) emphasized that the old debate among pathologists as to whether atherosclerosis is independent of old age or not has not yet been settled. Of course, juvenile cases of atherosclerosis are irrespective of age. In their opinion the above experiments have thrown some light on this problem suggesting that atherosclerosis is not a function of age, though a reduced elasticity of the vascular wall, i.e. an increased E. mod. and a lowered value of maximum tensibility are obligatory concomitants of old age.

Banga and Baló (1961a), in addition to studying the E. mod., investigated two further properties of the vascular wall, namely maximum tensibility (expressed in percentage) and tensile strength. The former has been expressed in the percentage by which a vascular wall is extensible without breaking, whereas the latter in the minimum weight (in g) breaking the strip. In Table 8 Banga and Baló (1961a) have classified carotids by age and present their maximum extension (column I), the minimum load causing breaking (column II), and the latter calculated for 1 g dry matter of vascular wall (column III). It is clearly seen that maximum tensibility and age show a well-defined negative correlation. The few discrepancies may be attributed to individual differences and possibly methodical inaccuracies. The

TABLE 8

Tensile strength of carotids according to age

	Carotids		Tensile strength			Diagnosis	Degree of athero-sclerosis (%)
No.	Age (years)	Dry matter (mg)	I maximum extension (%)	II load (g)	III breaking (g/mg)		
56	14	3·8	110	125	33	Cirrhosis hepatis	0
67	17	3·2	110	115	36	Lupus erythematosus	0
74	21	3·1	120	120	39	Nephritis chronica	0
53	24	3·0	100	84	28	Nephritis chronica	0
54	27	3·6	100	84	23	Endarteritis chronica	10
77	28	3·4	100	75	22	Nephritis chronica	20
52	30	4·2	100	75	18	Nephritis chronica	25
64	30	4·1	100	100	24·5	Embolia arteriae femor.	0
73	39	3·5	100	95	26	Mitral failure	0
75	43	4·4	80	85	19·2	Carcinoma coli rectalis	20
71	47	4·2	80	90	21·5	Angiosarcoma	0
87	47	4·1	90	75	18·2	Tumor ovarii	30
65	49	4·0	70	75	18·5	Carcinoma uteri	20
78	50	4.0	90	90	22	Atherosclerosis	75
62	57	4·7	70	82	17·5	Atherosclerosis	80
72	61	4·0	90	95	23·5	Plasmocytoma	10
81	61	4·1	90	75	19·0	Arterioscler. univ.	75
76	62	3·9	80	80	22	Endocarditis	35
66	70	4·1	70	72	17·5	Arterioscler. cerebri	75
57	72	4·0	70	75	18·5	Cirrhosis hepatis	75
61	74	4·1	70	72	17·5	Arterioscler. univ.	80
60	80	3·8	70	65	17	Arterioscler. univ.	85
63	82	5·0	70	65	13	Arterioscler. univ.	95
58	83	3·8	70	80	21	Atherosclerosis	70
70	86	4·1	70	75	18	Cirrhosis hepatis	75
55	86	5·0	50	80	16	Arterioscler. univ.	80
59	89	4·2	70	75	18	Tumor abdominalis	85

correlation to atherosclerosis is more pronounced in columns II and III, since the minimum load necessary for breaking (and the ratio of this to the dry matter of the carotid strip) are to a greater extent a function of the severity of atherosclerosis than of age. According to these investigators the indices of tensile strength are better indicators for atherosclerosis as an illness; the E. mod. values, on the other hand, are more definitely related to age.

THE INFLUENCE OF ELASTOLYTIC ENZYMES ON ELASTICITY

Banga and Baló (1961b) examined the effects of elastase (elastoproteinase) and elastomucoproteinase (EMPase) on the elastic tensibility of the same carotid strips in parallel experiments. Previously the same authors (Banga and Baló 1960b) demonstrated that EMPase is able to increase elastic tensibility; they expressed elastic tensibility in Wood's (1954) parameter. Since carotids contain elastin which is digestible by elastase, it was expected that this enzyme would alter the elasticity of the carotids. As to the mechanism of action EMPase is different from elastase, first of all in being unable to digest isolated elastin; besides, as shown in Chapter V, EMPase dissolves from the human aorta a protein-containing substance which has proved to be a mucolipoprotein. The effects of the two enzymes were analysed to demonstrate possible relationships between the quantity and E.U. activity of the enzymes, and the changes produced in E. mod. and Wood's parameter. Table 9 convincingly shows that small quantities of an EMPase preparation whose E.U. activity was only 1/100th that of elastase exerted a remarkable effect on the elastic tensibility of the aorta, whereas comparable quantities of elastase were ineffective. This is most definitely shown by the R values. While treatment in a buffer solution containing 0·25 or 0·5 mg elastase in 5 ml resulted in zero value of R, the same concentrations of EMPase produced $-0·17$ and $-0·35$ values, respectively. Similar differences were demonstrable when the effects of other concentrations were compared, e.g. the R value produced

TABLE 9

Comparative studies with elastase and elastomucoproteinase

Incubation in	Elastase				Elastomucoproteinase			
	mg	E.U.	E.mod$_1$ (g/mm^2)	R	mg	E.U.	E.mod$_1$ (g/mm^2)	R
Buffer control	—	—	9·1	—	—	—	9·1	—
Enzyme	0·25	20	9·0	0	0·25	0·25	8·0	−0·17
Enzyme	0·50	40	6·7	0	0·50	0·50	7·6	−0·33
Enzyme	1·0	80	4·6	−0·25	1·0	1·0	4·6	−0·50
Enzyme	1·50	120	4·6	−0·34	1·50	1·50	4·2	−0·58
Enzyme	1·75	140	3·8	−0·58	1·75	1·75	3·8	−0·67
Enzyme	2·0	160	2·6	−0·67	2·0	2·0	3·2	−0·75

Note: Material: carotids from a woman 49 years old. Enzyme in mg and E.U. are given for incubation in 5 ml solution

28

by 1 mg EMPase was twice that produced by elastase. The treatment of carotid strips with elastase or EMPase resulted in approximately the same E. mod. values, except when the lowest concentrations were used. In these cases EMPase was more effective in increasing elastic tensibility than was elastase. Between age and EMPase-sensitivity of the carotids no definite correlation could be established. The individual fluctuation made the small differences insignificant and the limited amount of EMPase available prevented us from continuing the experiments. Preliminary experiments of Banga and Baló (1960b), the results of which were expressed in Wood's parameter, suggested a correlation between enzyme effect and vascular lesion. However, the systematically performed experiments, during which all the data expressed in E. mod. were taken into consideration, failed to confirm such a correlation. A definite answer to this question needs a great number of experiments and, of course, large quantities of pure enzyme preparations.

CHAPTER III

ISOLATION OF ELASTOLYTIC ENZYMES

VERIFICATION OF THE EXISTENCE OF PANCREATIC ELASTASE, AN ENZYME INDEPENDENT OF TRYPSIN AND CHYMOTRYPSIN

THE DISCOVERY of elastase as a distinct enzyme with specific effect on elastic fibres was based on a theoretical conception (Baló and Banga 1948; Baló 1949). Baló as a pathologist had studied the pathogenesis of arteriosclerosis for many years. His histological observations have shown that the initial manifestations of arteriosclerosis could always be brought into relation with the destruction of elastic fibres of the arterial wall. For this reason he searched for chemicals which when reaching the circulation can destroy elastic fibres. In *in vivo* experiments Baló (1938, 1939 a, b) found that only highly toxic compounds, e.g. ammonium hydroxide, thyroxin which never occur in the circulation under normal conditions destroy elastic fibres. In his opinion (Baló 1938, 1939 a) the toxic substances produce acidosis resulting in disintegration of elastic fibres of the vascular wall (Baló 1963). The *in vitro* experiments of Baló and Banga (1949 a, b) confirmed the *in vivo* observations that only highly destructive acids and alkalis, i.e. substances never occurring in the organism, and even these substances only at temperatures higher than the physiological temperature, are able to attack elastic fibres. For this reason these authors postulated the existence of a substance which being present in one organ of the human (and animal) body is able to degrade elastic fibres enzymatically. Among the organ extracts tested only pancreatic and gastric extracts showed elastolytic activity (Baló and Banga 1949 a, b). Pepsin preparations were highly elastolytic at pH 1·8, suggesting that the effect of the gastric extracts was due to the presence of pepsin. Since the pancreatic extracts contained trypsin and chymotrypsin, the question arose whether or not these two well-known enzymes are responsible for the elastolytic activity of the pancreas. Ewald and Kühne (1878) and, subsequently, Ewald (1890) were the first to observe vacuoles appearing in histological sections of the lig. nuchae pretreated with pancreatic extracts; further treatment resulted in transversal splitting of the fibres. In similar experiments Schwalbe (1877) found that elastic fibres were enclosed in an envelope being relatively resistant to digestion. In his opinion elastic fibres consist of two different substances, viz. the envelope and a homogeneous substance filling the envelope.

It was reasonable to suppose that the pancreas contains a specific elastolytic enzyme in addition to trypsin and chymotrypsin. The problem seemed approachable in two different ways: 1. the effects of pure, isolated trypsin and chymotrypsin on the elastic fibres and on the isolated elastin had to be examined by histological and biochemical methods; 2. the specific enzyme had to be isolated and its distinctness from the two other enzymes had to be demonstrated. Baló and Banga (1950) prepared trypsin and chymotrypsin by the method of Kunitz and Northrop (1936), and the preparation so obtained was significantly less active on the aorta powder than another purified preparation called elastase. The experiments carried out by the authors with the trypsin and chymotrypsin preparations, kindly supplied by J. H. Northrop (Princeton N. J. USA), brought convincing proof. Since these preparations, when used either separately or together, failed to digest elastic fibres (Baló and Banga 1949b), it became clear that elastic fibres are digested by an enzyme other than the known proteolytic enzymes. The fact that elastase is a distinct enzyme, being specific for elastic fibres, was soon confirmed by several groups of investigators (Lansing et al. 1952; Hall et al. 1952; Pepler and Brandt 1954; Partridge and Davis 1955; Grant and Robbins 1955, 1957; Lewis et al. 1956; Robert and Samuel 1957a, and Thomas and Partridge 1960).

THE SITE OF PRODUCTION,
AND THE OCCURRENCE OF PANCREATIC ELASTASE

Kokas et al. (1951) were the first to demonstrate an elastolytic activity in the pancreas secretion of the dog. The activity was demonstrable irrespective of whether the secretion had been stimulated by secretin, HCl or pilocarpine. The pancreas secretion obtained after subcutaneous administration of pilocarpine was richer both in trypsin and elastase than that produced on the effect of secretin or HCl. The appearance of elastase in the pancreas secretion has proved that the enzyme is produced by the glands of the pancreas and suggests that the enzyme exerts its digestive effect in the small intestine. Grant and Robbins (1955) demonstrated the presence of elastase in the pancreatic duct, consequently they supposed that it is of exocrine origin. In the teleost *Lophius piscatorius*, having islet tissue separated from the acinar tissue, the enzyme was found by Lansing et al. (1953) in the islet tissue; the acinar tissue was free of elastase. For this reason these authors arrived at a contrary opinion. To elucidate the question, Carter (1956) used $CoCl_2$ and alloxan as cytotoxic agents and ligated the pancreatic duct in alternative experiments, yet their results were inconclusive. In similar experiments Butturini and Langer (1962) found that a decrease in the number of alpha cells runs parallel with reduced elastase activity. Cohen et al. (1958) followed the fluctuations in the elastase and lipase activities after various interventions. They concluded that elastase was produced by the acinar tissue. Lansing emphasizes in his book (1959) that Cohen et al. (1958) failed to realize the significance of their own observation, viz. the inhibition of elastase activity by $CoCl_2$ in the guinea-pig, suggesting that the enzyme is produced by the alpha cells.

Hall (1961b), considering the available data with criticism, suggested that neither the endocrine nor the exocrine origin can be excluded for elastase which, possessing both systemic and digestive functions, is an enzyme with extraordinary wide-scale activity.

Out of the pancreas, elastase has been found in the contents of the small intestine (Baló and Banga 1949a,b) and in the urine of man, rat and rabbit (Tolnay et al. 1962). The latter investigators suppose that elastase is excreted by the kidneys, thus it must be present in the blood, too.

BACTERIAL ELASTASE

Late in the last century Mall (1888, 1896) and Ewald (1890) and early in this century Eijkman (1903) reported that certain bacteria (Pseudomonas) were able to digest elastic fibres. Fifty years later Narayanan et al. (1953) found several elastase-producing strains of *V. cholerae*. Banga and Baló (1954) reported that keeping elastin suspensions in the refrigerator for a certain time led to elastolysis and an increased sensitivity to pancreatic elastase. They demonstrated elastolytic bacteria growing in the elastin preparations and succeeded in isolating three different bacteria, namely *Ps. pyocyanea*, *Staph. aureus* and *Staph. albus*. (The microbiological investigations were kindly carried out by Dr. M. Füzi.) The elastase activity of elastin preparations contaminated with these bacteria appeared to be higher by 60 to 70% than that of a fresh elastin preparation tested in parallel. When tested in Na_2CO_3 buffer at pH 8·6, the *Ps. pyocyanea* strain elicited the greatest activity, about twice the activity of the two Staphylococcus strains. To avoid bacterial contamination, Banga and Baló (1954) developed a new method for elastin production. They found boiling in 0·01% merthiolate solution for 10 minutes an appropriate method for making elastin incapable of supporting bacterial growth. Peppler and Brandt (1954) supposed as a result of their own experiments that bacterial elastase possesses chondroitinase activity. However, the existence of such an activity was not confirmed later. The preparation of pure elastase from a Flavobacterium is the great merit of Mandl and Cohen (1959, 1960a,b). As Mandl (1961) reported, the yield was low in their experiments, and their method was not suitable for production on a larger scale. Nevertheless, it is of theoretical interest that the specific enzyme so obtained was different in the mechanism of action from the enzymes exerting general proteolysis and failed to digest any other protein. Bacterial elastase is undoubtedly a proteolytic enzyme, and the bacterial elastolysis is associated with fission of peptide bonds; the appearance of free peptides is demonstrable by paper chromatography. Flavobacterium-elastase digestion of elastin proved to follow the zero-order kinetics up to approximately 70% hydrolysis. In the elastolysate N- and C-terminal amino acids were found. Among the former glycine was the commonest, while proline was never found.

In contrast to this C-terminal amino-acid glycine was never found, while proline, alanine and leucine were equally common. It seems, therefore, likely that proline-glycine linkages were hydrolysed. This mechanism is somewhat different from that found for pancreatic elastase (Naughton and Sanger 1958; Naughton et al. 1960).

32

Another bacterial enzyme, Protease B (Compte et al. 1961) also shows proteolytic activity but, unlike Flavobacterium elastase and like pancreatic elastase, it is inhibited by neutral salts. Thus, elastases derived from different bacteria may be somewhat different from one another.

ASSAY AND METHODS FOR ISOLATION OF PANCREATIC ELASTASE

Purified elastase was first prepared by Banga (1952) who applied ammonium-sulphate and alcohol fractionation. Needle-shaped crystals so obtained, assembled in bundles are seen in Fig. 10. To measure elastase activity Banga evolved a method

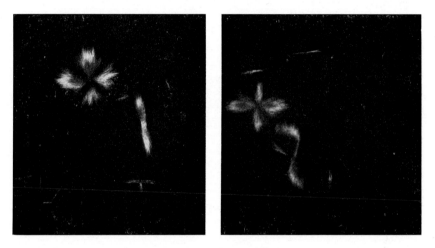

FIG. 10. Elastase crystallized from ammonium sulphate

based on the gravimetry of the substrate that remained undissolved after digestion with elastase. She used elastin as substrate and expressed elastase activity in elastolytic units (E.U.) representing the enzyme quantity that dissolves 1 mg elastin in 30 minutes under given experimental conditions. Almost every author has accepted as E.U. the enzyme quantity that, under specialized experimental conditions, dissolves 1 mg substrate, but the conditions have been variable. The methods for measuring elastase activity have been reviewed by Banga et al. (1959), Loeven (1960 a) and Mandl (1961). The same preparation may exhibit different E.U. values when assayed by different techniques. The discrepancies may be due to the quality of the applied buffer, the ionic strength, the ratio of substrate to enzyme, etc. These factors make the activity values obtained by different methods hardly, if at all, comparable.

Initially pancreas extracts containing crude elastase were compared with commercial trypsin preparations. Later efforts were made to isolate elastase, i.e.

33

obtain homogeneous preparations. Hall and Gardiner (1955) modified Banga's isolation procedure by introducing dialysis of the product of high elastase content obtained by precipitation with 45% ammonium sulphate and drying with acetone the fraction that became insoluble during dialysis. The method of assay used by these authors was significantly different from that of Banga, especially in the length of the incubation period (17 hours). Thus, the specific activity of Hall's Px preparation could not be compared with the crystalline elastase isolated by Banga. Subsequently, Hall and Czerkawski (1959) submitted their elastase preparation to further purification by alumina gel-adsorption methods. Hall (1957a) succeeded in separating two functionally distinct elastase fractions, namely fractions E_1 and E_2, on the basis of the different electrophoretic mobilities of these fractions. It is thought that E_1 splits the polysaccharide component of elastin, while E_2 is responsible for the proteolytic activity of elastase (Partridge and Davis 1955). The specific activity of the latter component, as prepared and assayed in the author's laboratories, was no higher than that of the elastase crystallized from ammonium sulphate solution. Later Hall and Czerkawski (1959) reduced the incubation period to three hours and measured the amount of solubilized elastin by means of the biuret reaction according to Sols (1947) or with Claesson's (1946) interferometer.

Lewis et al. (1956) obtained crystalline elastase by a procedure similar to that of Banga (1952). Like Hall and Gardiner (1955) they introduced the dialysis of the precipitate that had formed in 45% ammonium sulphate solution and crystallized the euglobulin fraction so obtained from ammonium sulphate. Electrophoretic analysis of this product resulted in two components, namely a slower-moving, larger component and a faster-moving, smaller one. In separating the two components the Aminco electrophoretic apparatus was used. Only the slower-moving, larger component possessed an elastolytic activity; the other was inactive. The activity of the electrophoretically homogeneous preparation of Lewis et al. (1956) was approximately twice as active as the crystalline elastase of Banga. The crystalline and the electrophoretically homogeneous products of these authors contained 106 and 132 E.U. per mg protein, respectively.

INACTIVE FORMS OF ELASTASE IN THE PANCREAS

Banga (1949a,b) described in her early reports that in the pancreas 75 to 80% of the elastase was in an inactive form. For this reason she introduced 4 or 5 times repeated freezing (at $-20\ ^\circ$C) and thawing of the native pancreas samples before assaying elastase in them. The acetone-dried powder so obtained contained all elastase in the active form. According to Banga's experiments the inactive elastase may exist either in the proenzyme form (zymogen) or may form a complex with an inhibitor. The presence of such an inhibitor in the pancreas has been confirmed since then (see below).

The existence of an enzyme-inhibitor complex was supported by the experiments showing that from the crude pancreas active elastase can only be extracted by

34

acid (pH 4·5) buffer mixtures; neutral and alkaline extracts of low activities can be activated by adding dilute acid (0·01 N H_2SO_4 or HCl) (Banga 1949). The acid activation can be explained by an elastase + elastase-inhibitor complex in which the inhibitor is acid-sensitive. Since trypsin can also be activated by acid, activated trypsin may also play a role in the release of elastase (Grant and Robbins 1955). The former mechanism of acid activation is supported by the fact that neutral pancreatic extracts are activated by precipitation with ammonium sulphate (Banga and Baló 1950). The presence of 45% ammonium sulphate shifts the pH to 4·5 to 5·0 and at this pH a considerable rise in the whole activity occurs during precipitation. Pancreatic extracts lacking elastolytic activity can be activated by dialysis as well as by acidification (Banga and Baló 1950). This kind of activation, however, needs a longer time. Within five hours no demonstrable activation occurred even when the outer fluid was continuously changed. Activation was significant after 24 hours, it showed further increase during the following 12 hours and reached its maximum at the 48th hour of dialysis. Further dialysis led to a decline in elastase activity. The slowness of activation during dialysis suggests that the molecule of the substance to be removed is relatively large; salts of low molecular weight disappear from the solution as soon as after five hours of dialysis. The fact that inactive extracts are activable by dialysis proves that an inhibitor is removed during dialysis, i.e. the activation by dialysis means removal of an inhibitor from the enzyme solution. Table 10 shows the degree of activation in a solution of low enzyme activity after different times of dialysis.

Mandl (1961) assumed that the supposed dialysable inhibitor is an inorganic salt which inhibits elastolysis even in physiological concentrations. This conception has, however, been opposed by the experimental conditions and by the fact that an acidified and subsequently reneutralized extract shows 5 to 6 times its original activity, although its salt concentration has increased as a result of these procedures. Thus, salt concentration plays no significant part in elastase activity measurements, except when it is extremely high.

The inactive form of elastase turning to active enzyme by trypsin treatment was designated proelastase by Grant and Robbins (1955). Lamy and Tauber (1962) partially purified and isolated the proelastase. They used trypsin to turn proelastase into elastase, whereas during the isolation procedure they prevented the transformation of proelastase into elastase by trypsin inhibitor. As regards transformation, the same authors demonstrated that the proenzyme was acti-

TABLE 10

Influence of the duration of dialysis on the activation of elastase

Period of dialysis (hour)	E.U./g pancreas	Activation (%)
Extract before dialysis	105	
5	105	0
24	520	395
36	560	435
48	580	450

Note: One g of powdered pancreas was agitated with 10 ml saline for 30 minutes. After centrifugation pH was adjusted to 8·6. After a dialysis at 15 °C for variable periods the elastolytic activity was assayed

vated only by native trypsin, i.e. the groups split off the proelastase molecule must be peptide groups in which the carboxyl groups of lysine or arginine residues play a role. Chymotrypsin and trypsinogen are weak activators of proelastase. The velocity of the activation by trypsin is high showing that the linkages responsible for the activation are readily accessible. Lamy and Tauber (1962) emphasize that these linkages resemble those present in myosin, being also easily attacked by trypsin (Mihályi and Harrington 1959). One of the fragments of the proelastase molecule may easily associate to trypsin, making the latter completely inactive. According to certain experiments the transformation of every unit of proelastase into elastase is accompanied by the inactivation of 48 units of trypsin. Consequently, activation of proelastase by a given amount of trypsin cannot last longer than for a limited period of time and the production of active elastase is proportional to the quantity of trypsin. This reaction is an interesting example for interactions between enzymes. The assay of active elastase is influenced not only by the elastase inhibitor but also by the active trypsin content of the pancreas. It is, therefore, clear why several investigators, e.g. Hall, were unable to demonstrate elastase in the pancreas. Practical observation prompted Baló and Banga to introduce the above activation procedure, i.e. repeated freezing (at $-20\,^{\circ}$C) and thawing of the native pancreas, by which elastase is released from the inhibitor and trypsin is activated. The latter process is important because transformation of proelastase into elastase depends on the trypsin concentration.

To isolate elastase from pancreas powder, Grant and Robbins (1957) prepared extracts with saline and added trypsin or pig duodenum as activator. In their purification procedure they introduced adsorption of elastase to elastin powder at pH 4·7 in the presence of 0·1 M NaCl and elution with 0·2 M acetic acid. According to these authors this method is the most suitable for the purification of proelastase, for in this case a single procedure resulted in a 15-fold enrichment. The trypsin content of the mixture used for the preparation of elastase was 0·0034%. The activity of the most purified elastase preparations of these authors was 23 to 26 times greater than that of the initial preparation, i.e. it remained below the specific activity of crystalline elastase.

LARGE-SCALE PRODUCTION OF ELASTASE

The early methods of elastase production, including Banga's (1952) method for producing crystalline elastase, had the disadvantage of having a low yield. It was thus reasonable to evolve procedures suitable for large-scale production of elastase. Bagdy and Banga (1957, 1958) developed the following two methods.

Method I. Pancreas powder was extracted with a solution of pH 4·5 to 4·7 containing 30 to 40% alcohol and 2 to 5% salt (sodium acetate) in water. Extraction was then continued with a volume ten times the weight of the pancreas for 30 minutes. The insoluble residuum was removed by centrifugation. As a result of this 90% of the initial elastase activity was detectable in the supernatant while the greatest part of the dry matter settled. To the supernatant an equal volume of alcohol was added at low temperature. A precipitate was so obtained which, after dehydration with alcohol and drying, contained 16 to 20 E.U. per mg, i.e. the yield was 80 to 85%. The authors call this preparation "crude elastase" for this has been the starting material for all their further purification and isolation procedures.

Method II. Elastase-containing extract was adsorbed to synthetic sodium-aluminium-silicate column (Decalso, Permutit Co.). For elution 40 to 50% aqueous ethanol or methanol was used. These contained 8 to 10% ammonium acetate at a pH between 4·5 and 5·0. The eluate was cooled to $-2\,°C$ and elastase was precipitated by adding three volumes of absolute alcohol of the same temperature, in a thin ray, under continuous stirring. The preparation was kept at $-2\,°C$ for several days and, after subsequent centrifugation, dehydrated and dried.

The activity of the preparations so obtained from "crude elastase" as starting material attained 70 to 80 E.U. per mg, and the yield as related to the activity of the initial pancreas powder was as high as 40%. Thus, by combining methods I and II large amounts of highly active elastase could be produced from powdered pig pancreas. However, as recognized later, these preparations were not homogeneous (see p. 38).

ENZYMES SEPARATED FROM THE ELASTASE ENZYME COMPLEX AND IDENTIFIED ACCORDING TO THEIR FUNCTION

The literature reviewed in the previous chapters has shown that the attempts to prepare homogeneous elastase resulted in heterogeneous preparations (Lewis and Thiele 1957). Furthermore, a growing number of observations has supported the existence of two enzymes active in the elastolysis (Hall 1953, 1957a; Banga and Baló 1956; Banga et al. 1957; Loeven 1960a, b). Most recently Loeven (1964a b, c, d, e) suggested the existence of a third enzyme, namely elastolipoproteinase, on the basis of chromatography and paper electrophoresis of the elastase enzyme complex.

This conception is in contrast to the observations of Lewis et al. (1956) who reported the isolation of "homogeneous", pure elastase by electrophoresis. However, these authors interpret purity as suggested by Colvin et al. (1954), i.e. they believe that because of the great lability and complex nature of proteins every protein preparation represents a group of several closely related protein molecules, instead of being a collection of identical molecules. With this restriction the elastase obtained by preparative electrophoresis may be considered to be homogeneous. Its homogeneity has been proved by ultracentrifugation, electrophoresis and diffusion. It is of interest, however, that even these authors found two components in elastase preparations which had been recrystallized several times when analysed by electrophoresis. One of the two components was larger and almost immobile, whereas the smaller component was fast-moving. What is more, the entire elastolytic activity, to our best knowledge the highest activity ever measured by that time, was found in the immobile component. We think that in this "elastase" preparation the two elastolytic enzymes might not have separated from each other, i.e. the preparation of Lewis et al. might have contained, in addition to elastase, a great quantity of the mucolytic enzyme, the EMPase of Banga and Baló (1956) which is also almost immobile when examined electrophoretically. In the Tiselius apparatus Lewis et al. (1959) found their pure elastase migrating together with the chymotrypsin, except when extremely high pH-s were used. In our experiments and in those of Hall (1957a) it was the mucolytic enzyme that appeared almost together with chymotrypsin. The same was shown by Loeven (1964e) by paper electrophoresis. This detail is to be emphasized for, as shown below, we have provided exact evidence of the participation of two enzymes in the elastolysis of native fibres. It can, however, not be excluded that elastase, i.e. the proteolytic component alone can digest the isolated elastin which has been submitted to denaturation by heat and chemicals during the isolation procedure.

Dvonch and Alburn (1959) separated two protease and two elastase factors (Elastase I and Elastase II) by starch-gel electrophoresis from the preparation called "Banga P_1" by Grant and Robbins (1957).

The purest elastase isolated in the author's laboratories from crude elastase by adsorption to synthetic sodium-aluminium-silicate (Decalso) and alcohol fractionation has proved to be heterogeneous electrophoretically. Paper electrophoresis showed three well-identifiable components (Bagdy et al. 1958) as shown in Fig. 11. The existence of three components was confirmed in the Tiselius apparatus. To produce larger quantities, the three components were separated by starch-gel electrophoresis using the method of Smithies (1955) as modified by Moretti et al. (1957). Electrophoresis was carried out in a horizontal apparatus (Banga and Baló 1962). On the basis of the mechanism of action the first, second and third components have been designated collagenmucoproteinase (CMPase), elastase and elastomucoproteinase (EMPase) respectively.

CMPase which will be discussed in detail under "Collagen" exerts a very characteristic effect on collagen fibres. Furthermore, it gives rise to collagenolysis in collagen-containing tissue powders. It is, therefore, regarded as a collagenase. The name collagenmucoproteinase was chosen because in early experiments the enzyme passed a mucoprotein into solution from native collagen fibres. This was termed mucoid$_2$ by Banga (1957, 1959a,b); Banga and Baló (1960a) and Baló et al. (1960) (Chapter XVI, p. 178).

The second component displayed an elastase activity. The purified preparations isolated by starch-gel electrophoresis always showed less specific activity than the starting preparation, in which all three components were still present. The loss in activity can be attributed partly to the long period of electrophoresis (24 hours), during which the enzymes were exposed to pH 8·6 at $+4\,°C$, and partly to the lack of EMPase in the second component. According to the present view (Chapter V, p. 60) EMPase stimulates elastolysis.

38

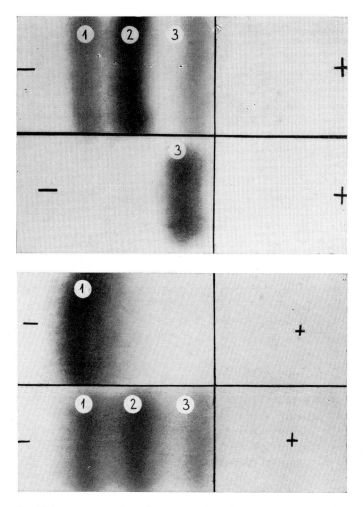

FIG 11. Paper-electrophoretic pattern of the elastase-enzyme complex. The upper part of the upper picture and the lower part of the lower picture show the three components of the elastase-enzyme complex: the lower part of the upper picture shows the isolated component No. 3 (elastomucoproteinase); the upper part of the lower picture shows the isolated component No. 1 (collagenmucoproteinase)

From a fraction purified by a special method combined with DEAE Sephadex chromatography an elastase (elastoproteinase) preparation showing the highest specific activity ever measured was obtained.

The third component is the elastomucoproteinase (EMPase). Until quite recently the specificity of this enzyme for the elastic fibres and its true mechanism of action could not be established. In sections prepared from the lungs of patients suffering from tuberculosis, Krompecher (1960) found an increase both in acid and neutral mucopolysaccharides (MPS) with Ritter and Oleson's (1950) staining. He reported that EMPase dissolved only the PAS-positive, neutral MPS; it was without effect on acid MPS-s. Similarly, only neutral MPS-s were dissolved by EMPase from sections prepared from tumours of the C_3H mouse strain. The experiments to be discussed in Chapter VI, pp. 72–78 have proved that the substrate of EMPase in the elastic fibres is different from the substrate of elastase.

We have prepared crystalline elastase in the following way as well (Banga and Bagdy, unpublished data). As starting material a preparation containing the elastase-enzyme complex purified with Decalso was used. This was dissolved in 0·1 M acetate buffer of pH 4·5 to make a 1% solution, and fractionated with alcohol. Crystals separating at 10 to 25% alcohol concentration at 0 °C showed no elastolytic, but possessed a considerable EMPase, activity. The preparation contained two components, a thermolabile and a thermostable one (Chapter V, p. 62). Although we have several times separated two or three subunits from EMPase preparations by starch-gel electrophoresis, we have never been able to produce and isolate from each other the thermolabile and the thermostable components of EMPase in quantities sufficient to verify any difference in other physical properties or mechanism of action.

On the basis of paper electrophoretic investigations the identity of Hall's E_1 preparation with the EMPase isolated by Banga and Baló (1962) may be assumed but has not yet been proved. The synergistic activation described by Hall (1957a) could inconsistently be demonstrated with EMPase and some of the experiments discussed below, also speak against the identity of the two preparations. The possible existence of two or more mucolytic enzymes is thus supported by starch-electrophoretic studies, and recently by Loeven's (1964e) experiments. Nevertheless, these being closely related to each other as regards physicochemical characteristics, their separation and identification and the examination of their mechanism of action encounter difficulties. In addition to these, Czerkawski and Hall (1958) reported on a denatured, inactive form which may be present in some preparations as a third component and inhibits the synergistic effect of the mucolytic component.

SEPARATION OF ELASTASE AND ELASTOMUCOPROTEINASE BY DEAE SEPHADEX CHROMATOGRAPHY

On the basis of the above data it is obvious that neither the elastase nor the EMPase fractions prepared in different laboratories can be considered entirely identical enzymes. Every elastase preparation was supposedly contaminated with the synergistic elastomucase and/or its inactive product. Czerkawski and Hall (1958) designated the latter E_2' because its electrophoretical mobility was almost the same as that of E_2. Since, however, E_2' is a denatured form of E_1, the designation E_1/den. as recommended by Loeven (1960a) appears to be preferable. The existence of more than one mucolytic enzyme as suggested by Loeven (1964a) would explain why in the author's laboratory neither the synergistic effect could be reproduced with the elastomucase prepared, according to the procedure of Hall and Czerkawski (1959), nor the elastomucase prepared by Loeven (1960b) activated Banga's elastase preparations. To avoid confusion, it seemed to be of importance to isolate homogeneous enzymes by a method including chromatography during which contamination of elastase (E_2) with EMPase (E_1) and vice versa can be excluded during elution. Loeven (1963a) produced elastase and EMPase preparations by Sephadex chromatography. However, the quantity of the preparations so obtained was too little to carry out the characteristic biochemical, histochemical and polarization-microscopic tests with the same preparation. Collaboration with Loeven (Banga and Loeven, unpublished experiments) has led to preparations sufficiently pure to be used for repeating earlier experiments. The experiments carried out with these preparations have provided the answer to a number of questions. Moreover, we succeeded in obtaining EMPase preparations which, on the basis of the histochemical reactions to be discussed below, have contributed to the fine submicroscopic structure of the elastic fibre. When using these preparations we were able to demonstrate, by polarization microscopy, two morphologically distinct components in the elastic fibre.

The isolation procedure including DEAE Sephadex chromatography consistently resulted in elastase (E_2) preparations of invariable activity (Banga and Loeven). In contrast to this, the activity of the E_1 preparation depended on the quality of the starting material (as to whether the AEI or the AES of Hall and Czerkawski (1959) was used for preparation.

The method of preparation was as follows. Bagdy and Banga's (1957) crude elastase served as starting material (p. 37). From this the AEI and AES fractions of Hall and Czerkawski were separated by long-term dialysis. E_2 and E_1 were prepared from both of these fractions by DEAE Sephadex chromatography. The two kinds of E_1 (E_1/AEI and E_1/AES) proved to be different both in synergistic effect and submicroscopic reactions. The results of the experiments carried out with these preparations are described in Chapter VI, p.79.

CHAPTER IV

ENZYMATIC DECOMPOSITION OF ELASTIC FIBRES WITH THE ELASTASE ENZYME COMPLEX

As SEEN in the preceding chapters, the first preparations employed in different laboratories for digestion of elastic fibres and elastin powder contained other pancreatic enzymes besides elastase (elastase-enzyme complex). Nevertheless, subsequent investigations have shown that the early results were acceptable since the hydrolysis of the elastic fibres was due, besides elastase, to the EMPase and the elastolipoproteinase components (Loeven 1964e), even in cases when the concentration of these enzymes was variable. The experiments (Chapter VI) that have revealed the effects of elastase and EMPase on the different morphological components also provided a firm basis for the detection of EMPase in some elastase preparations. These investigations revealed that neither Banga's ammonium-sulphate-fractionated crystalline elastase, nor the preparation separated in the Tiselius apparatus by Lewis et al. (1959) were homogeneous, whereas neither Hall's E_2, nor the elastase preparations of Grant and Robbins (1957) and Dvonch and Alburn (1959) contained EMPase in a concentration sufficient to disintegrate matrix-embedded filaments. Thus, elastolysis was attributable to the proteolytic activity of elastase in almost every experiment that has been published on this subject. Nevertheless, kinetic experiments (p. 80) have shown that the mechanism of elastolysis by the enzyme complex is different from that by pure elastoproteinase (Chapter VI, pp. 71–78). For this reason the kinetics of the elastase-enzyme complex and that of pure elastoproteinase will be discussed separately (see p. 46 and 80).

The experiments carried out with the elastase-enzyme complex have shown that some elastase preparations may contain ribonuclease and deoxyribonuclease enzymes as well. In separate experiments these enzymes failed to digest elastic fibres. However, in histological sections pretreated with these enzymes fibroblasts were not visible, showing that the two enzymes were active in these cells.

HISTOCHEMICAL EXAMINATION OF NORMAL TISSUE SECTIONS CONTAINING ELASTIC FIBRES AND OF ATHEROSCLEROTIC AORTAE

In some of these experiments frozen sections, in others fixed and embedded sections of vascular walls and of the lig. nuchae were used. Baló (1938, 1939a, 1951) was the first to demonstrate that swelling and lack of staining are the most characteristic, histologically detectable alterations in the arteriosclerotic aortae and carotids. Figure 12 shows a section of a normal and an arteriosclerotic aorta wall. The

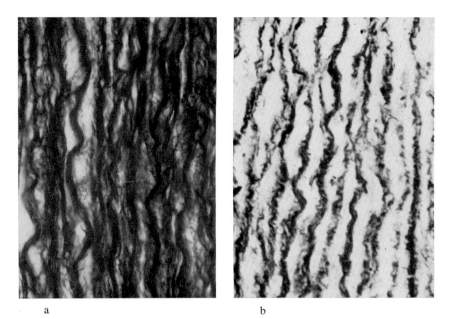

a   b

FIG. 12. Histological picture of the normal (a) and arteriosclerotic aorta wall (b).
Resorcin-fuchsin stain. Magnification is identical

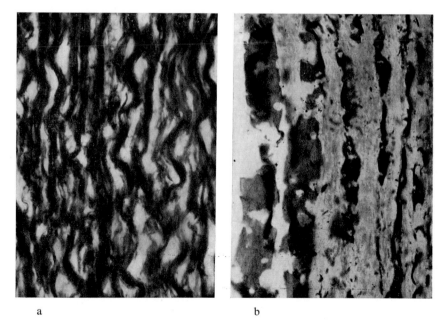

a   b

FIG. 13. Human aorta wall; (a) before and (b) after elastolysis. Incubation for two
hours with 0·5 mg/ml crystalline elastase

arteriosclerotic fibres being fragmented and swollen scarcely show any staining. Similar alterations are visible in sections of normal vascular walls preincubated in a highly active elastase solution for a short period (30 to 60 minutes). Longer incubation in elastase solution may lead to the complete disappearance of the

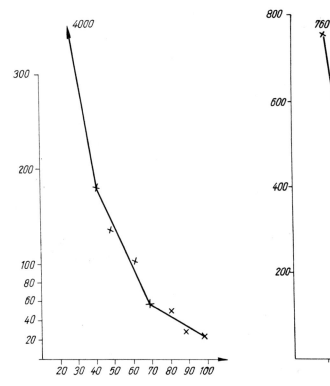

FIG. 14. Velocity of elastolysis as a function of age. Abscissa = age in years: ordinate = solubilization of the elastic fibres, minutes

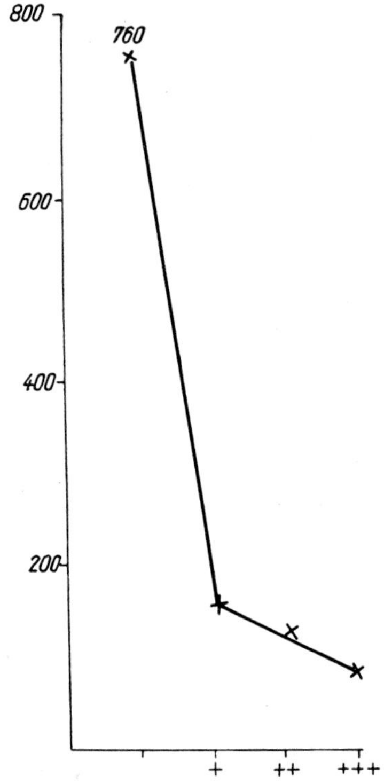

FIG. 15. Velocity of elastolysis as a function of atherosclerosis. Abscissa = severity of atherosclerosis. The highest degree of atherosclerosis is designated by + + +. Ordinate = solubilization of the elastic fibres, minutes

elastic fibres (Fig. 13). Elastic fibres are replaced by highly swollen, fragmented and vacuolated formations showing very pale staining if any.

Baló and Banga (1955) and, subsequently, Banga and Schuler (unpublished data) examined the velocity of the dissolution of elastic fibres by elastase in histological sections of carotids and aortae obtained from subjects of different ages. The time was determined that is needed for 50% reduction in the resorcin-fuchsin staining of elastic fibres. The velocity of elastolysis was found to be proportional to age (Fig. 14). It was significantly increased in case of the arteriosclerotic vascular wall (Fig. 15). The increased velocity may be explained by the changed chemical construction of the vascular wall (lipid accumulation). Similar observations were reported by Lansing et al. (1951), Findlay (1954) and Saxl (1957a, b). LaBella (1963) who, using isolated elastin, investigated the effects of age and atherosclerosis in biochemical experiments found a decrease in the elastolysis parallel with growing age and the degree of atherosclerosis. This question will be discussed below. When the temporal course of elastolysis was examined in sections of the lig. nuchae of the calf instead of those of the vascular wall, the picture was quite different

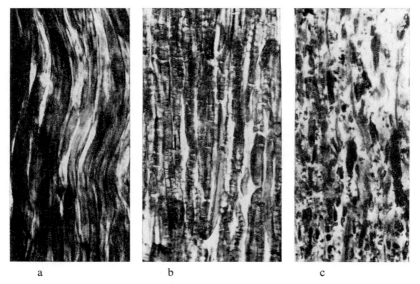

a   b   c

FIG. 16. Elastolysis in the lig. nuchae; (a) the parallel running elastic fibres of lig. nuchae; (b) fragmentation of the fibres in the initial stage of elastolysis; (c) disintegration and irregular arrangement of the fibres after longer elastolysis

(Baló et al. 1954). Figure 16 shows the untreated lig. nuchae (a), and the initial (b) and the final (c) phases of elastolysis. In the initial phase transversal fragmentation of the elastic fibres is visible, whereas in the final phase the fibre has lost its continuity, and only minute granules are present. Banga (1953) observed that the speed of solubilization for the Achilles tendon fibres that had undergone thermal contraction was 10 times that of elastin. Subsequently it was revealed that during thermal contraction of collagen a mucoid is dissolved; the presence of such a mucoid was supposed earlier by Partridge (1948). Unpublished experiments with tissue sections carried out by the author have shown that in human aortae and in the lig. nuchae thermal contraction of collagen proceeds less regularly than in the carotids and coronaries. The difference is caused by a strong association between collagen and elastin in the former tissues which prevents the physicochemical characteristics of collagen from being demonstrable. In sections of adult arteries, on the other hand, where thermal contraction of collagen proceeds, the solubilization rate of the thermally-shrunk collagen highly exceeds that of elastic fibres. Thus, placing a thermally-shrunk section in elastase solution for ten minutes results in full solubilization of the collagen fibres without any impairment of the elastic ones. Dissolution of the collagen fibres is indicated by a negative picro-fuchsin reaction according to van Gieson (Fig. 17). These experiments having been carried out with the elastase-enzyme complex cannot represent a specific effect. Thus, the effect presented in Fig. 17 might have been due to collagenmuco-proteinase as shown below in detail.

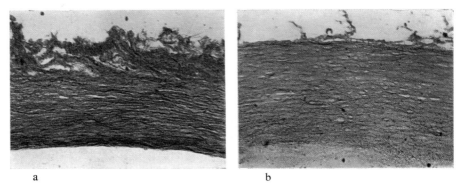

a   b

FIG. 17. Solubilization of thermally contracted collagen fibres with elastase; (a) human carotid section after thermal contraction, van Gieson stain. Red fibres indicate collagen, yellow fibres elastin; (b) the same after 10-minute elastolysis. The red collagen fibres have disappeared, the yellow ones remained

BIOCHEMICAL INVESTIGATIONS; KINETICS OF ELASTASE EFFECT

The elucidation of the kinetics of elastase effect was hindered by the insolubility of elastin and the consequent inhomogeneity of the system in which the reaction proceeds. Hall and Czerkawski (1961a,b,c) who studied the mechanism of the elastase-elastin reaction emphasized that, because of the heterogeneous nature of this reaction, the rules of the classical kinetics that are valid for the enzymatic reactions in general cannot be applied in this case. According to these authors the system shows an unusual empirical interrelation which can be expressed by the inverse Michaelis-Menten equation. The elastolysis time curve shows a sigmoid shape at pH 8·6, suggesting that the reaction proceeds in several steps.

After elastin was prepared in soluble form (Adair et al. 1951), Czerkawski (1958) and, subsequently, Hall and Czerkawski (1961b) investigated the elastin-elastase reaction in the presence of elastin solubilized with oxalic acid.

Partridge et al. (1955) were the first to prepare soluble elastin by boiling with dilute oxalic acid, under systematic physicochemical control of the reaction. They separated two kinds of molecules, viz. one of low (5500 to 6000), and another of high, molecular weight (60 000 to 84 000). The latter was termed α-elastin

46

by Partridge and Davis (1955). The majority of elastin proved to be α-elastin which is polydisperse and forms coacervate when heated. The low-molecule substance, i.e. β-elastin is monodisperse and does not form coacervate. It is of interest that the amino-acid composition of α- and β-elastin is almost the same; on the basis of the terminal amino and carboxyl groups the concept has developed that α-elastin is built up of β-elastin residues by cross-linkages of a hitherto unknown nature. It has only been demonstrated that these cannot be disulphide bonds.

Wood (1958) and, subsequently, Hall and Czerkawski (1961b) prepared α-elastin-like soluble components by using numerous solvents. The latter authors derived an empirical equation to explain the reaction between elastase and α-elastin. This equation consists of three terms: a linear function of substrate concentration, a hyperbolic function of enzyme concentration and a similar hyperbolic function of time. The fact that the reaction is of first-order with respect to the substrate indicates the fast formation of an enzyme-substrate complex, and the fact that it remains of this order throughout implies a step by step degradation of the substrate. The former observations have led to the establishment of a theoretical equation which is of the same form as the empirical one. The constants of the equation have sound physical meaning and can be obtained experimentally. Sachar et al. (1955), who used orcein-elastin as substrate, achieved zero-order reaction only until less than 35% of the 20 mg substrate had been solubilized. Unlike these authors, Lewis et al. (1956) who used electrophoretically homogeneous elastase, found a linear relation between enzyme concentration and solubilization of the substrate up to 70% solubilization. Similar results were reported by Campagnari and Greggia (1959).

Lamy et al. (1961) found the elastase-elastin reaction to be of zero-order in the only case when 0·4 mg elastase (Merck) was added to 50 mg elastin in the presence of 0·08 M Tris buffer at pH 8·6. When the substrate to enzyme ratio was changed or another buffer was used, e.g. veronal—acetate buffer, the kinetics of the reaction changed, viz. first-order or undeterminable reaction type was observed. These authors concluded that the elastolytic activity is bound to two distinct proteins, one of which is highly specific for elastin.

Hall and Czerkawski (1961b) investigated the effect of alterations in the elastin molecule on its affinity to elastase viz. modification or blocking of certain side-groups. They could speed up elastolysis by N-acetylation, deamination and, above all, by introduction of carboxyl groups by glyoxylization, whereas the reaction was slowed down by esterification, O-acetylation or dinitrophenylation. On this basis they concluded that elastolysis is preceded by adsorption of the enzyme to the solid, insoluble elastin substrate and that carboxyl groups are essential for the adsorption. In this respect the side-chain carboxyl groups of glutamic and aspartic acid are of particular importance. In our opinion (p. 51) all the carboxyl groups belonging to the fluorescent substance of elastin may play a role in the adsorption.

Histochemical investigations published by Romhányi (1959) agree well with the results of Hall and Czerkawski (1961b). Romhányi attempted to modify the course of elastolysis by substitution or blocking of the reactive side-groups in the structure of elastic fibres. Blocking of the basophilia of the tissue by methylation markedly slowed down the enzymatic dissolution of elastic fibres. Permanganate treatment, i.e. oxidation of the sulphhydryl groups into sulphone groups and of the OH groups into carboxyl groups markedly enhanced the basophilia of the toluidine-blue anisotropy, consequently accelerated the dissolution of elastic fibres. Deamination, another intervention enhancing the basophilia of elastic fibres, led to similar results. Romhányi (1959) attributed the association of elastase to elastin to the specially arranged acid side-groups of the latter. In his opinion the difference in enzymatic solubilization between the elastic fibres of new-borns and those of adults is related to the different degree of basophilia in these tissues.

Although the carboxyl group appears to be all-important for the elastase effect, Hall and Czerkawski (1961b) suggest that the presence of an unsubstituted hydroxyl group is also necessary for the actual reaction to proceed. It need not necessarily be inferred that the carboxyl and hydroxyl groups are present on adjacent amino acid residues nor even that they are on the same peptide chain. The net result must be, however, the production of a hydroxyl-carboxyl complex capable of reacting with a single, relatively small centre on the enzyme.

The Role of the Fluorescent Chromophorous Groups of Elastin in Elastolysis

Heim and Cseh (1933) Hungarian investigators were the first to observe fluorescence in elastic fibres in histological lung and aorta sections. However, their report having been published only in Hungarian has escaped attention. More recently Loomeijer (1958) called attention to the fluorescent substance of elastin. He cited the pioneer work of Szent-Györgyi (1957), suggestive of the existence of a close relationship between the fluorescence of a compound, and its activity in the energy transfer and, thus, in the metabolism. Accordingly, the fluorescent substance of elastin may be important in the decomposition and synthesis of elastic fibres. Partridge and Davis (1955) and LaBella (1957), who dealt with the yellow pigment of elastin, did not notice its strong fluorescence. Kärkelä and Kulonen (1959) attempted to isolate a yellow substance with maximum UV absorption at 330 mμ from elastin hydrolysate and achieved eight to tenfold purification. Loomeijer (1961) attributed the fluorescence of elastin to a fatty acid isolated by himself from the elastin's peptide chain using several kinds of hydrolytic methods. This substance is an organic acid with a branching chain of 12 C atoms and a supposed ketone function. Banga et al. (1964, 1965) examined the solubility of the fluorescent substance prepared from elastin powder by oxalic-acid hydrolysis and measured its fluorescence at 365 mμ. This component proved to be different from the yellow pigment. Partridge et al. (1963) isolated two closely related fluorescent peptides. Both of these (Compound A, i.e. "desmosin" and Compound M, i.e. "isodesmosin") may be regarded as tetracarboxylic tetraamino acid. The two compounds are different in the degree of unsaturation. Since, according to Partridge et al. (1963), they play a role in the cross-linkages of elastin, the fluorescent substances are thought to hold the peptide chains of the polydisperse elastin together and to bind elastase by their carboxyl groups, thus being of importance in the primary process of elastolysis.

The lack of data on a possible relationship between the fluorescent substance of the vascular wall and arteriosclerosis prompted Banga et al. (in the press) to examine this question systematically. They examined 6 normal and 19 sclerotic human aorta specimens. Powdered aorta was extracted with acetic acid, and the residue was used for short-term (30 minutes) and prolonged (24 hours) elastolysis experiments. The fluorescence of the elastolysates was measured by a Hilger UVISPEK spectrophotometer with fluorescence attachment. A 365 mμ filter was used. Depending on the intensity of fluorescence, 0·1 or 1·0 μg/ml quinine sulphate solution in 0·1 N H_2SO_4 as solvent was used as standard. The intensity of the fluorescence in the standard was taken as 100%. The solvent was used as blank. To make results comparable, the calculations were made as if the 0·1 μg/mg standard solution had been used throughout. Since the figures obtained were usually below 1·0, they were given as multiplied by 100. From these values the specific fluorescence, i.e. the fluorescence referred to 1 mg protein was also calculated.

Table 11 shows a marked accumulation of the fluorescent substance in the elastolysates of arteriosclerotic aortae as compared with the aorta specimens obtained from children, young adults and a calf. The difference is most striking between the children's aortae and the sclerotic ones.

According to LaBella's (1963) investigations both the yellow pigment and the fluorescent substance accumulate in the human aorta parallel with age, and the latter exerts a tanning effect on elastin. Consequently, the number of cross-linkages is growing with age and as a result of this a step by step accumulation of an elastase-resistant insoluble fraction ensues. The latter may amount to 50 to 55% of the elastin isolable from the oldest subjects. LaBella (1961, 1962, 1963) separated by chromatography the yellow pigment of elastin from a colourless substance fluorescing from 405 to 440 mμ. Walford et al. (1961) also separated two fractions from elastolysate, one of which was poor and the other rich in pigment. Sinex and Faris (1962) think that in purified elastin both the yellow pigment and the fluorescent substance arise from auto-oxidated lipids. The question as to whether these lipids are already present in young aortae, and so are only oxidated later needs further investigation. The answer to this question has become more uncertain since Banga et al. (1965) found that after shaking the oxalic-acid hydrolysate of elastin with lipid solvents, four-fifth of the fluorescence appeared in the aqueous phase. Presumably the substance obtained by us from arteriosclerotic aorta specimens (Chapter VIII) also contains the factor fluorescing from 405 to 440 mμ, but this question has not yet been studied.

The fluorescent substance demonstrated by Banga, Mayláth-Palágyi and Jobbágy (1965) appeared in the early phase of elastolysis (30 minutes) under the experi-

TABLE 11

Fluorescence measured at 365 mμ in elastolysates of normal and arteriosclerotic aortae

	AORTA			Fluorescence in elastolysate calculated for 1 mg protein, related to the fluorescence of a solution of 0·1 μg quinine sulphate/ml H₂SO₄, × 100	
Experiment No.	Aorta No.	Age	Condition, origin	30 min	from 30 min to 24 h
1	131	5 hours	Normal human	1	13
2	129	8 months		6	13
3	130	9 years		13	18
4	133	24 ,,		14	18
5	77	28 ,,		17	18
6	132	36 ,,		13	22
7	65	49 ,,		61	48
8	78	50 ,,		52	88
9	62	57 ,,		52	51
10	106	59 ,,		87	48
11	76	62 ,,		21	24
12	85	63 ,,	Sclerotic human	64	66
13	99	67 ,,		77	35
14	23	68 ,,		74	36
15	66	70 ,,		52	52
16	24	71 ,,		90	26
17	61	74 ,,		61	72
18	60	80 ,,		48	68
19	103	80 ,,		97	42
20	63	82 ,,		141	47
21	83	83 ,,		46	62
22	70	86 ,,		43	54
23	101	88 ,,		74	44
24	105	90 ,,		78	47
25	89	91 ,,		51	97

Note: Each figure indicates an average calculated from several parallel experiments

mental conditions given by these authors. Its fluorescence was observed at 365 mμ. In this fraction the substance fluorescing from 405 to 440 mμ could not be detected. It was, however, observed several years ago (Banga and Horváth, unpublished experiments) that the elastolysate contains two fluorescent substances; one of these is water-soluble, whereas the other appears in the chloroform-methanol fraction. Since arteriosclerosis is associated with increased basophilia, i.e. an increased number of acid groups (Romhányi 1959), Banga has supposed that in the arteriosclerotic elastin an increased number of active groups are available to adsorb elastase, consequently elastolysis is speeded up. It was assumed that in the case of arteriosclerosis the long peptide chains of elastin split off and association of the short chains needs an increased amount of the fluorescent substance. The accumulation of fluorescent substances was confirmed experimentally by Banga, Mayláth-Palágyi and Jobbágy (1966).

The supposed role of the fluorescent substances in elastolysis is inconsistent with the postulate of Hall and Czerkawski (1961b), namely that the carboxyl groups responsible for the adsorption of elastase derive from glutamic and aspartic acid. In fact, Lansing et al. (1951) found an increased level of aspartic + glutamic acid in arteriosclerotic aortae. Nevertheless, certain considerations speak against this concept. The concentration of glutamic + aspartic acid in collagen is five times that in elastin. In collagen the polar amino acids come to about 40%, whereas in elastin only 6·8% of the amino acids are polar. According to Hall and Czerkawski (1961b) 10^5 g of the elastin protein contains only 12 moles of dibasic acids, 12 moles of diamino acids, 33 moles of aliphatic hydroxy acids and 7 moles of tyrosine, i.e. 80 polar amino acids (6·8%) altogether. Consequently, if the polar groups of the side chains were responsible for elastolysis, elastase should be considerably more effective on collagen than on elastin. In fact, however, elastase fails to dissolve native collagen even if the latter is in the swollen state; consequently, the high concentration of polar, first of all dibasic, amino acids cannot be responsible for the enhanced elastolysis. Even the presence of the (yellow) fluorescent substance(s) in elastin is another chemically demonstrable difference between elastin and collagen, besides the dissimilar amino-acid composition.

The specific effect of elastase on elastin is different from the general proteolytic effect as shown by Tolnay and Bagdy (1962) who studied the effects of elastase derivatives. While elastolytic activity completely ceased as a result of iodination, formalin treatment, nitration or esterification of elastase, some reactions characteristic of proteolytic enzymes remained demonstrable to a certain extent. Thus, elastolytic activity appears to be different from trypsin activity.

The above data suggest that elastolysis involves two phases. In the first phase the insoluble elastin turns into soluble α-elastin. This process is not associated with the release of amino groups as shown by Hall and Czerkawski (1961a,b) by means of the so-called "controlled elastolysis"; in the presence of sodium dodecyl sulphate the reaction proceeded until the elastin was solubilized, but no release of amino groups could be demonstrated. During the second phase of the process, when by splitting of elastin shorter peptide chains were formed, amino groups were released. The second phase could be inhibited with sodium dodecyl sulphate. The controlled elastolysis experiments of these authors have, therefore, brought further evidence for the reaction described by Banga (1951) at the earliest times of the studies

51

on elastolysis, after the author had demonstrated that solubilization of elastin in itself was not accompanied by any release of amino groups. In repeated experiments she found no correlation in the initial phase of the reaction between the number of released amino groups and the degree of elastolysis (unpublished experiments). At that time the author attributed elastolysis to fission of the hydrogen bridges. Banga and Schuler (1953) submitted the production of amino and carboxyl groups in the course of elastolysis to systematic research. The number of released carboxyl groups was negligible as compared with that of amino groups. From these experiments it can be concluded, retrospectively, that the carboxyl groups were bound by elastase, thus escaped being determined.

The second phase of elastolysis was proved by Naughton and Sanger (1958) experimentally. These authors studied the specific effect of elastase as proteolytic enzyme on fraction B of oxidated insulin. An initially fast reaction was observed which, however, slowed down later; the quantity of the alkali measured in the autotitrator was equivalent to the fission of a single bond. According to the analysis, the fission took place between the leucine and tyrosine residues. When the reaction had not been suspended, fission of other peptide bonds was observed. Trypsin is known to attack primarily the peptide bonds in which carboxyl groups of strong basic amino acids (arginine and lysine) take part, whereas chymotrypsin is specific to the greatest degree for ester bonds of cyclic amino acids. Unlike these enzymes as shown by Naughton and Sanger (1961) elastase, being also a pancreatic proteolytic enzyme, attacks the bonds involving the carboxyl group of neutral amino acids that possess a long aliphatic side-chain (leucine and valine). The same enzyme is responsible for several kinds of fission catalyzed neither by trypsin nor by chymotrypsin.

The activity of elastase, like that of trypsin and chymotrypsin can be inhibited with diisopropyl phosphofluoride (D.F.P.); 10^{-4}M D.F.P. proved to be completely inhibitory. Naughton and Sanger (1961) prepared radioactive diisopropyl phosphoryl elastase from crystalline elastase by the procedure described by Naughton et al. (1960) using ^{32}P-labelled D.F.P. Experiments on insulin A and B fractions as substrate have shown that elastase splits off the bonds adjacent to neutral amino acids. This observation explains the specificity of elastase for elastin which is mainly built of amino-acid residues with aliphatic side-chains. Hartley et al. (1959) were able to demonstrate in elastase the Gly-Asp-Ser-Gly sequence in the neighbourhood of the reactive serine residue, i.e. the same sequence that had been found in the trypsin and chymotrypsin molecules. This finding explains the inhibition of elastase by D.F.P.

Hall (1954) assumed the role of a Ca atom in uniting elastase with its substrate, Ca being fixed to both of these proteins by chelate bonds. In the case of arteriosclerosis when the Ca level of the vascular wall is high (Lansing et al. 1948; Banga 1963b), Ca may be bound to the carboxyl group of the fluorescent lipid as well as to any free carboxyl group of the peptide side-chains.

The different observations can be unified. One of the fluorescent substances may be an organic substance (possibly fatty acid) of low molecular weight (Loo-

52

meijer 1961), the carboxyl group of which may bind the active amino groups of elastase. The reaction leads to fission of a lipopeptide and, consequently, to solubilization of elastin, provided the fluorescent fatty acid plays a role in keeping the polypeptide chains together. On this basis the primary effect of elastase should be manifested in some kind of decomposition of the fluorescent fatty acid, and this results in specific elastolysis. This process is thought to lead to formation of soluble α-elastin. The fission of peptide bonds, i.e. the appearance of the polydisperse substance with high amino-group content (121 mol/10^5 g elastin) demonstrated by Partridge and Davis (1955) is, in our opinion and according to Hall and Czerkawski (1961b,c), a secondary reaction being related to the general proteolytic effect of elastase. In the secondary reaction other groups of the enzyme are active than in the primary effect. Consequently elastase, i.e. the elastoproteinase component of the elastolytic system is a bifunctional enzyme with two active centres.

Wood's (1958) experiments on reconstituted elastin also support the view that, though the arrangement of the molecules seems to be identical both in the reconstituted and purified elastin, some stabilizing factors present in the purified elastin are lacking from the reconstituted elastin.

Solubilization of elastin by oxalic acid results in the same α-elastin which is obtained during the first phase of the elastase reaction. Terminal-group determinations (Partridge and Davis 1955) allow us to conclude that the average length of the elastin chain is markedly reduced during solubilization. It seems likely that in the course of the coacervation the peptide chains show no longitudinal association, consequently they are significantly shorter than the peptide chains of the initial elastin. As a result of this, the elasticity modulus (Young's modulus) for reconstituted elastin is only 1/100th of that of purified elastin, and the reconstituted elastin is digestible by trypsin. The factor securing great stability for elastin appears to be identical with the yellow fluorescent substance. This is thought to be the factor keeping the peptide chains together, and the fission of this bond results in the formation of the soluble α-elastin. During reconstitution this factor cannot incorporate into the molecule at all or, if so, not in the original position. This structural difference may explain further differences between reconstituted and purified elastin, first of all the inability of the precipitated elastin (coacervate) to form fibrils. Consequently, the fluorescent substance plays a primary role in the stability of the elastic fibre.

According to Hall and Czerkawski (1961c), in addition to the above two mechanisms of elastolysis, i.e. solubilization and secondary degradation in solution, there is a third reaction that was termed preliminary. Its presence may be demonstrated by a marked change in elasticity of elastin during the early stages of elastolysis. According to these authors fission of some bonds takes place which results in loosening of structure and increased elastic tensility. As regards this reaction and its explanation some doubts may arise. The elastin preparations used by the authors had been boiled in acetic acid. As a result of boiling the fibrils embedded in the cementing substance are solubilized faster than the matrix itself. Consequently, boiled preparations give a virtual "preliminary reaction" in the earliest phase of elastolysis. Preliminary reaction is not demonstrable when native preparation is used.

In Chapter I the differences between the results of Dettmer (1952) and Schwarz and Dettmer (1953), and those of Hall et al. (1952) and Lansing et al. (1952) are discussed in detail. According to the former group of investigators the filaments embedded in native elastic fibres are not solubilized by elastase, whereas the latter authors are of the opposite opinion. The divergency may be explained by the fact that the latter two teams used preparations which had been boiled with acetic acid or alkali. In the native state the filaments embedded in elastic fibres are solubilized by elastomucoproteinase, but not by elastase. Boiling, on the other hand, renders the filaments elastase-digestible, loosens the complex molecule and increases tensibility. It should be emphasized that any pre-treatment may markedly change the behaviour of an elastic fibre. It was thought for a long time that elastin being a stable scleroprotein is not altered by boiling. Since then our opinion has fundamentally changed. The cementing substance and the embedded filaments are chemically distinct substances and the filaments after being boiled solubilize faster than in the native state. Accordingly, the interpretation of the preliminary reaction described by Hall and Czerkawski (1961c) is not valid for native elastic fibres.

ELASTASE INHIBITORS

Simultaneously with the discovery of elastase, Baló and Banga (1949a,b,c) found elastase-inhibiting activity in human and animal blood sera as well as in the pancreas. Subsequently, numerous authors studied the inhibition of elastase and it has been shown that even salts may act as inhibitors in physiological or higher concentrations (Lewis et al. 1956; Winter and Fränkel 1956; Tolnay and Bagdy 1959; Thomas and Partridge 1960; Amati and Castelli 1961; Lamy et al. 1961). Physiological saline showed 50 to 75% inhibition, depending on the method of assay. Since the effects of different monovalent and divalent ions and the corresponding literature have been reviewed by Mandl (1961) as well as by Loeven (1963a), this question is not discussed in detail in the present work. As regards Ca^{++}, Hall's (1954) hypothesis is of interest. He suggests that this ion activates elastolysis. Tolnay and Bagdy (1959) found in the serum, in addition to the salt inhibitors, a specific elastase-inhibitor of high molecular weight.

Baló and Banga (1949a,b,c) supposed that in the pancreas a great part of elastase is not in an active state but it is present partly as proenzyme, partly bound to inhibitors. Baló and Banga (1953b) could increase the low elastase activity of pancreas extracts by dialysis, and found inhibitors in the dialysate. Such an inhibitory effect was demonstrated in the dialysate by Lewis et al. (1956) as well. Since, however, these authors found the same inhibitory effect in the ash of the dialysate, they denied the existence of a special elastin-inhibitor (E.I.) in the pancreas and attributed the effect to the salts present in the pancreatic extracts. Loeven

(1962a) separated from the elastase complex a non-dialysable protein component by starch-column chromatography; this component, designated IE_2, inhibited elastoproteinase (E_2). By these observations the existence of an elastase-specific pancreatic E.I. distinguishable from the salt effect as suggested by Baló and Banga has been confirmed. According to Loeven, however, only little amounts of this substance are present in the pancreas, and for this reason Lewis et al. (1956) could not identify it, furthermore, Loeven found the inhibitor to be dialysable under the conditions applied. Loeven (1962a) suggests that the controversy may be explained by the relative coarse porosity of the German dialysis tubes used by Baló and Banga. He employed tubes of finer porosity (made in England) and under these circumstances the pancreatic E.I. was found to be non-dialysable.

Banga (1963a) evolved a highly reliable test to assay E.I. both in the serum and the pancreas, using orcein-elastin as substrate. She plotted the standard curve on the basis of experiments carried out with pure, homogeneous elastase; the orcein-elastin was prepared with the optimum staining. The principle of the assay is as follows. To assay serum inhibitor, elastase of known activity, e.g. 20 E.U., was incubated with an aliquot of serum, and the activity of the mixture was measured on orcein-elastin. The difference between the number of E.U. added and the measured value gives the quantity of E.I. in units. Accordingly, one unit of E.I. represents the quantity that inhibits the activity of 1 E.U. (This method of estimation appears to be more reliable than that recommended by Loeven (1962a), i.e. the expression of the inhibition in per cent.) To demonstrate the inhibitor content of the pancreas, extracts were prepared with acetate buffer of pH 4·7. After the pH was adjusted to 7·4, the further procedure was the same as in the case of the blood serum. The inhibitor could only be detected in the pancreas specimens which showed no elastolytic activity, i.e. in those containing "free" inhibitor capable of binding the elastase added. Free inhibitor is mainly present in arteriosclerotic corpses. Banga (1963a) found 25 to 44 units of E.I. per g pancreas powder in atherosclerotic pancreas specimens, whereas the inhibitor was never detectable in the pancreas of corpses with normal vascular systems.

Animal and human sera contained 100 to 160 E.I. units per ml. Veres (1961) who studied E.I. activity histologically, found 70 to 80 units per ml human serum. This is about one half of the value demonstrated by the biochemical test on isolated orcein-elastin. When using our biochemical method, we incubated the mixture for 15 minutes and calculated the results for 30 minutes, i.e. the experimental results were multiplied by two. We calculated the E.I. values from the units so obtained; consequently, the E.I. values obtained by this method represented twice the number of E.U. inhibited in fact. The expression of inhibitor activity in E.I. units representing the number of elastase units inhibited under given conditions appears to be preferable to the calculation in per cent because a great number of tests have shown that the percentage inhibition depends on the specific activity of the enzyme preparation used. A preparation of low activity will dissolve less elastin during the unit of time than a highly purified enzyme, yet, e.g. both of these preparations may be completely inhibited by the same amount of a serum.

Similarly, when different elastase preparations are used, the same percentage inhibition may indicate different enzyme activities. In contrast to this, expression of inhibitor activity in E.I. units gives reproducible results even when different elastase preparations are used. In spite of this, it is recommended to use the same preparation in large series of experiments, and the incubation period as well as the other experimental conditions should be kept consistent.

A simple calculation will show the ratio of the elastase produced by the human pancreas to the inhibitor content of the human blood. On the basis of the histological assay, cited above, the average inhibitor concentration of the normal human serum may be estimated at 80 E.I. units per ml, i.e. the total inhibitor content of the approximately 5 l blood is able to inhibit the activity of about 400 000 E.U.

The pancreas of a young adult contains 200 E.U. as calculated for 1 g acetone-dried powder, i.e. for 5 g wet weight. If an adult pancreas in the wet state weighs 80 to 100 g and 1 g of the pancreas contains 40 E.U., the total elastase present in the whole organ amounts to approximately 4000 E.U., i.e. only 1/100th of the quantity that would be inhibited by the total E.I. content of the blood. If it is true that the inhibitor serves as a compensator of elastase activity, the latter must be highly over-compensated in the human organism. Thus, an experimentally, scarcely detectable decrease (10 to 20%) in the inhibitor level may lead to a significant imbalance in the elastolytic system. Such an imbalance might significantly influence the destructive and synthetic processes of elastic fibres.

In the case of essential haemosiderosis, an illness showing the highest incidence during childhood, the blood level of E.I. may rise to 180 to 200% of the normal level (Banga and Schuler, unpublished experiments). Since this disease is characterized by a supposedly enzymatic destruction of the vascular elastic fibres, the high inhibitor level may be considered an overcompensation. The enhanced elastolysis needs an increased amount of E.I. to be inhibited to such an extent that even the elevated E.I. level is unsatisfactory in preventing the vascular wall from being digested.

The E.I. of the blood is different both from the pancreatic elastase inhibitor and the trypsin inhibitor (Baló and Banga 1949c). In the course of the isolation procedure the elastase inhibitor of the blood was inactivated by 2·5% trichloro-acetic acid, while the trypsin inhibitor retained its activity. In addition, numerous trypsin-inhibitors such as soy-bean trypsin inhibitor, ovomucoid, kallikrein, (Veres and Mayláth-Palágyi 1964) proved to be ineffective when tested for inhibition of elastolysis (Walford and Schneider 1959; Giuseppe and Castelli 1957). The mucoprotein component of the bovine plasma should be regarded a special trypsin inhibitor (Wu and Laskowski 1960). This substance reacted with elastase stoichiometrically, but the dissociation rate of the complex so produced exceeded 100 times that of the trypsin-inhibitor complex. An observation of Graham (1960) also speaks against the identity of the serum E.I. with the trypsin inhibitor of the blood; serum-inhibited elastase could be freed from the inhibitor by trypsin, indicating that some inhibitors, though being inhibitors of a certain group of elastase, show a greater affinity to trypsin. These observations emphasize again the more or less proved hypothesis (pp. 51—52) suggesting that elastolysis proceeds in several steps, in each of which certain active groups of elastase take part. The fact that, like the trypsin and chymotrypsin molecules, elastase also possesses a Gly-Asp-Ser-Gly amino-acid sequence near the active serine may explain why the inhibitors of trypsin and chymotrypsin also inhibit elastase. Considering this concept we can accept some contradictory publications on this subject. Walford and Schneider (1959) showed that chicken and human sera, though they inhibit the elastin/elastase system, do not influence the casein/elastase one; according to these authors the serum inhibitor is specific for the elastolytic activity, i.e. it fails to inhibit the wide-scale proteolytic activity of elastase manifesting in the digestion of casein. Consequently, the serum contains a distinct elastase inhibitor. Bagdy et al. (1961, 1962) also demonstrated two distinct inhibitor systems in the serum, such as an elastase inhibitor and a trypsin inhibitor. In their experiments the specific elastolytic activity of elastase was scarcely inhibited by trypsin inhibitors, even when these were present in concentrations most favourable for the inhibition of trypsin. In contrast to this, the non-specific, proteolytic effect of elastase, i.e. that demonstrable on casein or haemoglobin, proved to be significantly more sensitive to trypsin inhibitors. Walford and Kickhöfen (1962) published similar results.

As to the nature of the elastase inhibitor of the blood inconsistent data have been published, and the foregoing explain the cause of the controversy. According to Banga et al. (1954b) the inhibitor activity of the serum is higher by about 30% than that of the whole blood. Consequently, the corpuscular elements of the blood contain no elastase inhibitor. Robert and Samuel (1957a) found the inhibitor activity in the α-lipoprotein fraction; according to these authors the β-lipoprotein fraction shows no inhibitor activity. Walford and Schneider (1959) who separated the components by starch-gel electrophoresis found the inhibitor at the junction of α_1-globulin and albumin. Saxl (1957a, b, 1961) thinks that a fraction rich in α_2-globulin is responsible for the inhibitor effect which, in her opinion, is necessary for the detection of the elastomucase clearing factor. The fact that in the author's laboratories, besides elastase inhibitor, an inhibitor of the elastomucoproteinase was demonstrable in the blood suggests that the two inhibitors may take place in different fractions of the blood. Such an assumption would explain the difference between the experimental results of Saxl and of Walford et al. In Loeven's (1963b) opinion the elastase inhibitor is contained in the α_2-globulin fraction, thus the authors who found it in the α_1 fraction worked with preparations contaminated with the α_2 fraction. Tolnay and Bagdy (1959) and Bagdy et al. (1961, 1962) found a marked inhibition in fractions containing pseudoglobulin and albumin. Considering the molecule weights, this specific inhibition was 1000 to 2000 times the inhibitor activity of the inorganic salts. Graham (1958) who fractionated the serum by the same method found the inhibitor in the $\alpha_1 + \alpha_2$ globulin fraction.

There are controversies even concerning the resistance of the elastase inhibitor to heat and pH. The lability of the serum inhibitor above 56 °C as demonstrated by Baló and Banga (1949b, c), Tolnay and Bagdy (1959) and Walford and Schneider

(1959) was not confirmed by Loeven (1963a), whereas Robert and Samuel (1957a) and Walford and Schneider (1959) observed a slow decrease in the inhibitor activity even at 37 °C. The former investigators think that the decrease at 37 °C is caused by a slow hydrolytic activity of the enzyme on the inhibitor. According to Loeven (1963b) no loss in the inhibitor activity is demonstrable when the inhibitor to enzyme ratio is so high that 100% of the enzyme is in the inactive state. If less inhibitor is present, the non-inhibited enzyme will slowly digest the elastin, i.e. the inhibitor activity appears to be lost.

The serum-inhibitor level has been extensively investigated in animals and in man in connection with senescence, pregnancy and several diseases.

Banga et al. (1954a) produced experimental arteriosclerosis in rabbits by the administration of ammonium hydroxide. They found that an increased serum cholesterol level was always accompanied by a decrease in the elastase inhibitor. According to Baló (1963) the acidosis produced by ammonium hydroxide might have been responsible for the destruction of the elastase inhibitor in these experiments. Alekseyeva (1956, 1959) who investigated the same problem confirmed the findings of the authors cited, viz. she produced atherosclerosis by feeding animals with cholesterol dissolved in helianthus oil (Anitschkow's method), and as a result of this she observed a decrease in the serum E.I. level.

Pretolani (1960a,b) found a rise in the E.I. content of the human serum up to 50 years of age; at this age the percentage inhibition was about twice that found for 20 to 30 years of age. Over 50 years the inhibitor level remained constant till the highest age studied. Salvini (1960) published similar results. In contrast to these, Walford and Schneider (1959) were unable to detect any change in the inhibitor activity of the serum parallel with age.

Schneider et al. (1960) found a significant rise in the E.I. level of pregnant women as well as in the rat, but not in the rabbit during pregnancy. In the author's laboratories Veres (1961) arrived at similar results. Accordingly, in the serum of pregnant women the E.I. level rises in the second month of pregnancy. Subsequently, it remains constant till delivery, and one month after it is at its normal level again. The similar fluctuation observed in the pregnant rat could not be suppressed significantly by either ACTH or oestrogens or progesteron. Schneider et al. (1960) attribute the quantitative changes in the E.I. during pregnancy to the mucoid substances accumulated in the interstitial tissue of the aorta. According to these authors the accumulation is accompanied by metabolic disturbances in the elastic tissues of the aorta. An observation of Gilfillan et al. (1960, 1961) is of special interest. These authors found the serum level of the E.I. during pregnancy to be three times higher compared with the normal value, while in the blood taken from the umbilical cord the E.I. level was markedly low.

Diabetes, hepatic cirrhosis and cardiovascular diseases were the conditions in which Pretolani et al. (1960b) found high E.I. levels. These could not be suppressed by elastase injections even when the latter were administered over several days. Elevated E.I. levels were found in cases of dermatomyositis and disseminated lupus erythematosus, both of which are considered to be collagen diseases, as well as in cases of the nephrosis syndrome (Walford and Schneider 1959). Also in diseases accompanied by an altered protein metabolism (Gilfillan et al. 1961), and probably by alterations in the structure of the elastin and of the collagen, an elevated E.I. level was observable in the blood.

In the serum of patients suffering from severe arteriosclerosis the quantity of the substance inhibiting the elastolytic enzyme was found to be at a low level (Baló and Banga 1949a). According to these authors 0·1 ml blood of healthy subjects inhibited six elastolytic units, whereas in extremely severe cases of arteriosclerosis 0·1 ml serum showed no inhibition under experimental conditions.

CHAPTER V

THE ROLE OF MUCOLYSIS AND LIPOLYSIS IN ELASTOLYSIS

ACTIVATION OF ELASTOPROTEINASE (E_2) BY ELASTOMUCASE (E_1) AND THE BIOCHEMICALLY VERIFIABLE MECHANISM OF THE ACTIVATION

THE ELASTOMUCASE fraction called E_1 was first isolated by Hall (1957a, b) by paper electrophoresis from elastase-containing preparations. This author demonstrated that the E_1 when added to the E_2 fraction was capable of activating the elastolytic effect of the latter by 80 to 100%. To give a possible explanation for the activation he suggested that the E_1 fraction which fails to be elastoproteolytic in itself is able to loosen the layer surrounding elastin fibrils. In this layer the elastin protein is kept together by polysaccharides. This system secures the stability of the elastic fibres. In the inner layer there are only fibrils consisting of elastin protein, running parallel with the axis of the fibre. These fibrils are kept together by forces other than polysaccharide linkages. Hall determined the polysaccharide contents of the elastolysates obtained by hydrolysis with mixtures of the E_1 and E_2 fractions. He found that the mucopolysaccharides solubilized by a mixture consisting of 10% E_2 in the E_1 fraction contained polysaccharides in 65%, whereas a mixture consisting of 10% E_1 in the E_2 fraction produced elastolysates with 29% polysaccharide content. Hall (1953, 1957a, b) supposed that the proteolytic component of elastase solubilized both the elastin of the outer layer and the internal fibrils which consist of proelastin, whereas elastomucase only attacked the outer layer which is stabilized by polysaccharides. The problem of the fine mechanism of elastomucase action has not yet been solved. Nevertheless, the submicroscopic investigations discussed below (Chapter VI, pp. 71–80) may approximate a possible solution of this question. In contrast to Hall's theory, Partridge et al. (1955) and Partridge and Davis (1955) are of the opinion that the elementary elastic fibre consists of a chemically homogeneous protein and contains no polysaccharide as stabilizing factor. It is, nevertheless, heterogeneous at the macromolecular level, being composed of α- and β-elastin. It has been mentioned that the amino-acid composition of these two components is the same, but the molecular weight of α-elastin is significantly higher than that of β-elastin. Accordingly, a single elastolytic agent, namely elastase is sufficient to solubilize, i.e. digest elastin. The typical physical characteristics of the elastic tissue, e.g. elastic tensibility, are explainable by the macromolecular structure of elastin and by the special coherence of the fibrils with collagen and mucoproteins or mucopolysaccharides. Loeven (1960a) was the most successful in confirming Hall's hypothesis. He employed two different substrates in experiments, viz. 1. alkali-treated, and 2. acid-treated elastin, both prepared from the lig. nuchae. He examined the effect of E_2 and E_1 on the velocity of elastolysis and on the tyrosine, hydroxyproline and hexosamine contents of the elastolysate. The two factors were used either separately or together. The difference in the mechanism of action between the two enzymes manifested, first of all, in the temporal appearance and in the quantity of hexosamine. By the end of the fifth hour of treatment with separated E_2 fraction (elastoproteinase) 50% of the alkali-treated elastin had been solubilized, but no hexosamine had been detectable. Hexosamine only appeared after the other 50% of the elastin has passed into solution. The solubilization of the second 50% of elastin needed less time (three hours), i.e. the reaction speeded up like autocatalytic reactions. A similar acceleration of elastolysis was observed when both E_1 and E_2 were added to elastin. In this case, however, the total amount of hexosamine had been released when only 30 to 40% of the elastin had been dissolved. In the case of acid-treated elastin the elastolysis with E_2 is faster, and hexosamine appears sooner than in alkali-treated elastin. In the presence of E_1, however, a great amount of hexosamine is released as early as in the first hour of elastolysis; later during elastolysis the ratio of dissolved hexosamine to the elastin protein declines. Besides the temporal course of elastolysis, the correlation between enzyme activity and the composition of the resulting elastolysate was investigated by Loeven (1960a) in the light of the mechanism of action of the two enzymes. His extensive experiments have convincingly proved the synergistic effect of E_1 on E_2.

It was in 1955 when in the author's laboratories Banga and Bagdy (unpublished experiments) first prepared elastase fractions with very small activity on elastic fibres. The supernatants, i.e. elastolysates produced by these enzyme fractions, nevertheless, contained a polysaccharide-like substance. Subsequently, in a preparative way (Chapter III, p. 37) a larger amount of this fraction was produced. Its effects on the elastic fibres of the lig. nuchae, on the Achilles tendon and on the collagen fibres of the rat tail were studied in parallel experiments. It was found (Banga and Baló 1956) that the preparation solubilized mucoid substances both from collagen and elastic fibres, but the mucoids dissolved from the two substrates proved to be distinguishable from each other, viz. the two reaction products gave different colour adsorptions with the Szára-Molisch reagent (Banga and Baló 1957) (Fig. 18).

Banga and Baló (1956) assumed that the two mucoid substances are dissolved by two distinct enzymes and termed the latter elastomucoproteinase and collagen-mucoproteinase, respectively (Chapter III, p. 39).

During the studies on the mucoproteinases of the connective tissue two problems arose (Banga and Baló 1957). The first one was related to the mucoproteins as substrates; 95 to 96% of the isolated fibres of the connective tissue (lig. nuchae, Achilles tendon and rat-tail tendon) consist of polypeptide chains; mucoproteins amount only to 3 to 5%. However, mucoproteins cannot be isolated from the connective tissue by chemical methods without causing substantial alterations in their molecules (e.g. some part of the mucoids of the connective tissue can be dissolved in strong alkali or concentrate $CaCl_2$ solution, but these agents split off the linkages between the protein and the mucopolysaccharide components, thus cease the native state of the mucoproteins). Because of the lack of any adequate method for preparing the substrate from the connective-tissue fibres, mucoproteinase activity has to be measured on native substrates, the majority of which represent ballast for the enzyme. Consequently, some classical methods of the enzyme analysis, e.g. determination of substrate-concentration curves are in these cases not feasible.

The other problem lies in the difficulty of separating some mucolytic enzymes from the proteolytic components. As a result of proteolysis, acid and neutral

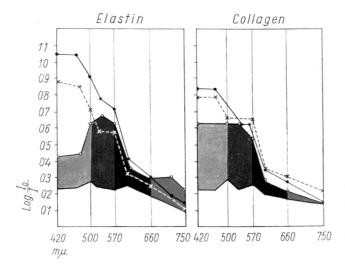

FIG. 18. Colour adsorption by the mucoid of the elastin (a), and of the collagen (b); (Szára-Molisch reagent); abscissa = wavelength in mμ; ordinate = extinction

TABLE 12

Characterization of mucoproteolytic enzymes

Enzyme	Substrate	Stability	End products
Elastomucoproteinase	Nuchal ligament (collagen-free) Aorta (collagen-free)	2 components: thermolabile + thermostable	2 components: non-dialysable mucoprotein (75%) + dialysable carbohydrate (25%)
Collagenmucoproteinase	Achilles tendon Procollagen Metacollagen Rat's tail tendon	2 components: thermolabile + thermostable	2 components: nondialysable mucoprotein (75%) + dialysable carbohydrate (25%)
Serum mucoproteinase	Serum protein	Thermolabile	Mucoprotein

62

mucopolysaccharides are also released. Consequently, the proteins that have been associated with the polysaccharide cannot be distinguished from those which were solubilized by any non-specific reaction. The use of radioactive isotopes and the introduction of quite new methods are expected to clarify the exact mechanism of action of these enzymes. Otherwise neither the components of acid MPS-s (hexuronic acid and hexosamine) nor the polysaccharides present in the neutral MPS can be determined accurately in the presence of proteins and/or protein hydrolysates.

Table 12 summarizes the characteristics and mechanism of action of the mucolytic enzymes having been isolated from the elastase-enzyme complex.

Loeven (1963b) pointed out that in order to explain the data obtained in this field it should be accepted that elastase has a group with mucolytic activity besides its proteolytic component.

THE LIPOPROTEINASE ACTIVITY OF ELASTOMUCOPROTEINASE

The assumption that also lipids are released from elastic fibres during elastolysis originates from Lansing et al. (1952) who observed lipids to appear while elastin was solubilized. According to LaBella (1957, 1958) elastin contains 0·5% lipid consisting of a cerebroside and a substance resembling plasmalogen. The positive PAS reaction of elastolysates is a function of the latter substance.

Banga and Baló (1962) and Banga (1962a) made efforts to find a substrate and a method, both suitable for demonstration of lipolytic activity in their EMPase preparations produced in a preparative way and by starch-gel electrophoresis. They found the acetone-dehydrated powder of the human aorta to be an appropriate substrate. From these EMPase dissolves a proteid amounting to 20 to 25% of the total protein content of the preparation. The latter contains neuramic acid, neutral and acid MPS-s and also lipids. For this reason it was termed mucolipoprotein complex or mucolipoproteid. To clarify the question Baló and Banga (1962) measured the activity of elastase and that of EMPase comparatively. They made attempts to demonstrate whether each of the two enzymes solubilizes different human aorta powders with consistent velocity and whether the difference in the reaction velocity of the two enzymes is constant when different aorta powders are used as substrate. Table 13 shows that different aorta powders were solubilized by the same enzyme at approximately the same rate, whereas elastase solubilized the aorta powders at a higher rate than did EMPase. The last column of the table shows that the activity of the elastase preparation was about twice that of the EMPase.

The difference between the two enzymes was demonstrable also in the mucopolysaccharide content of the elastolysates. In Table 14 the mucopolysaccharide contents of the proteins dissolved from various substrates by the two enzymes are presented in per cent. The percentages of the mucopolysaccharide components under study, viz. the Anthron-positive substance, hexosamine, hexuronic acid and neuramic acid were twice as high in the lysates obtained with EMPase as in

TABLE 13

Activity of elastase and elastomucoproteinase on the human aorta

Protocol No.	Substrate	Aorta age (years)	Activity		
			Elastase (E.U./mg)	Elastomuco-proteinase (E.M.U./mg)	E.U./mg per E.M.U./mg
15	Human aorta	83	96	42	2·28
16	Human aorta	73	96	49	2·07
17	Human aorta	88	86	43	2·00
19	Human aorta	67	90	42	1·90
21	Human aorta	73	100	48	2·08
22	Human aorta	79	94	32	2·90
24	Human aorta	71	94	46	2·05
28	Human aorta	79	90	40	2·24
37	Human aorta	19	96	46	2·28
40	Human aorta	74	96	56	1·70

Note: Substrate 100 mg; enzyme 0·5 mg; incubation 30 minutes

those solubilized by elastase. Table 14 shows that the neuramic acid and hexosamine content of the mucolipoproteide dissolved from arteriosclerotic aortae was higher by 110% and 60% respectively than of the mucolipoproteide derived from a calf aorta. Czerkawski (1962) suggests that elastin is a sialoprotein and, in his opinion, sialic acid is bound to hexuronic acid. Our own results have proved the existence of a linkage between sialic acid and hexosamine; one half of the hexosamine and

TABLE 14

Mucopolysaccharide content in per cent of the proteins solubilized by elastase or elastomucoproteinase

Substrate	Enzyme	Anthron-positive substance	Hexuronic acid	Hexosamine	Neuramic acid
		Expressed in per cent of the solubilized protein			
Human aorta	Elastase	2·9	0·94	2·98	1·50
Human aorta	EMPase	4·8	1·90	3·80	2·70
Calf aorta	Elastase	2·5	0·70	0·97	0·83
Calf aorta	EMPase	4·2	1·20	2·30	1·24

Note: Calculated for the materials solubilized by the enzymes during 30 minutes; 100 mg substrate and 0·5 mg enzyme in 5 ml

64

90% of the sialic acid were found in the protein spot (Table 16). Figure 19 shows the pattern of the electrophoretically separated mucolipoprotein.

The polypeptides in the elastolysates, obtained either by elastase or EMPase, are readily soluble in lipid solvents. The elastolysates of the lig. nuchae and of the isolated elastin were found to contain proteins soluble in methanol-chloroform (1 : 3) up to 65 to 72% and 83 to 95% respectively. The lipid determined in the

FIG. 19. Elpho pattern of the mucolipoprotein complex; (red colour indicates protein, bluish-red colour, metachromatic spot)

elastolysate that had been freed from protein by Bloor's (1943) procedure (summarized by Sperry 1955) was also measurable by Bragdon's (1951) method. In the case of the same aorta the lipid content of the elastolysate produced by EMPase was considerably higher than that of the elastase-produced lysate. The results are summarized in Table 15. In the last column of the table the total lipid content

TABLE 15

Lipid content of the protein solubilized from different substrates by elastase and elastomucoproteinase

Substrate	Age (years)	Enzyme	Solubilized from 100 mg of substrate		Lipid content of protein (%)
			protein (mg)	lipid (mg)	
Human aorta	30	Elastase	48	1·2	2·6
Human aorta	95	Elastase	43	2·8	6·5
Human aorta	19	EMPase	21	3·6	17·0
Human aorta	30	EMPase	25	3·0	12·0
Human aorta	67	EMPase	20	3·0	15·0
Human aorta	73	EMPase	24	4·8	20·0
Human aorta	83	EMPase	19	5·5	29·0
Human aorta	93	EMPase	20	4·5	22·5
Calf aorta	—	Elastase	60	0·9	1·5
Calf aorta	—	EMPase	25	4·8	19·4

is given in per cent of the polypeptides solubilized by the corresponding enzyme. It is seen that while in the EMPase-produced lysate the lipid content amounts to 16 to 25% of the protein content, the respective percentage for the elastase-produced lysate was only 1·5 to 6%. Banga and Baló (1962) determined the fatty-acid content and the iodine number in the EMPase-dissolved lipid which had been freed from polypeptides. They found both values to be relatively low, suggesting that the lipid is not a simple neutral fat.

On the basis of experimental data it has been supposed that the protein + mucopolysaccharide + lipid content of the elastolysate obtained with EMPase represents a single complex molecule which can thus be regarded a mucolipoprotein complex. Subsequently this hypothesis was proved by paper-electrophoretic analysis of the complex; the neutral MPS-s and the lipids migrated together with the protein component. On the other hand, the component containing the acid MPS migrated faster at pH 8·6 and gave a bluish-violet colour with toluidine blue. The same fraction gave neither the fuchsin nor the amido-black reaction, both specific for proteins. The other component was hardly shifted from the starting point towards the positive pole, but showed a strong protein reaction and gave a red colour, characteristic of lipids, with oilred; Fig. 19 shows the electrophoretograms.

Table 16 reflects the analysis of the components separated by paper electrophoresis from the mucolipoprotein complex of the aorta.

All these experiments unequivocally show that the human aorta is a substrate from which EMPase dissolves a complex containing both MPS-s and lipids. The acid MPS-s are not bound to the protein by covalent bonds (only heteropolar bonds have been demonstrated) and migrate separately in the electric field. Unlike these, the neutral MPS-s and the lipids show the same mobility as the protein component, suggesting that the lipid component is covalently bound to the protein.

Saxl (1957a, b) demonstrated by histochemical and electron-microscopic investigations that elastomucase takes part in the disintegration of the chylomicrons, and so can moderate the turbidity of the lipaemic serum. This means that E_1 shows *in vitro* clearing-factor activity. However, this effect cannot be brought about without the acid MPS-s of the elastolysates and certain serum components. As acid MPS-s, first of all chondroitin sulphate and heparin are taken into consideration, but the MPS-s liberated on the effect of elastase from the elastic tissue show a significantly greater activity.

Based on the concept that there is a close relationship between atherosclerosis and lipid metabolism, we made efforts to throw light on the effect exerted by the

TABLE 16

Analysis of the aorta mucolipoprotein separated by paper electrophoresis

	Percentage distribution	
	Protein spot	Meta-chromatic spot
Protein	90	10
Anthron-positive substance	71	29
Hexuronic acid	10	90
Neuramic acid	90	10
Lipid	90	—

elastase-enzyme complex on the lipids of the blood. It was found that when elastase complex was added *in vitro* to lipaemic serum (320 E.U. per ml serum) and the mixture was incubated for 10 to 16 hours, the serum became turbid, i.e. lactaemic (Fig. 20). Thus, in our experiments the elastase complex produced turbidity instead of showing the clearing effect. In some cases with certain EMPase preparations we observed a clearing effect but, owing to a shortage of enzyme, we could not continue these experiments systematically. The microscopic picture of a serum made turbid with the elastase complex is shown in Fig. 21. To clarify the cause of the increased turbidity, we examined the alteration brought about in the relative quantity of the fraction lipid-soluble protein + cholesterol. The results have unequivocally proved that the elastase-enzyme complex exerts its effect on the β-lipoproteins by splitting these substances into two separable components. Elastase double the quantity of the lipopeptides contained in the lipid-soluble fraction as com-

a   b

FIG. 20. Turbidization of the lipaemic serum on the effect of elastase; (a) control serum; (b) the same after incubation with elastase

pared with the lipaemic control serum. Furthermore, a new lipoprotein with dissimilar characteristics arose. The latter substance precipitated in lipid solvents from the lipaemic serum during storage and so it was separable from the

TABLE 17

Analysis of fractions isolated from human lipaemic sera by elastase

Serum	Treatment	Lipopeptide soluble in lipid solvents (%)	Protein insoluble in lipid solvents: cholesterol/protein %
Lipaemic serum$_1$	None	32	2·8
Lipaemic serum$_1$	Elastase	64	4·2
Lipaemic serum$_2$	None	33	2·9
Lipaemic serum$_2$	Elastase	66	4·4

β-lipoprotein. Its cholesterol content was higher than that of the β-lipoprotein (Table 17). It seems likely that the appearance of the new lipoprotein was due to the elastolipoproteinase activity of the elastase-enzyme complex (Loeven 1964a, d).

The rise of a new lipoprotein with higher cholesterol content was confirmed by paper electrophoresis. As the latter had separated, the β-lipoprotein spot disappeared from the paper strip and a diffuse spot could be seen at the same site. In addition, a much more intensely stained lipid spot was seen at the site of the α-globulin, confirming the existence of the lipoprotein fraction insoluble in lipid solvents.

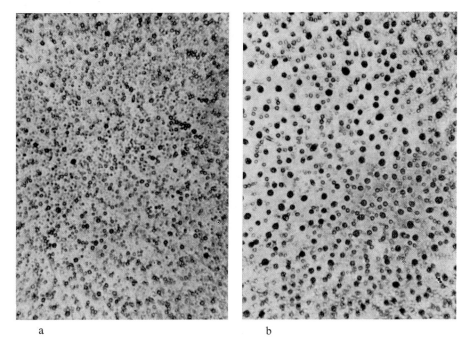

a   b

FIG. 21. Microscopic picture of a lipaemic serum made turbid by incubation with elastase; (a) control serum; (b) the same serum after incubation

The elastolipoproteinase activity of the elastase-enzyme complex could also be demonstrated when a lipoprotein which was isolated from the lipaemic blood of cholesterol-fed rabbits was used as substrate (Baló and Banga 1962). Using the ten methods of the Cohn fractionation, we found the β-lipoprotein in fraction III. The isoelectric point of this protein was at pH 4·6. The lipoprotein precipitated at this pH contained 32% cholesterol. If the same serum fraction was submitted to elastase digestion, the precipitation at the isoelectric point resulted in a lipoprotein with only 14% cholesterol. On the basis of this observation we have concluded that the elastolipoproteinase component of the elastase complex is capable of binding cholesterol; 1 mg of the enzyme-complex protein with an activity of 80 E.U. is capable of binding 0·4 mg of cholesterol.

Hall (1958) observed only a slight clearing effect with E_1 in sera with alimentary lipaemia, for the concentration of acid MPS-s was too low in the sera of this

kind of lipaemia. A substantially more pronounced effect was observed in cholesterolaemic chicken sera which contains more acid MPS. In Hall's opinion an
interaction between elastomucase, α-globulin and acid polysaccharides results
in a lipoprotein-lipase activity which is comparable with the lipoprotein-lipase
activity of the post-heparin serum. As a result of this activity non-esterified fatty
acids are liberated from the lipaemic-blood serum or from triglyceride substrates.
Using Tween as substrate, Hall (1961c) found the esterolytic activity of elastomucase (crude preparation) to be different from that of pancreatic lipase. He
examined the effect of the latter in control experiments. In the same publication
Hall refers to the β-globulin (not to the α-globulin) as a factor playing a role in
the clearing reaction.

Szabó and Cseh (1962) examined the lipoproteide-lipase activity of the elastase-enzyme complex as compared with the heparin effect. As substrate an artificial lipoprotein (Ediol-albumin activated with fresh human serum) was used in these experiments. The lipolytic activity of elastase and that of heparin were determined when
each of these agents was added alone and after preincubation of each of these substances with acetone-dried powders of preparations obtained from various vascular walls.

The elastase complex in itself was found to exert a lipolytic effect on the artificial lipoproteide complex. This effect was, however, only about one half of that
exerted by heparin. Unlike this, the lipolytic effect of the elastase complex often
exceeded that of the heparin if the former had been preincubated with the acetone-
dried powder of certain vascular walls. In the case of powdered veins and coronaries
this excess amounted to 50 to 80% and a considerable excess was observed in the
case of powdered aorta as well. After preincubation with powdered carotids the two
activities were equal, whereas the heart heparin showed a higher activity than
did elastase. In the case of veins another interesting phenomenon was observed;
the clearing effect of preincubated elastase exceeded the activities that were measured
when heparin or elastase were applied alone. This observation could be explained
by assuming that elastase solubilized lipoproteine-lipase from the veins or that a
heparin-like substance was released which exerted a more intensive clearing
effect than did heparin. Elastase-treatment of acetonized powders prepared from
the vena cava resulted in the solubilization of at least two substances, viz. a thermolabile clearing-lipase and a thermostable component which, like heparin, was
able to enhance enzyme activity. The authors suppose that veins play a role in
the decomposition of chylomicrons and that the elastase-enzyme complex also
plays a part in this function.

THE ELASTOMUCOPROTEINASE INHIBITOR

It has been shown (see p. 61) that the assay of elastomucoproteinase activity
encounters some difficulties. Consequently, demonstration of an inhibitor of
this enzyme also requires severe criticism. A highly-purified EMPase preparation
which in the applied concentration does not dissolve the isolated elastin at all

is a prerequisite of an appropriate assay. In addition, the enzyme should be capable of increasing the elasticity of carotid stripes (Banga and Baló 1960a) and passing into solution from human aorta powders a mucolipoprotein up to 20 to 25% (p. 63).

It appears to be of great importance whether or not the human serum contains a distinct EMPase inhibitor besides the trypsin and elastase inhibitors. Banga and Baló (partly unpublished experiments) found blood serum to be inhibitory to the elasticity-enhancing effect of EMPase which is demonstrable by loading carotid stripes. The EMPase preparations had been separated by starch-gel electrophoresis. To prepare the load-extension curve, the enzyme was applied in a concentration of 0·2 mg per ml at pH 7·4 in 0·025 M veronal-acetate buffer at 37 °C. The samples were incubated with and without serum. The amount of the human serum capable of completely preventing the effect of 1·0 mg pure EMPase was estimated at 0·2 ml.

The human serum showed considerably less inhibitory effect when aorta powders were digested with EMPase. Under the experimental conditions 1 mg EMPase was totally inhibited by 0·4 to 0·6 ml human serum. In these experiments all the serum samples tested originated from old arteriosclerotic subjects. The inhibitory effect of the same serum sample was always approximately identical regardless of whether elastase or EMPase was to be inhibited. Banga (1963a) using orcein-elastin as substrate calculates the elastase-inhibitor (E.I.) value of a serum from the number of E.U. which is inhibited by 1 ml serum (or pancreatic extract). The same method of calculation can be applied for the estimation of the EMPase inhibitor when aorta is used as substrate. In this case, too, the use of the same enzyme preparation under consistent experimental conditions is a prerequisite of comparative studies.

In the powdered pancreas of arteriosclerotic subjects the EMPase inhibitor cannot be demonstrated consistently. Out of the ten samples tested the EMPase inhibitor was only detectable in two cases, whereas the elastase inhibitor was present in every sample.

CHAPTER VI

VERIFICATION OF THE COMPLEX STRUCTURE OF ELASTIC FIBRES; STUDIES WITH ELASTASE AND ELASTOMUCOPROTEINASE PREPARATIONS SEPARATED BY DEAE SEPHADEX CHROMATOGRAPHY

THE EXPERIMENTS to be described in this chapter provided the first topochemical evidence showing that the elastic fibres, though appearing to be homogeneous and uniform when examined by histological staining methods, are in fact built of two or possibly three components as regards enzyme chemistry. This could not be proved by the use of classical, histochemical reactions as mentioned. These had to be combined with anisotropic staining procedures which were evaluable by the polarization-microscopic technique (Banga, Loeven and Romhányi 1965). These combined methods enabled the demonstration that EMPase (E_1) acts by disrupting the arrangement of the spiral fibrils in the cementing material as visualized by means of the aniline reaction by Romhányi (1955, 1962; Figs 4 and 5). The homogeneous, pure elastase preparation (E_2) dissolves the matrix, but fails to attack the embedded fibrils.

The following experiments were carried out with preparations E_2 and E_1/AEI, both characterized in Chapter III, p. 41. At the end of this chapter the comparative investigations will be published that were performed with other E_1 preparations also obtained by Sephadex chromatography.

SUBMICROSCOPIC HISTOCHEMICAL METHODS

To compare the mechanism of action of the two kinds of enzyme, formalin-fixed and paraffin-embedded sections were examined. Several kinds of tissue were used, i.e. new-born and adult human aorta tissues, three-month-old human embryos, human intervertebral discs and bovine lig. nuchae. Extensive studies were only carried out on the human aorta and the lig. nuchae of the calf.

Three methods of preparation were used for histological and submicroscopic examination.

a) Elastica staining with orcein and resorcin-fuchsin (RF).

b) Anisotropic staining with toluidine-blue (TB)—ferricyanide. This method was evolved by Romhányi (1958, 1959). It is based on the principle that transversally oriented TB molecules are deposited on the polysaccharide component of the elastic fibres and so make them birefringent. The elastic fibres stained by TB show anomalous colours between blue and green. This phenomenon has been termed anisotropic staining by Romhányi (1958, 1962). The resulting double refraction by the elastic fibres is measurable quantitatively in Leitz microscope by compensator (using red filter) and so the enzyme activity can be expressed numerically as a function of time. According to our experiments the evaluation of this reaction in the human aorta is a function of age (Banga, Loeven and Romhányi 1965), giving measurable results only in aorta sections derived from adults. Aortae of the new-born being enzyme-resistant are less suitable to demonstrate the difference between elastase and EMPase by this reaction. Using bovine lig. nuchae, on the other hand, in comparative studies has led to other interesting results.

c) The phenol reaction of elastic fibres. While the phenol reaction of collagen fibres (Ebner 1894) is a well-known and thoroughly investigated phenomenon, the same reaction for the elastic fibres can only be demonstrated by the submicroscopic, morphological technique developed by Romhányi (1955). The reaction is based in the case of the adult human aorta, on the morphological arrangement verifiable by the aniline reaction (Figs 3 to 5).

As shown in Fig. 3a the elastic fibres of the new-born show an undulated course. Unlike these, the elastic fibres of the adult are extended and show an almost straight course (Fig. 3b). These fibres are surrounded by collagen, the latter showing a ring-shaped spiral or helical form (Fig. 7). The phenol reaction of the almost straight and horizontal elastic fibres is, owing to this arrangement, readily distinguishable from that of the perpendicularly running ring-shaped, spiral-like collagen fibre. Although phenol makes both elastic and collagen fibres birefringent, on the basis of the characteristic morphological appearance one can easily ascertain which kind of fibre disappears enzymatically. Using this reaction we have found a substantial difference between the adult human aorta and the bovine lig. nuchae as shown in detail below.

ELASTOLYSIS IN FIXED AND EMBEDDED HUMAN AORTA PREPARATIONS

RF-stained elastic fibres of the aorta when treated with E_2, even if the concentration of the enzyme is as low as 0·05 mg per ml, show a sudden lysis after a short latent period (about 30 minutes). By the end of the first hour no traces of elastic fibres are detectable any longer, only minimal, vacuolized remnants of tissue, scarcely staining with orcein remain. The histological pictures so obtained are identical with those seen in native, frozen sections (Fig. 13), suggesting that there is no difference in the appearance of elastolysis proceeding either in native or fixed sections.

In contrast to this an incubation of elastic fibres with E_1, even if the concentration of the enzyme is as high as 1 mg per ml, results in only 20 to 30% solubilization after three hours of incubation. Accordingly, E_1 fails to attack the cementing substance which stains with RF. To demonstrate a possible synergistic effect of E_1, E_2 must have been applied in such a low concentration in which it did not alter the RF staining of elastic fibres whithin three hours. This concentration was found

72

to be 0·005 mg per ml. When E_1 was added in 1 mg per ml concentration to the above concentration of E_2, almost complete lysis ensued within three hours of incubation (Table 18).

TABLE 18

Synergistic effect of EMPase as tested by resorcin-fuchsin staining

E_1 mg/ml	E_2 mg/ml	Incubation period (hours)	Disappearance of resorcin-fuchsin staining (%)
1	—	3	20·0
—	0·005	3	0·0
1	0·005	3	90·0
—	0·1	3	100·0

The investigation of elastolysis in elastic fibres by the toluidine-blue (TB) anisotropic-staining technique led to an interesting result; incubation with E_1 which, as seen above, scarcely altered the RF staining of the fibres, disrupted their anisotropic staining (Table 19). In Table 19 the intensity of RF staining is presented in per cent, whereas TB anisotropic staining is expressed in the retardation (mμ) measured in the Leitz compensator.

TABLE 19

Effect of EMPase on the toluidine-blue anisotropic staining

Enzyme	Incubation period (hours)	Intensity of resorcin-fuchsin staining	Toluidine-blue anisotropic staining, retardation (mμ)
E_1 1 mg/ml	1	100	−22
E_1 1 mg/ml	2	90	−8
E_1 1 mg/ml	3	80	0·0
Buffer control	3	100	−24

On the effect of elastase (E_2), on the other hand, the TB anisotropic staining will only cease when the cementing substance stainable with RF has been digested completely. It is assumed that in this case the loss of the anisotropic staining was a secondary effect resulting from the solubilization of the cementing substance which ceased the stability and submicroscopic arrangement of the embedded fibres and, consequently, prevented toluidine molecules from being associated in an oriented arrangement to the surface of the fibrils. Figure 22 shows the effect of E_1 on the TB anisotropic staining. In the control sections the anisotropically stained elastic fibres are located in the part surrounded by the ring-shaped collagen-mucoid, termed by us collagenmucoid$_1$ (Chapter II, p. 19). After enzymatic

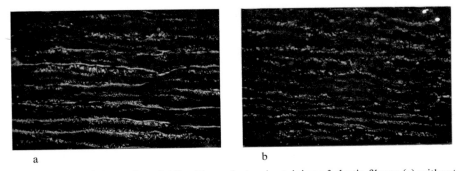

a   b

FIG. 22. Effect of E_1 on the toluidine-blue anisotropic staining of elastic fibres; (a) without enzyme (b) after enzyme treatment

digestion the white stripes replace the sites of elastic fibres. These appear to be empty, i.e. unstained, showing that this component has been specifically dissolved by E_1.

Table 20 shows the joint effect on the human adult aorta of EMPase and elastase. The present concentration of each of the enzymes, when applied separately, failed to cease TB anisotropic staining. However, at incubation in the presence

TABLE 20

Combined effect of elastase and EMPase on toluidine-blue anisotropic staining

Enzyme (mg/ml)	Incubation period (hours)	Toluidine-blue anisotropic staining	
		mμ	decrease (%)
E_1 0·5 mg	1	−22	0·0
E_2 0·005 mg	1	−20	10·0
E_1 0·5 + E_2 0·005 mg	1	−10	50·0
Control	1	−22	0·0

of both EMPase and elastase the retardation decreased by 50% as compared with the initial values. Naturally E_2 will cease the TB anisotropic staining of elastic fibres even without EMPase when the former is applied in high concentrations and the incubation period is prolonged. However, neither EMPase nor elastase will alter the anisotropic staining of the surrounding collagenmucoid. While the anisotropic staining of the elastic fibres ceases on the separate effect of E_1, the surrounding collagenmucoid (photograph is shown in Fig. 7) will never disappear totally, not even after a long period of incubation with E_1 or $E_1 + E_2$. Using the data of the compensator the negative birefringence of the two kinds of mucoid, viz. collagenmucoid and elastinmucoid, can be expressed in retardation ($m\mu$) and the mucoids themselves are separable from each other on the grounds of their distinct morphological construction. The enzymatic disappearance of elastinmucoid is measurable, whereas collagenmucoid is made recognizable by its resistance to enzymes as shown in Table 21.

TABLE 21

Toluidine-blue anisotropic staining of elastinmucoid and of collagenmucoid in human adult aorta

Enzymes (mg/ml)	Incubation period (hours)	Toluidine-blue anisotropic staining retardation ($m\mu$)	
		Elastin-mucoid	Collagen-mucoid
Buffer control	1	-20	-20
E_2 0·005 mg	1	-19	-19
E_1 1 mg/ml	2	-7	-19
E_2 0·005 + E_1 1 mg	3	0·0	-19

In another series of experiments the phenol reaction was utilized to demonstrate the effect of E_1 on the disintegration of filaments. It was mentioned in connection with the description of the reaction that besides collagen the filaments embedded in the elastic fibres give the reaction with phenol. The substance reacting with phenol was termed phenolelastoid. The surrounding collagenmucoid and the phenolelastoid are well distinguishable from each other submicroscopically. Figure 23 shows that the latter is surrounded by the collagenmucoid enveloping in a spiral form. Both of these substances show negative double refraction, consequently the rings of the collagenmucoid are alternatively light and dark, according to their refraction. Unlike this, phenolelastoid appears as a straight light stripe. Figure 23a and b show the distinctness of the two substances. While phenolelastoid is completely disintegrated by EMPase, i.e. the light stripes are replaced by empty areas, the collagenmucoid$_1$ remains unchanged, its birefringence as measured by the compensator after treatment is the same as it was at the start of the experiment.

The phenol reaction has proved to be appropriate for the demonstration of the specific EMPase effect. In the course of an incubation of one hour in the presence of 1 mg E_1 per ml the RF staining showed no change, while the phenol reaction

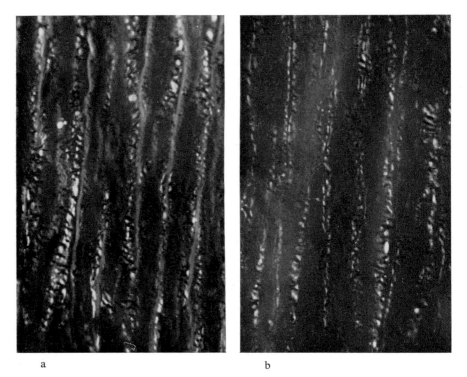

a   b

Fig. 23. Disappearance of phenolelastoid on the effect of E_1; (a) control; (b) the same after incubation in 1 mg/ml E_1. In (a) the elastic fibres are well visible; in (b) the site of the elastic fibres is empty

of the elastic fibres disappeared. On the effect of E_2, on the other hand, the reaction did not disappear until the elastic fibres had lost their RF staining.

The experiments carried out in new-born aorta sections as substrate have proved even more convincingly that E_2 exerts its effect on the RF-stainable component of elastic fibres, whereas E_1 disintegrates the phenolelastoid component which, consequently, loses its phenol-fixing capacity. The results so obtained are presented in Table 22. High concentrations of E_2 make the RF staining of the fibres disappear

TABLE 22

Effect of elastase on new-born aorta sections

Enzyme	Incubation period (hours)	Resorcin-fuchsin staining (%)	Phenol-elastoid (mμ)	Collagen-mucoid (mμ)
Buffer control	2	100·0	−13	−19
Elastase(E_2) 1 mg/ml	2	0·0	−12	−19
EMPase 1 mg/ml	3	90·0	−3	−19

76

within two hours, whilst it is without effect on the phenolelastoid; the intensity of the latter reaction is not altered by the enzyme treatment. On the effect of E_1, on the other hand, scarcely any reduction (about 10%) is observable in the RF staining, whilst the negative double refraction of the phenolelastoid falls to one-fourth of the initial value. The negative double refraction of the collagenmucoid is resistant to both enzymes. The negative birefringence of the latter substance is not reduced significantly by either of the enzymes. Collagenmucoid shows more intensive negative birefringence than phenolelastoid, a further property differentiating the two substances from each other.

The results obtained by this reaction provide strong evidence that E_1 causes the disappearance of the arrangement of the elastin-embedded filaments which is responsible for the oriented fixation of the phenol molecules. The digestion by EMPase of the TB anisotropic staining and that of the phenolelastoid do not run parallel in time. The loss of the phenolelastoid precedes that of the TB anisotropic staining; in the case of the adult aorta and an enzyme concentration of 1 mg per ml the former process is completed within one hour, whereas the latter needs three hours. (In the new-born aorta even the former reaction needs three hours.) Consequently, two different chemical groups are responsible for the two reactions and, supposedly, two groups are split off by two different components of E_1. The groups that play a part in fixing phenol are still unknown, whereas the TB anisotropic staining is most probably a polysaccharide reaction. We termed the component elastinmucoid because it is a special mucoid component of elastin that reacts with toluidine blue.

The three staining reactions under discussion and the specific effects of elastase and EMPase on different morphological components throw a new light on the results published by Dettmer (1952) and Schwarz and Dettmer (1953) (see Chapter I). Though it cannot be checked retrospectively, it is highly probable that the preparations used by these investigators mainly contained E_2. Consequently, in their experiments only the cementing substance was digested, the embedded filaments remained intact as confirmed by their electron micrographs. The reality of this concept is supported by one of our observations. We found E_2 to be effective even in a concentration as low as 0·05 mg/ml, in contrast to E_1, of which at least 1 mg/ml was needed to attack filaments, i.e. the digestion of the mucoid component (elastinmucoid) of the elastin-matrix-embedded filaments required E_1 in a quantity 20 times that sufficient for E_2 to digest the cementing substance. Although E_1 contains less protein than does E_2, the difference in the specific activity is another striking difference between the two enzymes. It should be added that E_1 is very labile (Czerkawski and Hall 1958, Loeven 1960a), consequently elastase preparations produced in certain laboratories might have been free of the E_1 component.

When using Romhányi's (1955) aniline reaction for measuring the velocity of the elastolysis we were able to demonstrate fibres with intensive double refraction as a result of association of aniline molecules to the elastic fibres (Figs 3 and 4). An analysis of this submicroscopic structure led us to prove the spiral structure of the elastic fibre (Figs 4 and 5). Romhányi who combined the aniline reaction with elastolysis studies, found E_2 to be active on the same elastin component which is responsible for the aniline reaction. Based on comparative studies carried out in RF-stained tissues, he concluded that components (according to the author, mucoids) capable of oriented fixation of certain groups of molecules, e.g. aniline, are also present in the cementing substance of elastin. However, this component is not identical with the filaments giving the phenol reaction. Further investigations are necessary to reveal the relationship between the elastinmucoid giving the TB reaction, on the one hand, and the aniline reaction on the other. According to experiments carried out with E_2 the aniline reaction and RF staining disappeared exactly at the same time.

ELASTOLYSIS IN FIXED AND EMBEDDED LIG. NUCHAE OF THE CALF

Experiments were carried out to demonstrate the differences between elastase and EMPase concerning their effects on the submicroscopic components of the lig. nuchae. The effects were examined by three different histochemical methods: 1. RF stain, 2. TB anisotropic stain, and 3. the phenol reaction. Unlike human aorta, lig. nuchae preparations had to be incubated for a long period (17 hours) with the enzymes to demonstrate enzyme activity. In the following the most characteristic difference between the two enzymes, as demonstrable on the lig. nuchae, is described.

E_2 makes the RF staining of the elastic fibres disappear without affecting their TB anisotropic staining. This phenomenon is a result of the stability of the substance termed elastinmucoid. This component also disappears from adult aorta

TABLE 23

Demonstration by toluidine-blue anisotropic staining of residual collagen-type fibres on the site of the elastinmucoid of lig. nuchae

Enzyme incubated for 17 hours	Resorcin-fuchsin staining (%)	Toluidine-blue anisotropic staining retardation (mμ)	
		Elastin-mucoid	Collagen-type fibre
Control	100	-9	0·0
E_2 0·05 mg/ml	0·0	-9	0·0
E_1 1 mg/ml	Fragmentation	0·0	$+6$

sections on the effect of E_2, but only after the fibres have lost their TB anisotropic staining. Presumably in the lig. nuchae elastinmucoid is much more stable than it is in the adult aorta. Accordingly, when the RF-stainable matrix has been completely disintegrated, the elastinmucoid giving the TB reaction still shows its characteristic submicroscopic arrangement. In the case of E_1 the reaction is just the opposite. After a long period of incubation with 1 mg/ml E_1 solution RF stain only shows a transversal fragmentation (see Fig. 13b), but the fragments have retained their RF staining. On the other hand, the TB anisotropic staining completely disappears, indicating that the specific effect of E_1 is manifested in splitting off the elastinmucoid, a phenomenon leading to transversal fragmentation. At the same time the phenol reaction, i.e. the phenol-inducible negative birefringence of the elastic fibres has also ceased by E_1. However, at the site of the elastic fibres the TB anisotropic staining shows some kind of positive double refraction, supposedly of the collagen type, in contrast to the adult human aorta in which the elastic fibres are replaced by empty stripes. The results of the quantitative studies are presented in Table 23.

COMPARATIVE STUDY OF ELASTOMUCOPROTEINASE FRACTIONS OBTAINED BY DIFFERENT PREPARATION TECHNIQUES

The above experiments have brought evidence for the existence of filaments inside the cementing substance of elastic fibres; these filaments should be variable not only in morphological appearance but also in chemical structure. Furthermore, an analysis of the TB anisotropic staining of adult human aorta and bovine lig. nuchae preparations in the study of elastase and EMPase digestion supports the view that the cementing substance is inhomogeneous in construction; it contains a component which reacts with TB as well as another which fails to give this reaction. The former component is solubilized by the EMPase preparations which are capable of activating the proteolytic activity of elastase (e.g. the E_1 preparation isolated by Hall 1957a). This appears to be identical with the component that was thought by Hall et al. (1952) to be elastomucin. It is termed in this chapter elastinmucoid to be distinguished from the collagenmucoid, and from the phenolelastoid, both giving negative double refraction with phenol. These two substances are well distinguishable morphologically as shown in Figs 7 and 23.

In the course of our experiments it was found that only the E_1/AEI preparations, i.e. those obtained from the euglobulin fraction of the pancreas, disintegrated the phenolelastoid; the E_1/AES preparations obtained by us from Hall's AES supernatant failed to attack this component. Furthermore, after elastinmucoid has been removed from the lig. nuchae, a component showing positive double refraction is demonstrable in the remnants. This component was termed collagen-type fibre in Table 23 because only this type of fibre may show positive double refraction. This is, however, completely hidden as if it were enclosed by elastinmucoid. It becomes only visible after elastinmucoid has been removed by E_1/AEI. The component has never been demonstrated except in the lig. nuchae. Presumably it is also present in the elastic fibres of young human aortae, but cannot be detected because of the more complex structure and higher resistance of these fibres to enzymes.

All these experiments support the view that the DEAE Sephadex chromatography developed by Banga, Loeven and Romhányi (1965) supplies consistent EMPase preparations; these have shown different mechanisms of action, depending on the source of the preparation which was either the AES or the AEI fraction of Hall. By paper electrophoresis Loeven (1964 d) demonstrated two mucases which he termed Em-I and Em-S. Further investigations are necessary to throw light on the specific effect of these enzymes on the components of the elastic fibre.

It can be concluded that elastic fibres are built up of three components. One of these is the cementing substance which stains with RF. The elastinmucoid and the phenolelastoid, both giving the TB anisotropic staining are embedded in the cementing substance. A specific enzyme appears to belong to each of the three components.

KINETICS OF THE ELASTOPROTEINASE (E_2 = TRUE ELASTASE).
ACTION ON ORCEIN-ELASTIN SUBSTRATE

The observations of Czerkawski (1958) and Hall and Czerkawski (1961a) suggesting that the kinetics of the so-called homogeneous reaction between elastin and elastase does not follow the rules of classical kinetics have raised the suspicion that this irregularity might be due to a contamination of the enzyme preparations with E_1 or E_1 (den.). To clarify this problem experiments were carried out in the author's laboratory with the elastoproteinase preparation produced by Banga and Loeven by DEAE Sephadex chromatography (Chapter III, p. 40). This preparation as demonstrated by Loeven (1963a) gave a single, homogeneous protein stripe when examined by paper electrophoresis. To measure the kinetics of this reaction, an orcein-elastin adequately prepared with Merck orcein by Banga (1963a) served as substrate. It was shown that at pH 8·6 the time curve of the reaction was always of zero-order, irrespective of the quality of the buffer (Tris, veronal-acetate or $Na_2CO_3 - HCl$ buffer was used) and the substrate concentration. The K_M value

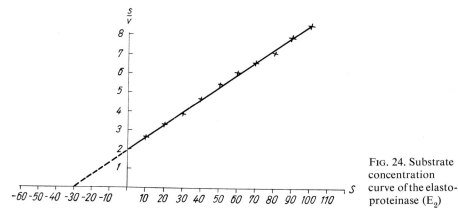

FIG. 24. Substrate concentration curve of the elastoproteinase (E_2)

calculated from the substrate concentration curve, according to the method recommended by Lineweaver-Burk, proved to be equal to 30. Figure 24 demonstrates the relationship obtained between the substrate concentration (S) and the ratio of substrate to reaction velocity (S/V). Accordingly, the enzyme was half-saturated by the substrate at 0·6% concentration of orcein-elastin. It is concluded from these experiments that the reaction does follow the rules of classical kinetics, provided it is carried out with orcein-elastin and pure, homogeneous elastoproteinase. In this case the Michaelis constant can be calculated for the reaction.

CHAPTER VII

CHANGES IN ARTERIOSCLEROSIS AND THE IN VIVO EFFECT OF
PANCREATIC ELASTASE

ELASTASE, under *in vitro* conditions, dissolves the elastic fibres and in the vascular
wall gives rise to alterations identical with those observable in the arteriosclerotic
organism (Figs 12 and 13). It was thus reasonable to suppose that in so far as
there is any relationship between the elastase enzyme and the pathogenesis of
atherosclerosis, it may be manifested in an increased production of pancreatic
elastase. Baló and Banga (1953 a, b) and Baló (1957) submitted this question to
a systematic investigation by comparing the elastase content in the pancreas of
young and old cadavers. Two groups served as control. One of these consisted
of subjects 18 to 41 years of age who had died as a result of accidents. The members
of the other control group, aged 16 to 45, had died of various diseases; their vascular
system was also free of atherosclerosis. Whilst in the two control groups the average
elastase content of the pancreas was 200 and 155 E.U. respectively, as calculated
for 1 g of the acetonized dry powder of the organ, the corresponding value for the
arteriosclerotic cadavers was as low as nine, and in a considerable number of
the pancreas specimens elastase activity could not be demonstrated at all. Accordingly, instead of the initial assumption, its opposite was proved experimentally:
elastase disappears from the arterio- (athero-) sclerotic pancreas. The above authors
supposed that, since enzymes are active not only in decomposition but also in the
synthesis, the lack of elastase might disturb the metabolism of the elastic fibres.
As a result of this, regeneration of the elastic fibres may become defective and
finally may lead to atherosclerotic lesions. Consequently, Baló and Banga (1953b)
considered the introduction of elastase for the prevention and therapy of arteriosclerosis to be reasonable.

Based on this hypothesis, Lansing (1954, 1955) submitted the *in vivo* elastase
effect to systematic study. He administered elastase-containing pancreas powder
orally to rabbits in which he had induced atherosclerosis and fatty liver by feeding
with cholesterol. He found that the development of both atheromatous lesions
of the intima and fatty liver were suppressed by elastase. Consequently, he attributes also a systemic effect to elastase. Lansing (1959) entered into debate
with Tennent et al. (1956) who published contrary experimental results, and
convincingly demonstrated that the cholesterol dose administered to chickens
by the latter authors was too large to be neutralized by the given dose of elastase.
When examining the effect of elastase on the metabolism of the elastic fibres of
the aorta, Lansing (1955) administered radioactive isotopes to rabbits, in addition
to elastase. Both the control animals and the experimental group received ^{14}C-

labelled acetate and glycine intraperitoneally; the latter group was given elastase, too. It was shown that the incorporation of the isotope was reduced compared with the control.

These experimental results were confirmed by Citi et al. (1960) and by Salvini et al. (1960) who suppose that the systemic effect following the administration of elastase may be produced in two different ways. The reduced turnover of elastin may result from a rise in the elastase content or from a decreased inhibitor concentration. Grandonico et al. (1960) when studying the incorporation of ^{35}S-labelled sulphate, found a reduced mucopolysaccharide level both in the isolated elastin and the aorta as a result of the *in vivo* elastase effect. These authors attribute the increase in the serum clearing factor to the mucopolysaccharides released from the aorta tissue on the effect of elastase. These experiments have provided evidence for the absorption of the orally administered elastase, and its ability to influence the metabolism of the elastic fibres, but have not supplied any information on the fine mechanism of these processes.

Baló et al. (1957) administered elastase doses, one-fifth of the lethal dose per day to white rats for 90 days, intraperitoneally. The pancreas of the animals enlarged singificantly, owing to a hypertrophy of the glandular tissue and an increase in the cell number, i.e. hyperplasia. It is of interest that the enlargement of the pancreas led to a rise in its specific elastase activity (E.U. per g pancreas).

Butturini et al. (1958, 1959a,b,c) examined the effect of elastase alone and in combination with glucagon in serial experiments carried out in rabbits fed with cholesterol. Glucagon increased and elastase reduced the intensity of the development of atheromatous plaques. Furthermore, elastase reduced the total amount of plasma cholesterol, first of all by inducing the disappearance of the free cholesterol; at the same time, elastase prevented the development of fatty liver. Elastase exerted a protective effect against the atherosclerosis of the chickens even in the presence of glucagon.

Lapicirella et al. (1960a,b) attribute an importance to *in vivo* administration of elastase. In their opinion small doses of elastase exert a protective effect against atherosclerosis, whereas large doses, in spite of reducing blood cholesterol, disintegrate and, finally, digest the elastic fibres of the arteries.

Atherosclerosis has been produced by elastase in *in vivo* experiments in dogs (Nasbeth et al. 1963). A segment of the abdominal aorta was exposed to 4 ml of a 0·1 % solution of elastase for 90 minutes and subsequently the dogs were thyroidectomized. The animals were kept on a diet of high fat and cholesterol content, and killed after two months. Elastase produced deterioration of the elastic tissue and 50% loss of the elastin content. These lesions were accompanied by the initial form of atherosclerosis, viz. subintimal fibrous plaques, and in several cases small aneurysms were observable. In this case the elastin showed the same effect as *in vitro*, i.e. it dissolved the elastic fibres.

The effect of elastase on the lipolytic activity of the aorta was examined by Salvini et al. (1960). This activity was found to be increased compared with the control.

The pharmacological effect of the purified elastase was investigated by Borsy et al. (1959). They observed transient hypotension in cats given 120 to 240 E.U. per kg body weight. Larger doses led to irreversible effects. The resulting hypotension could not be inhibited by vagotomy, atropine or phenergan, i.e. it was not based on excitation of the vascular nerve ends of the vagus (Bezold reflex) or of the parasympathetic nerve endings. The elastase-induced hypotension is well distinguishable from the effects of histamine, serotonine or kallikrein. Extensive animal experiments have shown that the dilatation of peripheral arteries and capillaries is responsible for the hypotension following the administration of elastase. However, some effect on the central vasomotor centre cannot be excluded. The effect of elastase on the smooth-muscle organs resembles that of trypsin.

The intravenous toxicity of enzyme preparations ran parallel with their elastolytic activity. The more active a preparation the more toxic it proved to be when given to mice or rats intravenously. The toxic and subtoxic effects of the intravenously administered enzyme were most pronounced in the lungs and in the spleen, both of which are rich in elastic fibres. In addition, the permeability of the vascular wall increased markedly. In further experiments Borsy et al. (1959) demonstrated that occasionally fatal pulmonary oedema and haemorrhage following intravenous administration of toxic doses of the enzyme can be prevented by elastase inhibitor, or by antirheumatic drugs which also have an antiphlogistic effect.

Biological and pharmacological studies on elastase have revealed that in its digesting capacity elastase is superior to the proteolytic enzyme preparations which have been introduced in therapy. Thus, it seemed to be reasonable to study the therapeutic effect of elastase in patients suffering from diseases usually treated with streptokinase, streptodernase, trypsin or other enzymes. Accordingly, Kovács and Bagdy (1958a,b, 1959) administered elastase intrabronchially in cases of lung abscesses, chronic pneumonitis, bronchiectasis and chronic suppurative bronchitis. In addition, they attempted to use the enzyme in cases of cavernous tuberculosis as well as in cases of atelectasis of tuberculous origin. They achieved complete clinical recovery of patients suffering from lung abscess; the bronchoscopic findings became normal in 58 out of 100 cases. Furthermore, significant improvement was observed in 34 cases, whereas in eight cases elastase treatment was without effect. The eight cases of chronic pneumonitis showed complete recovery, the X-ray shadows disappeared and the patients had no complaints after 3 to 8 treatments. Clinical improvement ensued in the 18 patients with bronchiectasis as well. They became apyretic, the sputum decreased in volume and became odourless. The bronchogram showed no change. Consequently, in cases of bronchiectasis elastase can be used in preparation of surgery and as symptomatic therapy. Good results were achieved in cases of chronic suppurative bronchitis, atelectasis and empyema. According to the observations of Kovács and Bagdy (1958a,b, 1959) elastase caused neither local nor general side-effects; it is excellently suitable for inhalation from an aerosol apparatus. Bagdy et al. (1960) reported that in

Hungary other clinicians (Marton, Kertes and Boda) also used elastase in the form of aerosol in the therapy of bronchopulmonary suppurations (60 cases). They found elastase to be an enzyme preparation of excellent effect; when inhaled it was less irritative than the imported trypsin preparations used by them earlier. As a single dose for inhalation 360 E.U. are recommended.

Raffay and Richter (1962) treated 25 cases of bronchial asthma with elastase aerosol. They measured the volume of the sputum in a pneumometer and found

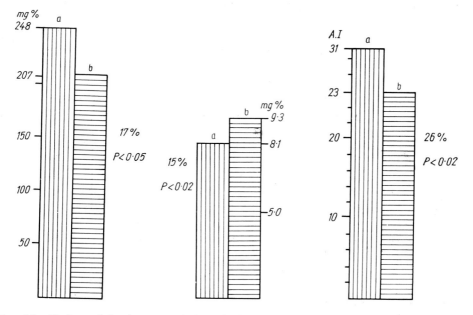

FIG. 25. Cholesterol level after administration of elastase

FIG. 26. Quantitative changes in the ketone-bodies after administration of elastase

FIG. 27. Arteriosclerotic index after administration of elastase

a continuous increase in its quantity during elastase therapy. The maximum was reached after ten days of treatment. During this time the bronchi became empty, mucus secretion ceased and a transient improvement ensued. As regards the mechanism of the solubilization of mucinoid substances, the authors demonstrated that it was the sialic acid component of the glucoproteide present in the asthmatic sputum that splits off and is solubilized on the effect of elastase. Consequently, the glucoproteide of the sputum may be considered as sialomucin and the effect of the enzyme as sialolysis.

These experiments are in accordance with the observations of Banga (unpublished experiments), viz. the adhesive, viscous sputum obtained from patients with bronchial asthma was liquified on the effect of elastase. The great amount of glucoprotein contained in these sputa suggests that it is the EMPase component of the elastase-enzyme complex that exerts the mucolytic effect on the glucopro-

7 S.F.E.C.

teide. This mechanism resembles the effect of EMPase on the mucolipoprotein complex of the aorta (Chapter V, p. 64) .The latter complex also contains sialic acid which, however, remains in the non-migrating protein component after electrophoresis. No experiments have been carried out to demonstrate whether or not sialic acid can be split off from mucolipoprotein with elastase.

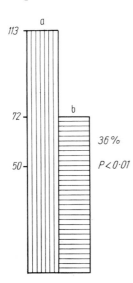

FIG. 28. Elastase inhibitor after administration of elastase

Butturini and Langer (1962) examined the effects of elastolytic pancreas extracts in subjects suffering from atherosclerosis or hypercholesterolaemia. Twenty-five atherosclerotic patients were given elastase in a daily dose, 300 E.U. contained in 5 mg of the elastase preparation, intramuscularly. As a result of this treatment the cholesterol level of the blood decreased, whereas the relative quantity of cholesterol esters increased; the ratio of β-lipoprotein to α-lipoprotein also decreased.

Nagy and Medgyesi (1962) administered elastase to a patient suffering from essential lipaemia in dragées containing 200 E.U. each. The patient was given four dragées three times a day over a period of six weeks. After the first three weeks of this therapy the lactaemic serum of the patient, which could not be cleared up in any other way, became transparent, i.e. complete clearing ensued. During this period the total lipid value of the serum decreased from 2460 mg/100 ml to 790 mg/100 ml, the total fatty acid in the serum from 1680 mg/100 ml to 420 mg/100 ml and the total cholesterol in the serum from 370 mg/100 ml to 150 mg/100 ml. The authors believe that the orally administered elastase exerted a heparin-like effect.

Mayláth-Palágyi et al. (1965) observed 30 patients from 54 to 78 years of age, each suffered from arteriosclerosis and hypertension. The patients who were kept on a normal diet were given a daily dose of three times two dragées, each containing 200 E.U. over a period of six weeks. The authors followed the changes in the blood cholesterol and ketone-bodies and the ratio of the former to the latter (arteriosclerosis index of Kiss and Mayláth 1962). The blood samples were taken on an empty stomach. In addition, they assayed the elastase inhibitor in the blood and related the values obtained during therapy to the initial values.

Figures 25 to 28 illustrate the results. Blood cholesterol, being on average 248 mg/100 ml initially, dropped to 207 mg/100 ml (17% reduction). The difference proved to be significant (P < 0·05). Accordingly, the cholesterol excess disappeared. The average blood level of ketone-bodies rose from 8·1 mg/100 ml which is a value below the normal level to 9·3 mg/100 ml. The 15% increase proved to be significant again (P < 0·02). The authors attribute the low level of the ketone-bodies in the blood of sclerotic patients to a reduced fat oxidation. Thus, a rise

86

of this level would indicate an enhanced fat metabolism. The average arteriosclerosis index was 31, i.e. it exceeded the normal level (18 to 20) at the beginning of the therapy. By the end of the experiment the average index had fallen to 23 (26% reduction), a value near the normal level ($P < 0.02$). The average elastase-inhibitor value was 113/ml serum, i.e. 1 ml serum was capable of inhibiting 113 units of elastase measured biochemically (Chapter IV, p. 54). At the end of the therapy the corresponding value was 72 E.I./ml serum, indicating a reduction by 36%. The difference is highly significant ($P < 0.01$). The authors have concluded that orally administered elastase is capable of altering the fat metabolism of arteriosclerotic patients as shown by the normalized cholesterol and ketone-body levels and the resultant normalization of the arteriosclerosis index. The decrease in the inhibitor values appears to indicate that elastase is not a simple digestive enzyme; it is absorbed in the blood, and so exerts a systemic effect.

CHAPTER VIII

CHANGES IN THE CHEMICAL STRUCTURE OF ELASTIC ARTERIAE
PARALLEL WITH AGE AND ARTERIOSCLEROSIS

IT IS an old observation that the connective-tissue fibres building up the vascular wall are altered in old age and during illness. However, understanding of these phenomena had not been approached until similar alterations were produced in experimental animals. Josué (1903) was able to give rise to experimental arteriosclerosis in rabbits by systematic intravenous administration of adrenalin. Adrenalin-induced sclerosis is characterized by necrosis of the smooth-muscle fibres of the media. This is followed by a compression of the neighbouring elastic fibres, fragmentation of the fibres and calcification of the media. The sclerogenic effect of adrenalin was attributed to the consequent hypertension. However, arteriosclerosis, in every respect similar to that induced by adrenalin, can be produced by various acids and other chemicals, none of which can cause hypertension. Thus, the vascular lesions should be ascribed to other factors than hypertension. According to Baló (1939a) alterations in, and destruction of, the elastic fibres of the vascular wall are the phenomena most characteristic of arteriosclerosis. Based on his own animal experiments and on his observations on several hundreds of subjects Baló (1938, 1939a, 1963) has put forward the theory that the destruction of elastic lamellae is caused by acidosis.

Histologists and pathologists (Lansing et al. 1948, 1950; Blumenthal et al. 1944) distinguish arteriosclerosis from atherosclerosis, the former being characterized by a well-defined deposition of calcium, whereas the latter by lipid-containing plaques in the intima of the vascular wall. The main component of the lipids is cholesterol. Anitschkow and Chalatow (1913) were the first to produce experimental atherosclerosis in rabbits by feeding the animals with cholesterol dissolved in helianthus oil. Anitschkow (1934) suggests that the experimental atherosclerosis is identical with the human disease. Gerő (1963) believes, on the other hand, that there is no relationship between hypercholesterolaemia and atherosclerosis.

Undoubtedly one of the most pronounced concomitant phenomena of old age is the calcification (Verkalkung) and resultant thickening and induration of the vascular wall. As a result of these the vascular lumen becomes constricted. These alterations are caused by deposition of calcium salts, neutral fat and cholesterol in the vascular wall. Baló (1939a) as well as other investigators have pointed out that progress in age and arterio- (athero-) sclerosis are accompanied by a reduction in the number of elastic fibres as it is histologically most clearly demonstrable in the aorta. Troitzkaja-Andreewa (1931) and Romhányi (personal communication) who also studied the question histologically, found an increase in the number of collagen fibres parallel with age. According to these authors the disappeared elastic fibres are replaced by collagen fibres.

CHEMICAL STUDIES ON STRUCTURAL PROTEINS AND THEIR
CHANGES PARALLEL WITH AGE AND ARTERIOSCLEROSIS

As mentioned, it is an old observation of pathologists that parallel with age and arteriosclerosis the structural proteins (i.e. scleroproteins, namely elastin, collagen and reticulin) of the vascular wall undergo alterations demonstrable by histological staining techniques. For obvious reasons efforts have been made to support these observations by exact, quantitative biochemical data.

Lowry et al. (1941) were the first to carry out biochemical investigations concerning the elastin and collagen contents of the vascular wall. Their technique was modified and employed for the determination of elastin, collagen and calcium in human arteriosclerotic aorta specimens by Lansing et al. (1950). The modified technique, in brief, is as follows. Aorta powder made free from fat is boiled in 0·1 N NaOH for 45 minutes. The authors supposed and proved experimentally that the alkali-soluble proteins and the collagen are solubilized by this treatment and the residuum consists of elastin and calcium. By using this method the authors demonstrated how the elastin and calcium contents of the aorta wall change in relation to age. The elastin level showed only a little, according to the authors an insignificant, decrease in old age, whereas the increase in calcium − from 0·5 to 6% − was considered highly important. The elastin values varied between 48% and 41% from 10 to 100 years of age.

In the author's laboratory aorta specimens taken from 20 cadavers of persons who died of various diseases were analysed according to the method of Lansing et al. (1950) (Table 24). An aliquot (collagen + elastin) was weighed and was taken as 100%. Elastin was weighed gravimetrically; the quantity of the collagen was calculated from the difference. In addition, from the same specimens we attempted to separate the collagen and elastin fractions from each other by elastolysis. We assumed that elastase solubilized the elastin and, by its general proteolytic activity, all soluble protein; the insoluble residuum was thought to be the collagen. The initial sum of the weights of the two scleroproteins was taken as 100% here, too. The experiments were carried out with native aorta sections, and a residuum extracted with a buffer solution of pH 7·4 served as control for the initial value. Table 24 shows that the sum of the elastin obtained by Lansing's method and of the collagen calculated from the gravimetrical value obtained after elastolysis (see column I + IV in Table 24) varied from 61% to 156%. In this case soluble protein was not measured. On the other hand, the sum of elastin as determined according to Lansing and that of collagen after elastolysis (see column II + III) also showed great variations (from 44% to 139%). We had presumed that the excess percentage values over 100% should have given the soluble protein that had solubilized in

TABLE 24

Combination of the Lansing technique with elastolysis to assay the elastin and collagen content of the vascular wall

Speci-men No.	Age in years	Cause of death	Elastin (%)		Collagen (%)		Elastin + collagen (%)		Degree of athero-sclerosis
			Lansing's technique I	Elastolysis II	Lansing's technique III	Elastolysis IV	I + IV	II + III	
2	17	St. p. commiss.	30	64	70	36	66	134	0
16	17	Combined mitral failure	58	70	42	30	88	112	0
1	26	Carcinoma. Embolia	59	72	41	28	87	113	0
15	37	Diabetes mellitus. Uraemia	52	64	48	36	88	112	+ +
19	39	St. p. pneumonect.	52	75	48	25	77	123	+
9	41	Nephritis. Uraemia	36	72	64	28	64	136	+
20	41	Reticulosis	38	77	62	23	61	139	+
25	47	Tumor oesophagi	32	69	68	31	63	137	+
14	48	Myodegeneratio cordis	40	60	60	40	80	120	+
21	52	Tumor pulmonis	43	71	57	29	72	128	+
6	53	Coronary thrombosis	50	56	50	44	94	106	+ +
17	56	Tumor pulmonis	30	33	70	67	97	103	+
18	65	Tumor pulmonis	36	47	64	53	89	111	+ + +
5	57	Carcinoma hepatis	36	61	64	39	75	125	+
4	59	Cardial decompensation. Uraemia	53	43	47	57	110	90	+
7	60	Myodegeneratio cordis. Arteritis	50	56	50	44	94	106	+ +
24	60	Cirrhosis hepatis	40	63	60	37	77	123	+ + +
22	69	Carcinoma prostatae	39	78	61	22	61	139	+ +
3	76	Myodegeneratio cordis. Hypertensio.	75	19	25	81	156	44	+ + +
28	76	Carcinoma colli uteri	83	44	17	56	139	61	+ + +

the buffer. The great variation in the data of Table 24 points to enormous diver-gencies in the scleroproteins of individual aorta specimens. It has been concluded from these studies that neither the technique described by Lansing et al. (1950) nor the gravimetrical assay combined with the elastolysis of native aortae is an appropriate method for the quantitative determination of scleroproteins.

Since by the methods available the two scleroproteins could not be separated satisfactorily, especially not from old and arteriosclerotic aorta specimens, several investigators (Sachar et al. 1955; Scarcelli 1958) attempted the separation by the elastolysis of orcein-stained aortae. According to the concept of the latter author mucoids, collagen and soluble proteins were extracted from the human aorta with 0·1 N NaOH, and the residue was stained with orcein and submitted to elastoly-sis; from the extinction by the supernatant the author estimated the elastin on the basis of a standard curve plotted for pure elastin. Scarcelli (1961) demonstrated a rise from 19 to 50% in the elastin content of the aorta wall from infancy till 20 years of age. Elastin was shown to be continuously rising parallel with age in the lungs as well (Scarcelli and Repetto 1959).

In our laboratory we assayed the elastin in 30 old, arteriosclerotic human aorta specimens (Banga 1963a) after staining with orcein, with and without combining the method with Scarcelli's alkali extraction. We found no significant difference between the two values. When after solubilization of the orcein-stained elastin by elastase the elastin content was calculated either from the extinction of the dissolved orcein or from the gravimetrical values, the values obtained were slightly higher than the 30% average given by Lowry et al. (1941). It was concluded that elastin was not the only component of the aorta which was stained by orcein. The non-specific staining of another scleroprotein was added to that of elastin and thus raised the "elastin" value obtained either by Scarcelli's method or by gravimetry. However, this scleroprotein is insoluble in alkali. Thus it seemed reasonable to modify Scarcelli's method by postponing alkali extraction to stain-ing. When doing so a great amount of stain was extracted by the alkali and the purplish-blue colour of the aorta and of the elastin changed into plum-blue. This colour did not change after further alkali treatment. It can, therefore, be supposed that the residual staining is really fixed to elastin, thus insoluble in alkali. The aortae so treated supplied colourless residue after elastolysis and the elastin values obtained were lower. (Naturally, the elastin values should be calculated from a standard curve plotted on the basis of data obtained by using a plum-blue preparation which was stained with orcein after alkali extraction.) According to our experience these elastin values may be regarded as correct.

The hydroxyproline tests carried out in the author's laboratory have shown that collagen is not totally dissolved by the Scarcelli extraction, therefore, it may be responsible for the high elastin values. For this reason we removed collagen by treatment with a 40% solution of KI, and subsequent extraction with water or at 70 °C by heating with acetic acid. The KI-treated elastin showed a reddish colour when stained with orcein, whereas boiling with acetic acid did not change the original colours of the orcein-elastins. Figure 29 shows aorta preparations stained with orcein after different extractions, whereas in Table 25, the elastin values obtained after these extractions are shown together with the collagen content and the percentage values of the unknown scleroprotein. The so-called unknown scleroprotein was not solubilized in the course of boiling with alkali or acetic acid, i.e. it was not identical with collagen. It proved to be resistant to elastase as well. Its quantity in human (old) aorta specimens ranged from 5 to 25%. In most cases it contained Ca in a high percentage (30 to 40%) as well as Mg and polysaccharides.

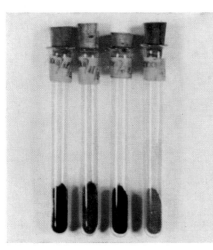

FIG. 29. Elastin powder stained after different chemical reactions. The tubes from the left: first = orcein-elastin; second = after extraction with KI; third = after extraction with acetic acid; fourth = after alkali extraction

The unknown scleroprotein appears to be identical with the substance isolated by LaBella (1963) from old aorta specimens. This substance could not be solubilized with elastase in its majority. The findings of Lansing et al. (1951), that by elastase the elastin of the young aorta is solubilized to 100%, whereas those of the old aorta only to a lesser extent are in accordance with the presence of this substance.

La Bella (1963) examined the velocity of elastolysis in young and old aorta specimens. In contrast to the results of Baló and Banga (1955) he found that the elastin of young subjects was solubilized faster than that of old persons. This statement is erroneous and it is attributable to the inadequate turbidimetric technique used by this author. Owing to their high Ca content the old, "elastase-resistant" elastins are insoluble and so increase the turbidity of the suspension which fails to clear up even during a long-term elastolysis. Thus, in old aorta specimens elastolysis seems to be retarded when checked by turbidimetry. When the velocity of the elastolysis is calculated from the solubilized nitrogen, and this is related to the initial elastin-nitrogen, the result will be the same as reported by Baló and Banga (1955), i.e. the quantity of the elastase-soluble elastin is in direct relation to age. Accordingly, parallel with age elastin undergoes a change resulting in an accelerated elastolysis. Consequently, the high values obtained for the aorta of old subjects by turbidimetry are explainable by the unknown scleroprotein which is present besides the homogeneous elastin. This substance appears during the isolation of elastin in the insoluble fraction and totally resists elastase.

The change in the elastin content of the aorta parallel with age and arteriosclerosis is well demonstrable by histological methods. The best biochemical method for

TABLE 25

Aorta elastin values obtained by KI extraction as compared with the data obtained by Scarcelli's method; collagen and unknown scleroprotein contents

Aorta No.	Age (years)	Sex	Diagnosis	Elastin percentage assayed			Collagen++ %	Unknown sclero-protein %	Degree of athero-sclerosis
				by Scarcelli's method	after extraction with 40% KI+	alkali extraction after staining with orcein			
65	49	♀	Carcinoma	60	32	32	32	6	++
78	50	♀	Arteriosclerosis	42	—	35	24	7	++
62	57	♂	Atherosclerosis univ.	45	28	26	31	12	+++
85	63	♀	Cor pulmonale	45	—	22	17	10	+++
66	70	♂	Arteriosclerosis cordis	42	31	25	28	5	+++
61	74	♀	Atherosclerosis univ.	37	27	32	18	25	+++
60	80	♀	Atherosclerosis univ.	42	31	25	20	9	+++
83	83	♀	Arteriosclerosis	45	—	29	17	9	+++
70	86	♀	Cirrhosis hepatis	42	—	25	25	8	+++
89	91	♀	Tumor pulmonum	36	—	26	18	14	+++

Note: + = elastin percentage calculated from elastolysis following treatment with 40% KI, boiling in water and subsequent staining with orcein
++ = assay of collagen: aortae were boiled with 1% acetic acid for one hour, three times; collagen was calculated from the Hypro values of the protein soluble in acetic acid

its demonstration includes the removal of soluble proteins and mucoprotein by extracting acetonized aorta powders with three consecutive alkali extractions (0·1 N NaOH, 20 °C, 24 hours, 10-fold volume). In this case elastin is digested by incubation with pure, homogeneous elastase and determined by the Folin-phenol method. The results obtained by combining the biochemical and histological methods are shown in Table 26. The percentage values of soluble protein + mucoprotein, elastin, the total amount of the collagen fractions, and the degree of arteriosclerosis are presented.

The severity of arteriosclerosis as established in the histological tests was in accordance with the decreasing elastin content. Loss of elastin was frequently, but not regularly, accompanied by a rise in collagen. In some cases, however, collagen decreased parallel with elastin.

The collagen content was also checked by assaying the protein-N and the hydroxyproline solubilized by boiling in 1% acetic acid. It was, however, demonstrated long ago (Banga et al. 1949) that the collagen of the aorta differs from that present in other tissues not only morphologically and functionally but also in its physicochemical characteristics. Collagen can be extracted with 1% acetic acid even without heating from the Achilles tendon as well as from the skin. From the aorta, on the other hand, under these circumstances a collagen is extracted (Banga et al. 1949) that is not viscous and fails to show double refraction when flowing. In the serial experiments shown in Table 25 solubilization of collagen from the aorta was still incomplete after three consecutive boilings with acetic acid as shown by the fact that the third boiling scarcely solubilized any hydroxyproline-containing protein, while in the residuum, in the so-called elastin fraction, 3·5 to 4% hydroxyproline was demonstrable. This is further evidence for the absence of pure elastin in the aorta of old subjects. The amino-acid composition of these elastins have undergone characteristic changes as shown also by Lansing et al. (1951) in comparing the elastins of young and old subjects. These differed from each other in the specific weight, in Ca content and in the relative number of free carboxyl groups. According to the amino-acid analysis the quantity of aspartic and glutamic acid displayed a significant rise parallel with age. Accordingly, in old age the amino-acid composition is shifted towards collagenization. Based on the specific weight, the elastin obtainable from the aorta of young subjects is called "light" in contrast to the "heavy" elastin characteristic of the old aorta.

A substance capable of binding orcein remains insoluble in the lig. nuchae, too, after two cold extractions with alkali and subsequent complete elastolysis. Figure 30 shows that in lig. nuchae fibres stained with 2%, 1% or 0·5% solution of orcein and subsequently subjected to elastolysis a coloured substance is still demonstrable. Consequently, orcein is fixed not only by elastin but also by some other substance. Since orcein may be fixed by metacollagen as well (Chapter XIII, p. 155) it is reasonable to suppose that a part of the collagen in the lig. nuchae is present as metacollagen. The unknown scleroprotein whose greater amounts are demonstrable in the aorta does not exceed 2 or 3% in the lig. nuchae. It is of interest, however, that it is detectable even in the ligaments of young calves

94

which indicates that this substance is contained not only in the old and sclerotic aortae, although its quantity in these is considerably higher.

Miller et al. (1952) determined the carbohydrate content of the scleroproteins of human aorta specimens ("albuminoids" termed by the authors) as a function of age. Their results appear to prove that it is independent of age, sex and pathological conditions. The carbohydrate content of the albuminoids showed a slight fluctuation around 1%. However, these findings do not agree with subsequent information in the literature, nor are the findings of Kraemer and Miller (1953) on the elastin content in accordance with the data shown in Tables 25 and 26.

FIG. 30. Left: lig. nuchae fibre fascicles stained with 2, 1 and 0·5% orcein. Right: the same after complete elastolysis. It is well visible that the residuum still contains orcein

These authors investigated the elastin content in 43 aorta specimens ranging from infancy to 89 years of age. At the same time they estimated the degree of arteriosclerosis by a method described in their publication and classified the aortae into four groups according to the severity of arteriosclerosis. They claimed that the elastin content of the albuminoids of the aorta is independent of age, sex and atherosclerosis. The average elastin content of the aorta specimens was 34·8% for both sexes as calculated from the 43 specimens. The elastin content of the pathologically altered vascular wall was significantly higher, but the authors attributed this increase to the increased calcium content of the pathological aortae. According to our present knowledge the failure of these authors to demonstrate the decrease in the elastin of the vascular wall during arteriosclerosis may be attributed to the methods of Lowry et al. (1941) and Lansing et al. (1952) used by them with the modification that the aorta tissues were, in addition, washed with NaCl and extracted by Ca(OH)$_2$. The insoluble fraction qualified to be elastin contained all the deposited inorganic salts and water-insoluble lipids, although the latter ought to have been saponified when boiled with alkali. In the carbohydrate content, on the other hand, they could not find any change because all mucoids and acid polysaccharides were extracted by Ca(OH)$_2$ and by boiling with alkali. The residual fraction is bound to elastin too strongly to be removable by the methods applied.

95

TABLE 26

Separation of scleroproteins from human aortae

Aorta No.	Age (years)	Sex	Diagnosis	Soluble protein + Mucoprotein (%)	Elastin (%)	Collagen (collastromin + metacollagen)	Degree of arteriosclerosis
8	16	♀	Sarcoma	41	45	14	0
XVI	17	♂	Combined mitral failure	35	35	30	0
I	26	♀	Carcinoma. Embolia	29	43	28	0
6	28	♀	Hodgkin's disease	36	43	21	0
XV	37	♂	Diabetes mellitus. Uraemia	26	38	36	++
XIX	39	♂	Pneumonectomy	30	45	25	+
IX	41	♂	Nephritis. Uraemia	29	43	28	+
XX	41	♂	Reticulosis	31	46	23	+
18	44	♂	Carcinoma pulmonis	38	40	22	+
XXV	47	♂	Tumor oesophagi	28	41	31	+
12	47	♀	Peritonitis	40	35	25	++
XIV	48	♂	Myodegeneratio cordis	24	36	40	+
4	50	♂	Endothelioma	42	40	18	+
XXI	52	♂	Tumor pulmonis	29	42	29	+
7	52	♂	Tumor pulmonis	45	35	20	0
VI	53	♂	Coronary thrombosis	23	33	44	++
20	53	♀	Tumor cerebri	37	43	20	+
11	57	♀	Tumor pancreatis	39	37	24	+
9	59	♀	Carcinoma pancreatis	34	44	22	+
VII	60	♂	Myodegeneratio cordis. Arteritis	23	33	44	++
5	60	♂	Tumor cardiae	32	46	22	+
XVIII	65	♂	Tumor pulmonis	21	26	53	+++
14	67	♀	Carcinoma uteri	33	40	27	++
19	67	♀	Carcinoma ventriculi	37	42	21	+
23	68	♀	Embolia pulmonum	37	42	21	+
24	71	♀	Embolia cerebri	36	42	22	+
16	73	♀	Atherosclerosis univ.	37	34	29	+++
21	73	♀	Tumor pancreatis	37	38	25	+
22	79	♀	Atherosclerosis univ.	34	32	34	+++
13	79	♀	Embolia pulmonum	38	36	25	++
15	83	♂	Embolia cerebri	42	33	25	+++
17	88	♂	Arteriosclerosis	40	35	26	+++
10	90	♀	Decompensatio cordis	37	38	25	++

Note: Soluble protein + mucoprotein (%): alkali-soluble protein was assayed by the biuret method; elastin (%): after alkali extraction the elastase-soluble protein was assayed by the Folin-phenol method; collagen (%): the elastase-insoluble residue was assayed by the hydroxyproline test

Buddecke (1958a, b, c) dealt with the chemistry of the human and animal aorta wall in several reports. He studied the alteration in the scleroproteins of the aorta wall as a function of age, and also the alkali-soluble ground substance. These experiments were combined with investigations of the acid mucopolysaccharides and sulphur- and hexosamine-containing mucoids of the ground substance. In addition to the age factor, a possible dependence of the scleroproteins on the severity of arteriosclerosis was also studied. According to these experiments the quantity both of the alkali-soluble ground substance and the hexosamine shows a marked rise parallel with age and atherosclerosis. Even the sulphur content increased, indicating an accumulation of the sulphated polysaccharide. Buddecke found no quantitative change in the collagen. Reduction in elastin was the only change he was able to demonstrate; 50 or even 75% of the elastin may disappear, depending on the severity of arteriosclerosis. It is emphasized and supported by experimental data that senescence is associated with a marked increase in the dry matter of the aorta (the data are calculated for aorta fragments $1\cdot33$ cm^2 in size). This is unexplainable by either the increased amount of the alkali-soluble ground substance or a fat accumulation in the intima. Buddecke attempts to explain the increase in the dry matter by a proliferation of *de novo* formed connective tissue around the arteriosclerotic lesions. The accumulated substance may be identical with the so-called unknown scleroprotein. Besides an increase in quantity, even an alteration in the spectrum of the mucopolysaccharides is demonstrable when arteriosclerosis proceeds (Buddecke 1960). A characteristic rise in the chondroitin-sulphate value is accompained by reduced hyaluronic acid and chondroitin levels. The accumulation of chondroitin sulphate is in connection with an increased deposition of calcium.

During the last ten years more than 100 papers have dealt with the alterations of the connective tissue concerning the structure proteins, in relation to age and atherosclerosis. The results are not equivocal because, depending on the method applied and the type of the connective tissue studied, disappearance and accumulation may equally be demonstrated for elastin as well as for collagen. In connection with the alterations occurring in the aorta Bertelsen (1961a,b) pointed out that the age-dependent alterations in the scleroproteins of the media-intima are independent of the accumulation of lipids in the intima. Although the formation of the latter may be in relation to the accumulation primarily of the acid MPS-s and also of the glycoproteins, it cannot as yet be decided whether or not it may serve as a basis for plaque formation in the intima.

THE ROLE OF MUCOPOLYSACCHARIDES AND LIPIDS IN ATHEROSCLEROSIS

On studying the hexosamine and neuramic-acid contents of the ground substance of the vascular wall, Lindner (1961) emphasized the significance of these substances in the metabolism. Their quantity depends on age and arteriosclerosis. The alterations in the fibrous substance of the vascular wall depend on several constituents

97

of the chromotropic ground substance. However, Lindner also emphasizes that, if the conditions of the ground-substance constituents are variable even within a small area, none of the biochemical, histological and histochemical techniques in itself is sufficiently satisfactory for an opinion to be formed on the alterations in the ground substance. This variability is why the processes to be investigated and their many-sided interrelations cannot be determined satisfactorily. According to Lindner, histochemistry, being closely related both to morphology and biochemistry, is expected to promote the clarification of the problem of arteriosclerosis.

Dyrbye and Kirk (1957) evolved a technique for the isolation of the MPS-s from young and old arterial tissues which yields isolated MPS of satisfactory purity. From aorta specimens of children and adults 2·4% MPS was obtained, whereas those of persons from 60 to 76 years of age yielded only 1·2%. The authors have concluded that the isolable MPS decreases parallel with age. The analysis of the isolated MPS (Kirk and Dyrbye 1957), including the assays of total hexosamine, uronic acid, sulphate and protein, showed no considerable differences between age groups. As regards the amino-sugar components of the MPS, higher galactosamine and lower glucosamine levels were found in the group of subjects from 60 to 76 years of age compared with the data of children and young adults. From the isolated MPS-s two fractions, viz. a faster-moving and a slow-moving one were separated by paper electrophoresis (Dyrbye et al. 1958). Both fractions showed metachromasia with toluidine blue. The faster-moving component resembling chondroitin sulphate contained 62·2% MPS and the total amino-sugar content of this fraction consisted of galactosamine. The MPS in the slower component amounted to 37·5% and consisted of almost equal amounts of galactosamine and glucosamine. Dyrbye (1959) investigated the metabolism of the acid sulphomucopolysaccharides of human aortae by using inorganic sulphate labelled with ^{35}S. He ascertained an inverse relationship between age and the incorporation of labelled sulphate.

Gerő et al. (1959, 1960) dealt with the relationship between the genesis of cholesterol-containing lipid plaques in the vascular intima and the quantity and fluctuation of blood lipids. According to their theory the β-lipoprotein of the blood has an antigenic capacity; by the administration of this fraction atherosclerosis may be prevented. As to the pathomechanism of atherosclerosis the authors assume that a great amount of MPS is deposited in the vascular wall and forms a complex with the β-lipoprotein accumulated as a result of the disturbed metabolism of the blood lipids. Thus, β-lipoprotein of blood origin is fixed in the vascular wall by complex bonds in a quantity which is presumably in close relation to the increased amount of the MPS in the vascular wall. These investigations were based on immunoelectrophoretic studies which have shown that in the aorta only the intima contains β-lipoprotein of plasma origin, whereas the other components of the vascular wall are free of this lipid fraction. This finding was confirmed by Tracy et al. (1961).

The important starting point of the investigations of Gerő et al. (1959, 1960) was Bernfeld's (1958) observation which has shown that only two fractions, namely the β-lipoprotein and the fibrinogen are the factors forming specific complexes with certain macromolecular polyanions. According to Gerő's hypothesis a similar complex may be formed with the mucoid substance accumulated in the vascular wall and this would represent the first step in the process leading to deposition of lipids and fibrin in the intima. To decide whether such complexes occur at all, MPS-s isolated from the intima of atherosclerotic human aortae, and the reactions of these MPS-s with the β-lipoprotein complex of the plasma and with fibrinogen, were studied. The acid MPS-s of the aorta were found to be the factors that react with the β-lipoprotein and with fibrinogen by forming complex bonds. According to this concept the acid MPS-s, accumulated in the course of atherosclerosis, trap the β-lipoproteins from the blood, and the plaques of the intima come about by fixation of the latter.

As regards the explanation of the complex formation from acid MPS and lipid, there exist some controversies between Gerő et al. (1961a, b, c, 1962), Bihari-Varga et al. (1963) and the results of Banga and Baló (1962) and Banga (1962b). The former investigators attribute no role to the mucoid-fixed protein components of the aorta, supposing that only the reactivity of the components containing acid sulphate are decisive factors in the development of MPS $-\beta$-lipoprotein complexes. In contrast to this, the investigations carried out in the author's laboratory have proved that neuramic-acid-containing neutral heteropolysaccharides form covalent bonds with a certain protein fraction which might be responsible for lipid fixation. The lipid component of the mucolipoproteide of the aorta (Chapter V, p. 65) may originate from the β-lipoprotein of the blood serum. We assume that in the aorta this lipid is fixed by covalent bonds to the protein as in the electric field the two components migrate together. The lipid component of the β-lipoprotein is incorporated in the complex either by a covalent bond with a protein already present in the complex or by exchanging the two protein components; in the latter case the protein component of the β-lipoprotein is incorporated. It is also possible that a mucoprotein complex of low molecular weight originally develops into a macromolecular mucoprotein complex by addition of the two proteins.

In contrast to the view of Gerő as well as to that of Banga and Baló, Boucek and Noble (1959) assumed, on the basis of their experiments carried out with labelled acetate, that the lipids and the steroids are synthesized in the vascular wall locally, i.e. the accumulation does not originate from circulating lipids.

According to Loeven's (1963a) experiments EMPase as a component of the clearing factor is demonstrable in the blood. Thus, Saxl's (1957a, b) suggestion, viz. the in vitro produced clearing factor would be capable of solubilizing the neutral fat deposited in atheromatous plaques, may be attributed to a presumable EMPase content of the blood serum used. The fact that this enzyme in itself, or an associated enzyme being closely related physicochemically to it, possesses lipolytic activity as well (Banga and Baló 1962; Banga 1962b; Loeven 1964e) may explain the effects observed.

Zemplényi and Grafnetter (1958) and Zemplényi et al. (1959) dealt with the lipolytic and esterolytic activities of the aorta wall with special regard to senescence and atherosclerosis. Using lipaemic blood as substrate, these authors determined the quantity of the non-esterified fatty acids released from the substrate on the effect of the lipolytic enzymes of the aorta wall. The lipolytic activity of the rat's aorta was found to be considerably higher than that of the aorta of species inclined to atherosclerosis. It is well-known that atherosclerosis can hardly be produced in rats, in contrast to the rabbit, guinea-pig and rooster which are susceptible to this disease. It has been ascertained that the lipolytic activity of the aorta wall shows a marked decline parallel with age as well as with atherosclerosis. The above investigators attribute the lipid deposition during the development of athero-sclerosis to a reduced lipolysis due to the disturbed dynamic equilibrium. As a result of this, the fat deposited on the intima fails to be degraded into fatty acids. Instead, it is accumulated in the vascular wall. On the other hand, according to these authors besides the lipids even the sulphated MPS-s of the vascular wall increase in amount. This increase presumably results from enzymatic effects as suggested by an increase in the sulphatase activity associated with declining lipolytic activity.

Based on the data available numerous groups of investigators believe that the MPS-s present in the ground substance play a central role in the aetiology of atherosclerosis; they are thought to be primarily responsible for upsetting the local metabolism of the vascular wall which is finally manifested in the dismeta-bolism of the entire vascular tissue.

Kayahan (1959) opposed this view and suggested that alterations in the α- and β-globulins of the serum are important factors in the development of atherosclero-sis. According to the experiments of this author the serum globulin of athero-sclerotic subjects with detectable hypercholesterolaemia shows an increased lipid-fixing capacity in contrast to the sera of normal cholesterol level. Kayahan evolved an elegant assay for the lipid-fixing capacity of globulins. He has shown that, besides the local metabolism of the vascular wall, the altered composition of the blood should not be neglected either. Furthermore, these investigations point to a possible significance of proteins, first of all of the serum globulins, besides the MPS-s, in the pathogenesis of atherosclerosis.

Saxl (1961) studied the genesis of the complex of lipids with elastic tissue in young human and chicken aorta specimens. She found the complex to be held together by van der Waals forces. In the aorta of cholesterolaemic chickens she followed the disintegration and conversion of the lipids into lipoprotein by electron microscopy. On the effect of elastomucase and serum globulin she found a clear-ing reaction in the intima tissue, indicating that the lipids in the plaques of the intima had been solubilized. Baló (1963) observed the same phenomenon in healed cases of experimental atherosclerosis. In such cases the lipids deposited in the intima of the aorta and other arteries become absorbed and disappear entirely. Baló pointed out that Krylov (1916) and Anitschkow (1925) were the first to observe regression of initial lesions in experimental atherosclerosis. Since then numerous authors have observed the disappearance of plaques in the intima.

SUMMARY

The view that the elastic fibre is a complex structure, i.e. inhomogeneous both chemically and morphologically, began to develop only after the discovery and study of the mechanism of action of elastase. Until then the elastic fibres had been distinguished from collagen and reticular fibres partly by staining techniques, partly by biochemical experiments based on physicochemical differences. Studies with elastase, the enzyme decomposing elastic fibres and the study of its subfractions, such as elastoproteinase, elastomucoproteinase and elastolipoproteinase, have proved the complex structure of the elastic fibre as far as each of these enzymes attack a special component of the elastic fibre.

Polarization-optical studies appear to prove the existence of two or even three submicroscopic components inside the elastic fibre which had been thought to be integral. These components are: a) the matrix which is demonstrable histologically by resorcin staining; b) the elastin-mucoid giving anisotropic staining with toluidine blue, and c) the phenol-elastoid which gives the phenol reaction, though it is not identical with collagen. Under the electron microscope only two morphologically distinguishable components have been detected: the matrix and the embedded fibrils. Polarization optics owes its greater resolution to the anisotrope reaction, whereas the poor results obtained by electron microscopy are attributable to the fact that for the investigators working with high-resolution electron microscopes highly-purified elastomucolytic and elastolipolytic enzymes are not available in sufficient quantities. The lipid-containing component of the elastic fibre has not yet been demonstrated morphologically.

Biochemical investigations appear to prove the existence of three components unequivocally, mainly: a) one consisting of protein; b) another containing besides protein acid and neutral mucopolysaccharide, and c) a lipid-containing component. At present only the histochemical existence of the components seems to be proved; their isolation and preparation in a pure state needs further studies. It seems likely that the relationship of these components to each other is age-dependent and it is also a function of arteriosclerosis, and these inconsistencies hinder their preparation and isolation.

Functional studies seem to throw light on two circumstances; a) the function of the elastic fibre depends not only on the integrity of its chemical construction, but it may be influenced by physicochemical and chemical changes in other components of the connective tissue, such as collagen and reticular fibres and/or the mucoids of the ground substance; b) the elastase-enzyme complex and its inhibitors

may, through their synthesizing and decomposing activities, indirectly influence the condition, and consequently the function, of the elastic fibres.

In our opinion the elastase-enzyme complex and its inhibitors represent a regulating mechanism which is responsible for the integrity of the normal fibres capable of the maximal function under physiological conditions. Old age and arteriosclerosis are associated with an alteration in the production and relative amount of the enzymes and their inhibitors, not only in the pancreas but also in the blood serum. This imbalance brings about the morphological changes in the vascular wall, characteristic of old age and arteriosclerosis.

In order to study, *in vivo* and *in vitro*, the mechanism of action of the elastolytic-enzyme components it would be greatly important to solve their mass production in the preparative way. The preparation of specific inhibitors would be equally important. While injection of the highly active elastoproteinase into living objects is unreasonable because of the strong tissue-destructive effect of this enzyme, the mucolytic and lipolytic enzymes are free of such an activity, thus are expected to be suitable for *in vivo* experiments. Such experiments will prove the role of the elastolytic enzymes in the pathogenesis of arteriosclerosis, a hypothesis first suggested by Baló.

Macromolecular Structure of the Collagen Fibre;
Submicroscopical, Chemical, Histochemical
and Physical Evidence of their Complex Structure

CHAPTER IX

MOLECULAR STRUCTURE OF COLLAGEN PROTEIN

WHILE our ideas concerning the molecular and macromolecular structure of elastin are uncertain, our knowledge of collagen is much more profound. This is primarily due to the fact that, unlike elastin, collagen shows a crystal-like arrangement at the molecular level, and the aggregation of molecules follows a well-defined regularity in native collagen fibres. At the macromolecular level, as will be shown, structures different from those occurring in the native collagen fibre can also be produced *in vitro*. The discovery of these structures has significantly advanced our knowledge in this field. The fine molecular structure is analysed by the wide-angle X-ray diffraction technique (Astbury 1938), whereas for revealing the macromolecular arrangement the small-angle X-ray technique (Bear 1942) proved to be appropriate. Under the electron microscope the native fibres show a characteristic cross-striation, 640 Å in periodicity as recognized independently in two laboratories (Schmitt et al. 1942, Wolpers 1943).

The small-angle diffraction patterns and the cross-striation observed by electron microscopy prove the same macromolecular arrangement.

Like elastin, collagen belongs to the group of so-called insoluble scleroproteins. The chemical analysis of these substances is considerably hindered by their insolubility. In most cases they cannot be purified satisfactorily, unless they are submitted to drastic physicochemical and chemical procedures. The fact that in spite of these difficulties our knowledge is more precise about collagen than about elastin is partly due to the many-sided, wide interest focussed on collagen.

From the biological and medical point of view collagen is an important substance because it constitutes 25 to 35% of the total skeleton proteins. Since it is a component of the bone, the skin, the tendon, the fascia and of both loose and compact connective tissues, it is present in every organ. It is, therefore, reasonable that certain diseases displaying morphological lesions in the connective tissue have been described as collagen diseases (Klemperer et al. 1942). In connection with these collagen has had an extensive literature.

In industry the role of collagen in the tanning of leather is all-important. Furthermore, gelatin and glue the well-known degradation products of collagen are of universal industrial importance. The lack of antigenicity in the collagen-containing fibres allows their use as bandages in surgery.

The investigations during the last 20 years have considerably advanced our knowledge of the chemical composition and molecular and macromolecular structure of collagen. However, the connection between the function of the fibre and its molecular structure is still lacking. The question has arisen whether chemical substances and linkages similar to those being so important in the function of elastin are of primary significance for the function of collagen as well. Research concerning this question is, naturally, rather difficult, for like in elastin, only minute amounts of the functionally important substances are present in the collagen. These substances are mucoproteins and mucopolysaccharides in nature. The main subject of this work is to isolate these substances and to prove their participation in the structure of the functioning fibre. As in the case of elastin enzymatic analysis has brought the final proof here, too. Collagenmucoproteinase (CMPase, see Chapter III, p. 39), the enzyme isolated first by us is produced in the pancreas, just like elastolytic enzymes and trypsin. In our opinion CMPase is able to exert even a collagenase effect, provided the substrate is adequately disintegrated.

The test applied in the study of function includes denaturation of the fibre; yet the outcome of the reactions and the end-product supply important information concerning the working capacity of the fibre.

Before describing our own investigation in the field of the function of collagen, the present stage of collagen research is reviewed.

AMINO-ACID COMPOSITION AND AMINO-ACID SEQUENCE

The amino-acid composition of a preparation is greatly influenced by the degree of its homogeneity and purity. However, during the preparation of pure collagen protein the concentrated salt and alkali solutions dissolve other soluble proteins from the tissue in addition to collagen. As a result of this, also mucopolysaccharides (MPS), particularly acid MPS-s and possibly mucoproteins which are integrant components of the native, functionable fibre will be extracted. Naturally, investigators have consistently iamed at obtaining a protein product which may be regarded as pure collagen. Table 27 shows the amino-acid composition of the pure collagen and pure gelatin as published by Bowes and Kenten (1949), Chibnal (1946) and Eastoe (1955).

During the last ten years efforts were made to determine the amino-acid sequence of collagen, but the knowledge in this field is far from being complete. It was thought for a long time that the collagen chain is characterized by a simple G-P-R sequence (Astbury 1940), in which G = glycine (Gly), P = proline (Pro) or hydroxyproline (Hypro) and R may indicate any other amino acid. The most recent data do not seem to confirm this view. Grassmann (1955) divided the peptides isolated from the acid or alkali hydrolysates of collagen into neutral, acid and basic peptides and peptides containing Pro or Hypro. From these investigations it is clear that in the so-called "small peptide molecules" Gly is the most common residue and the majority of the peptides contain Pro and Hypro. The Gly-Pro-Hypro sequence is the most common and Gly-(Pro-Hypro)-Gly tetrapeptide has also been isolated. Besides the small peptides obtained by acid and alkali hydrolysis, Grassmann et al. (1956, 1960) isolated larger peptide frag-

TABLE 27

Amino-acid composition of collagen and gelatin, M/10^5 *g protein*

	Collagen		Gelatin			Collagen		Gelatin
	Bovine skin	Human bone	Prepared with acid from porcine skin			Bovine skin	Human bone	Prepared with acid from porcine skin
Glycine	350	344	352	Hydroxyproline		107	108	103
Alanine	106	122	119	Lysine		31	30	28
Leucine	—	27	25	Hydroxylysine		8	4	6
Isoleucine	42	14	10	Arginine		51	51	52
Valine	29	25	24	Histidine		5	6	6
Phenylalanine	25	15	16	Aspartic acid		47	51	50
Tyrosine	8	5	3	Glutamic acid		77	78	78
Serine	33	39	39	Tryptophane		—	—	—
Threonine	20	20	18	Cystine		—	—	—
Methionine	5	6	6	Amide nitrogen		47	40	44
Proline	132	133	141					

ments by tryptic digestion. These peptides contained from 3 to 131 amino-acid residues each and comprised more than 50% of the native collagen protein. The fact that in this case, too, one-third of the amino-acid residues was glycine has strengthened the view that in the collagen chain every third amino acid has to be Gly. Nevertheless, some of the peptides did not contain Gly in sequence of 4 or 5 amino acids. It was another interesting observation that the peptides in which imino acids were predominant contained no polar residues and vice versa; e.g. in a peptide consisting of 33 residues the number of imino-acid residues was 15 and only one of the amino acids was polar, whereas another peptide consisting of 20 residues contained neither Pro nor Hypro, while more than one-third of the residues was polar.

The amino-acid sequence of the collagen was also studied with the pure collagenase prepared from *Clostridium histolyticum*. Nordwig (1962) summarized the literature of these works. Accordingly, a P-R-R'-P sequence is a prerequisite in the collagenase action to split the R-R' bond of collagen. In this case P means proline, but it may mean Hypro. However, in the latter case the enzyme is less active. A synthetic peptide, namely Cbo-Gly-Pro-Gly-Gly-Pro-Ala proved to be an excellent substrate. This was split into Cbo-Gly-Pro-Gly and Gly-Pro-Ala by the enzyme (Cbo = carbobenzoxy component). In collagen hydrolysates Manahan and Mandl (1961) and a number of other investigators (Schrohenloher et al. 1959; Sakakibara et al. 1960; Ogle et al. 1961) found the peptides Gly-Pro-Ala and Gly-Pro-Hypro most frequently. According to others the Gly-Ala-Hypro and

Ala-Hypro with Ala occur much less frequently as N-terminal. However, these data are inconsistent with the observations of Grassmann et al. (1961a) who found Gly as the most common N-terminal, and Pro (82%) or Ala (18%) in position two. They never found Hypro either in position two or in position three. In the native collagen neither Grassmann and Hörmann (1953) nor Bowes and Moss (1951, 1953) could reveal N-terminal groups. However, after heat treatment or denaturation with urea or some other denaturing agent a small number of N-terminal residues could be detected. It was claimed that the terminal groups might have been masked by mucopolysaccharides (Ramachandran 1963). In this Institute Banga (1953) and Banga and Baló (1954) were able to detect a mucoid which can be liberated by a heat treatment too short to lead to gelatinization. This mucoid (mucoid$_1$) is bound by covalent bonds to the collagen protein.

By a modified thiohydantoin method Deasy (1956) found Gly, Ala and Leu C-terminal residues in the collagen of the bovine tendon. The original C-terminal is presumably serine which converted into alanine or glycine during the alkali hydrolysis applied by the author. Accordingly, Gly and Ala are considered split products and not true C-terminals. An existence of three C-terminals, namely Ser, Val and Leu, appears to be consistent with the triple-helical structure of collagen.

EVIDENCE OF A HELICAL STRUCTURE CONSISTING
OF THREE PEPTIDE CHAINS

On the basis of wide-angle X-ray diffraction patterns, Astbury put forward a collagen model consisting of extended polypeptide chains. In this model the $C=O$ and $N-H$ groups of the amino-acid residues are partly in the *cis*, partly in the *trans* position, whereas the P residues are in *cis* position. According to more recent studies, however, P residues comprise less than one-third of the amino-acid residues and the *cis* configuration does not exist in the collagen structure. In spite of this, Astbury's theory suggesting that in the collagen regular sequences are predominant and Gly is present in every third position has proved to be acceptable. Astbury's model was followed by some others supposing extended chains in the structure (Huggins 1943; Zahn 1948; Ambrose and Elliott 1951; Randall et al. 1953). However, these models are not consistent with certain obvious properties of the collagen. Pauling and Corey (1951a, b, c) put forward the revolutionary theory that in a biological helix the number of members per turn is not necessarily an integer number, the neighbouring turns of a helix may approach to, or deviate from, each other and so the distance between the single members of the turns may be inconsistent (puckered chain). On this basis Pauling and Corey (1951b) succeeded in creating the so-called α-helix model for the keratine group of fibrous proteins, and the same structure has proved to be most acceptable for synthetic polypeptides as well. Several helical models with single, double or triple helices were proposed for the collagen, but none of these could explain all its known properties. The structure most adequate to explain all these characteristics is a triple-chained model which was first proposed by Ramachandran and Kartha in 1954 and 1955 and was established in its ultimate form by Ramachandran and Sasisekharan (1961). Unlike the earlier structures, this model consists of three helices running beside one another and stabilized by interchain hydrogen bonds of the NH...O=C type. The helices form a so-called coiled-coil triple helix, indicating that they are coiled up not only around one another but also around a central axis. In such a structure every third residue should be a glycyl one, for every third alpha C atom occupies such a position that there is no space for a side-group. The glycyl residue must be inside, otherwise the compact five-member rings of Pro and Hypro would not fit into the triple helix. It is also essential in this structure that only two interchain hydrogen bonds belong to every three residues. This complicated triple helix considerably inhibits the free motility of the peptide chains. According to Pauling and Corey (1954) 40% of the peptide bonds are double-bonded. Consequently, every third bond is immobile along the peptide chain. In the collagen the motility is even more limited because of the direct incorporation of Pro and Hypro molecules in the peptide chain. Owing to the five-member ring of these amino acids another linkage is fixed along the peptide chain. Consequently, only every third bond remains free-moving. For this reason in the collagen the chains form rigid, extended spirals which will be even more rigid by interchain linkages.

Ramachandran (Madras school) based his model on wide-angle X-ray diffraction studies. From these he obtained three kinds of information (Ramachandran 1963): a) from the distances of the layer lines he ascertained that the structure is helical; b) the position of the individual spots proved the latticed arrangement of the protofibril; c) the intensity of the spots supplied information on the arrangement of the atoms inside the protofibrils. It was shown that the pattern given by the non-extended collagen fibre never gives sharp outlines because the fibrils inside enclose an angle with the axis instead of running parallel with it. Accordingly, the spots appear around the centre of the pattern and form a layer line. As a result of extension the fibrils will be arranged along a straight line and sharply outlined spots appear instead of layer lines. Thus, only the photographs of extended fibres can be used in the construction of a model for the molecular structure.

The configuration of the polymers synthesized from Gly, Pro and Hypro is also triple-chained, but it is somewhat different from that of the collagen. Recently Andreeva et al. (1961) synthesized a Gly-Pro-Hypro polymer with a molecular weight of 25 000. The X-ray pattern and infrared absorption of this polymer are very similar to those of the collagen.

As to the amino-acid construction of the three polypeptide chains, two alternative structures have been proposed: a) the special Gly-Pro-Hypro sequence occurs only in one of the chains; b) it occurs in all three chains. Both alternatives are very similar to the configuration of the supposed standard structure, and either of them may be accepted without postulating that any of the atoms in the backbone deviates by more than 0·5 Å from its standard position. The final settlement of this question needs a more precise knowledge of the amino-acid sequences.

Also Rich and Crick (1955, 1958) proposed two alternative models which they termed Collagen I and Collagen II. At that time they were still unable to construct a satisfactory collagen model with two interchain hydrogen bonds for each residue. For this reason they put forward models in which only one hydrogen bond belongs to every three residues. Topologically two alternative structures may arise, in one the NH−O hydrogen bond is clockwise, in the other it is anticlockwise. These alternatives correspond to the Collagen I and Collagen II models of Rich and Crick. Later Rich and Crick (1961) considered the Collagen II model to be more adequate for many reasons.

However, in the infrared absorption spectrum the frequency of the NH vibration agrees better with the Ramachandran structure than with the Collagen II model.

According to Ramachandran the physical and chemical characteristics of the collagen are as follows: a) one third of the amino-acid residues is glycyl and about 20% are imino-acid residues; b) typical wide-angle X-ray diffraction pattern showing meridional reflection at 3 Å and equatorial reflection at 12 Å; c) the electron microscope shows cross-striation with a periodicity of 640 Å; d) in the infrared absorption spectrum the peak corresponding to the NH group is at 3330 cm^{-1}, i.e. it is shifted by 30 cm^{-1} from the 3300 value characteristic of other proteins; e) strong negative optical rotation ($-350°$) in solutions which falls to $-120°$ when collagen is heated to the contraction temperature in the presence of water; f) heating results in the shrinkage of the rigid structure, and a simultaneous conversion of the crystalline structure into amorphous. Although these criteria are characteristic of native collagen fibres, it would be groundless to state that a substance is not collagen if it fails to show any of these characteristics (Ramachandran 1963). Thus, fibrils reconstituted from collagen solutions may or may not show the characteristic periodicity under the electron microscope or even may show a completely different periodicity. Accordingly, the criterion given under c) appears to be insignificant. The collagen of invertebrates contains less glycine and amino acid, i.e. it does not cover requirement a). It does cover criteria b) and c) but not d) and e). The lower glycine content and the lack of other characteristics suggest that the collagen of invertebrates is linked with another protein.

CHAPTER X

The Tropocollagen Macromolecule

Electron-microscopic Studies

WHILE the wide-angle X-ray diffraction patterns have supplied information only on the molecular construction of collagen, electron-microscopic studies have thrown light on the structure of the collagen fibre. Since 1942 the Cambridge school (Mass.), headed by Gross, Highberger and Schmitt, and the German Grassmann school (Munich) have been the most successful in this field.

Simultaneously with electron-microscopic experiments Bear (1942) demonstrated that the small-angle X-ray diffraction pattern of the natural collagen fibre corresponds to a periodicity of 640 to 700 Å. Owing to the experiments of Zacchariades (1900) and Nageotte (1927) the solubility of collagen in dilute acids, e.g. acetic acid, was known. Collagen when precipitated from such solutions forms fibrils showing the typical wide-angle diffraction pattern (Wyckoff and Corey 1936), and under the electron microscope a periodicity of 640 Å (Schmitt et al. 1942). Furthermore, the collagen of the skin is soluble also in citrate buffer, and when such solutions are dialyzed, a fibrillar precipitate is produced. This consists of procollagen crystals as termed by Orekhovich et al. (1948). Highberger et al. (1950) examined the substance so obtained under the electron microscope and demonstrated, besides the fibrils of 640 Å periodicity, so-called "long-spacing" fibrils with a periodicity of 2000 to 3000 Å ("fibre long-spacing" = FLS form). Measurable amounts of such fibrils arise only if serum glycoprotein or mucopolysaccharides (MPS) of high molecular weight are added to the solution before dialysis. According to Highberger et al. (1951) and Gross et al. (1952) the presence of MPS only induces the FLS-formation, but does not play any part in the chemical reaction. The amino-acid composition of FLS is identical with that of the normal collagen fibres, both giving the typical wide-angle diffraction pattern.

Schmitt et al. (1953) found another long-spacing modification, the so-called "segment long-spacing" (SLS) form. The SLS collagen is precipitated from acid solutions by adenosine triphosphate (ATP) and it can also be prepared from phosphate solutions by adding ribonucleic acid (RNA), deoxyribonucleic acid (DNA), heparin or chondroitin sulphate before dialysis. Dialysis should be performed against a citrate buffer (Schmitt et al. 1955). In contrast to the FLS type being fibrillar in nature, the protofibrils show a lateral aggregation resulting in short segments, 2800 Å in length. This form shows the same amino-acid composition and wide-angle diffraction pattern as the normal collagen. In Fig. 31 electron micrographs of the FLS and SLS forms are presented. Schmitt et al. (1953) and Gross et al. (1954) showed that the three different modifications can be converted

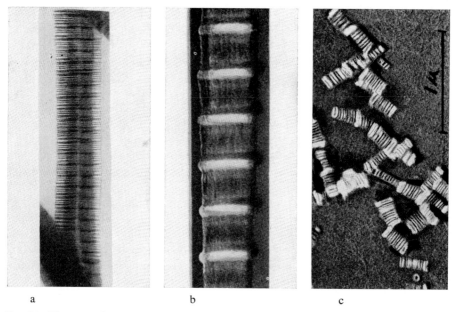

FIG. 31. Electron-microscopic picture of the native (a); FLS (b); and SLS collagen (c); (after Highberger et al. 1950)

into one another quantitatively. It can, therefore, be concluded that collagen has a fundamental unit which forms different modifications depending on the type of aggregation. The fundamental form is a single protofibril (triple helix) which is 2800 Å in length. Gross et al. (1954) termed this "tropocollagen macromolecule" (Tc.) because it is not built up of a single, but of three peptide chains which are linked to one another by hydrogen bonds.

It is of interest that physicochemical studies have led to the evidence of the dimensions of the tropocollagen macromolecule which is, according to these studies, 2800 Å in length and 14 Å in diameter. In general, it has been accepted that the SLS form of collagen may be considered the molecular finger print of collagen, for in the SLS form the tropocollagen molecules are aggregated in parallel and this type of aggregation shows the distribution of the side-chains in the fibrils most clearly.

AGGREGATION OF TROPOCOLLAGEN MOLECULES;

FORMATION OF ITS QUATERNARY STRUCTURE

The amino-acid composition and the amino-acid sequence are characteristic in the primary structure of collagen. In Chapter IX (p. 109) we have pointed out that the characteristic amino-acid sequence of collagen, particularly the presence of imino acids (Pro and Hypro) in the primary chain, is a prerequisite of the formation of a triple-helical structure. According to Kühn (1962) the extended spiral

112

structure of the single peptide chains forms the secondary structure, whereas the tertiary structure is due to the triple peptide chain turning around a central axis. The stability of the tertiary structure is secured by hydrogen bridges inside the triple-helix. However, both the secondary and tertiary structures will cease when the citrate-dissolved collagen is heated to 38 °C. In this case the collagen molecule assumes the form of an irregular conglomerate. Ultracentrifugal analysis has shown that in such denatured solutions fractions occur with molecular weights amounting to one-third or two-thirds of the original molecular weight, i.e., single

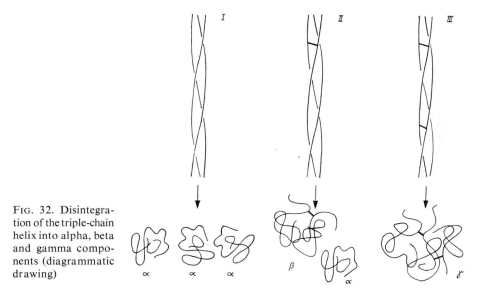

FIG. 32. Disintegration of the triple-chain helix into alpha, beta and gamma components (diagrammatic drawing)

and double peptide chains arise from the disintegrating collagen molecule. The single chain is called alpha particle. It is of importance that, as shown by Orekhovich and Shpikiter (1957, 1958), certain denatured solutions contain two or three kinds of molecules, different in molecular weight. According to Boedtker and Doty (1955) the triple-chain helix has a molecular weight of 300 000 to 330 000; that of the alpha particle is 70 000 to 80 000, whereas the molecular weight of a second component also different in sedimentation velocity, is 120 000 to 130 000 (Orekhovich and Shpikiter 1958; Doty and Nishihara 1958). In this molecule (beta component) two peptide chains are bound together. Grassmann et al. (1961) found a third degradation component (gamma particle) in addition to the alpha and beta molecules. The molecular weight of this was found to be 290 000. It is thought that all three peptide chains are contained in this component without the hydrogen bonds securing the secondary and tertiary structure for the Tc. macromolecule. Figure 32 illustrates the degradation of the triple helix into alpha, beta and gamma particles.

In the primary structure, along the molecule, regularly-arranged sequences mainly consisting of light amino acids and irregular sequences of polar amino acids follow each other alternately. In order to understand the structure of the Tc. molecule, the knowledge of the position of the polar amino acids is of particular importance. Along the molecule there are areas where basic amino acids (Arg and Lys) are predominant, whereas in other areas acid amino acids (Glut, Asp) are more frequent. The presence of ammonium or guanidine groups with positive charge at the end of the side-chains of the basic amino acids and of negatively-charged carboxyl ions at the corresponding site of the acid amino acids produces centres with positive and negative charge, respectively, on the surface of the mole-

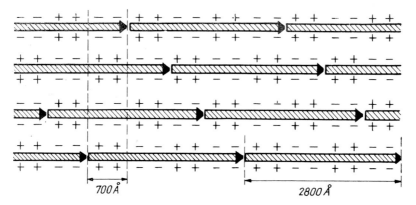

FIG. 33. Simplified, diagrammatic arrangement of tropocollagen molecules in the fibrils. As a result of a shift by one-fourth of the period the negatively and positively charged centres of the adjacent tropocollagen molecules show this pattern (after Kühn 1962)

cule. This characteristic polarization determines the formation of collagen fibrils and the development of a quaternary structure. In the linkage of Tc. molecules the attractive electrostatical forces between the negative and positive charges represent the cohesive force. The negatively-charged areas tend to approach a segment with a positive charge. Owing to the characteristic distribution of the electrostatic charges, the most favourable combination of the adjacent molecules will ensue if they lie parallel but shifted by one-fourth of their length beside each other. Nature has solved the problem of fibril formation in this way (Kühn 1962) (Fig. 33). Considering that the Tc. molecule is 2800 Å in length, a shift by one-fourth this distance means 700 Å. This arrangement is a clear-cut explanation of the periodicity of 640 to 700 Å consistently shown in the electron micrographs of the collagen tissue. The polar "heavy areas" (with long side-chains) will be visible as dark cross-striations, whereas the neutral "light areas" (short side-chains) will show light cross-triations under the electron microscope. These segments show the subperiods within the 700 Å periods. The more precisely the molecules of the polar areas fit with each other, the sharper are the cross-striations and the more subunits are shown. The arrangement is especially well demonstrable when the fibrils are treated with phosphotungstic acid or with the

114

tanning chrome complex (III) or with uranyl acetate. These heavy metal complexes are transversally fixed to the basic or acid areas of the molecule so strongly that the polar areas cannot separate from one another.

The hypothesis suggesting that the periodicity recognizable in the native collagen fibre is due to the alternate construction of the Tc. macromolecule has been confirmed by Hodge and Schmitt (1960) and Kühn (1960). From the tropocollagen solution native fibrils or long-spacing-segments will separate, depending on the presence or absence of ATP during fibril formation (Fig. 34). These observations

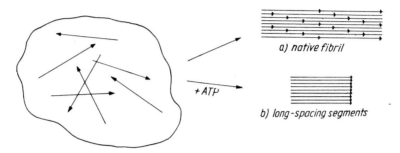

a) native fibril

b) long-spacing segments

+ ATP

Fig. 34. Formation of native fibril (a), and long-spacing segments (b) from tropocollagen solution (after Kühn 1962)

were confirmed by further interesting experiments (Hodge and Schmitt 1960). When native-type fibrils were placed in ATP-containing tropocollagen solution at a pH favourable for the arisal of SLS particles, the native-type fibrils behaved as nuclei in the formation of SLS segments. The SLS segments "grew out" of the surface of the native fibres in a periodical arrangement. Owing to the orientation of the SLS particle grown out of a native fibril, the periodicity of the latter was exactly continued in the former (Fig. 35).

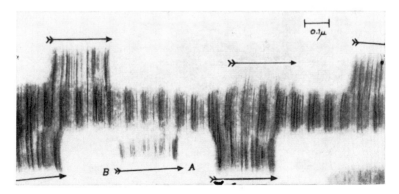

Fig. 35. SLS particles growing out of the native fibre. Electron micrograph (Schmitt and Hodge 1960)

115

In the foregoing, the formation of the quaternary structure of the collagen fibril was followed from the single peptide chain, over the triple-helical structure (so called Tc. molecule) to the fibrillar structure. We have seen that the existence of the individual phases are based, in addition to X-ray diffraction investigations, on other physicochemical studies and excellent electron micrographs. According to Kühn and Zimmer (1961) the lateral linkages are brought about by electrostatical forces in relation to each of the three types of the Tc. molecule. These forces arise from the positive and negative charges accumulated on the molecular surface. Regarding the formation of native fibres, as shown in the preceding chapter, it is thought that, as a result of attractive forces between positively- and negatively-charged centres, the adjacent Tc. molecules are shifted beside each other by one-fourth of their length. SLS types arise only in acid solutions, where Tc. molecules may possess only positive charge. The ATP molecules which have multiple negative charges form a network across these molecules and so keep them together. The linkages are brought about by the distribution of polar amino acids along the molecule. If the basic amino acids and the associated positive charges were arranged statistically, linkages would also come about by chance, i.e. unarranged. In fact, however, owing to the presence of ATP ions, areas with the same degree of positive charge will be linked together. For such linkages parallel molecules whose end is cut off are most favourable.

In the presence of a great quantity of chondroitin sulphate (when the ratio of collagen to MPS ranges from 6 : 1 to 3 : 1) Tc. molecules show at neutral pH a position characteristic of the FLS type. In the case of such an arrangement (so-called antiparallel arrangement) strongly positive areas lie beside one another while certain negative charges will miss one another. However, the molecules are forced by the chondroitin sulphate to assume an arrangement resembling the SLS form, for every second neighbour of each of the Tc. molecules run parallel. Kühn (1962) and Kühn and Zimmer (1961) claimed that under special circumstances a previously unknown FLS form comes about. This form was termed FLS II to distinguish it from the known FLS I.

The experiences available have obviously proved that native-type fibrils are mainly formed in collagen solutions (procollagen or tropocollagen) in which the fibril formation is induced by certain inorganic ions, mainly phosphate ions. Sharp electron micrographs of high contrast are only obtained with unpurified procollagen as starting material which contains polysaccharides in about 1% (acid and neutral sugars). A prerequisite for the formation of SLS-type fibrils is the presence of ATP. FLS-type fibrils, on the other hand, require acid MPS-s to be formed. It has been suggested also on theoretical grounds (Kühn 1962) that in fibril formation neither inorganic phosphate ions nor ATP, nor acid MPS-s play any chemical role; yet we are of the opinion that the fibre capable of functioning represents a unit in which neutral and acid MPS-s are essential components.

As to the longitudinal, i.e. end-to-end interfibrillar linkages, a uniform view has not yet developed, and the role of neutral glycoproteids and acid MPS-s is also obscure in the functioning collagen fibre as well as in the relationship of the ground substance building up the collagen tissue from the collagen protein itself.

It is known that ultrasonically-fragmented Tc. molecules are able to be linked together, as observed (Hodge and Schmitt 1958) at the longitudinal ends. It was, therefore, assumed that Tc. molecules have some end groups consisting of short

a   b

Fig. 36. Formation of monomers on trypsin effect (a) from SLS (b); (after Schmitt and Hodge 1960)

appendages, so-called tail peptides. Linkages between these end groups make Tc. molecules capable of fibril formation. To reveal the characteristics of these end groups Hodge et al. (1960) studied the aggregation in Tc. solutions following treatment with proteolytic enzymes. As a result of proteolysis, the viscosity of the Tc. solutions was considerably reduced, but their optical rotation showed no change. They obtained no SLS polymers from enzyme-treated sonicates. Instead, only a few, fragmented SLS particles formed (Fig. 36). These results are consistent with the hypothesis suggesting that the end groups of the Tc. molecule are attacked by the enzyme, while its helical configuration remains unaffected. According to the experiments of Hodge et al. (1960) tyrosine-containing peptides which are important in the end-to-end linkage are released on the effect of proteolytic enzymes. However, this hypothesis was not accepted by Kühn et al. (1961) who claimed that Tc. preparations intensely digested with pepsin and trypsin were able to be linked together and formed native-type fibrils. According to these authors the end-to-end linkage is not due to the tail peptides but, like lateral aggregation, results from electrostatical attractive forces. They suggest that the peptides decomposed by pepsin and trypsin are of no importance in fibril formation. These enzymes give rise to preparations resembling highly purified collagen. The fibrils formed in such preparations are thinner and show less contrast than non-purified preparations. Hexose, hexosamine and tyrosine fall to a lower level both in enzyme-treated and purified preparations. It is thought that a tyrosine-containing glyco-proteid which is not an essential component of collagen is split off. As regards the role of the acid α-glycoproteid, Kühn (1962) pointed out that even minute amounts of this substance promote the formation of native-type fibrils; fibril formation is speeded up and the electron micrographs of the resulting fibrils show particularly clear structure and contrast. Kühn attributes this phenomenon to the electrostatical interrelation between the polar groups of the collagen mole-cules and the glycoproteid.

In Chapters XIV (p. 166) and XV (p. 171) we present evidence of an essential role of certain mucoproteins in the formation of collagen fibrils. These not only induce fibril formation but also form a covalent bond with collagen. Since they contain a great number of tyrosine-containing peptides they might be supposed to be related to the tail peptides. This view is supported by the fact that an enzyme of collagenmucoproteinase activity which is present in trypsin preparations liberates polysaccharide-containing peptides being essential in fibril formation. Up to now neither X-ray-diffraction studies nor electron-microscopic investigations have been able to provide certain evidence of the existence of these substances.* Only the studies discussed in the following chapters have proved their existence convincingly.

---

* T. Nemetschek recently (1965) published that the collagen fibres treated with CMPase show a symmetric cross-striation, while the native ones are asymmetric.

CHAPTER XI

SOLUBLE AND INSOLUBLE COLLAGENS

DURING the history of collagen research over half a century investigators have been most interested in the problem of the soluble and insoluble collagen. Zacchariades (1900) and subsequently Nageotte (1927) were the first to prepare soluble collagen by extraction with dilute, mainly acetic acid. Certain kinds of collagen such as the tail's tendon of the young rat, ichthyocolla, the swimming bladder of fish, etc. give rise to a thin gel in adequate amounts (100 to 200-fold in weight) of dilute (0·2 M) acetic acid. The gel can then be separated from the relatively small amount of insoluble fraction. Such collagen gels were termed collagen A by Delaunay et al. (1955, 1956) who, among others, employ these gels in their investigations. However, the collagen gels so prepared still contain both forms of collagen, and the Nageotte method is inadequate to make a distinction between soluble and insoluble collagen. Tustanovsky (1947) and Orekhovich et al. (1948) first succeeded in their complete separation; they extracted the soluble collagen from various tissues (mainly from animals' skins) by citrate solutions of pH 3 to 4. By this solution 15 to 20% of the collagen could be extracted from the skin of young animals, whereas the yield from old animals was only 5 to 10%. Soviet authors call the collagen soluble in citrate buffer procollagen (Orekhovich 1952), for experiments with radioisotopes have shown that *in vivo* this fraction is formed earlier than the insoluble fraction. They found considerably low procollagen values and consequent defective fibrillogenesis in scurvied animals.

From procollagen solutions a crystalline substance can be obtained by various methods, most favourably by dialysis against distilled water adjusted to pH 7·5 or against dilute phosphate buffer of pH 7·5. Banga et al. (1956a) obtained similar procollagen crystals from young rats' tendons. The photograph of these crystals is shown in Fig. 37.

Bressler et al. (1950) studied the physicochemistry of procollagen crystals. However, in the light of the latest knowledge the published data suggest that the procollagen studied of these authors might have been in a partially decomposed state as shown also by its molecular weight which was 60 000 to 70 000, whereas the molecular weight of the intact Tc. molecule is between 300 000 and 330 000 as shown in Chapter X (p. 113). More recent works of Orekhovich and Shpikiter (1957, 1958) made it likely that the earliest procollagen crystals contained the alpha component of the triple-helical Tc. molecule.

The results of the Soviet investigators in the preparation of soluble procollagen have impelled other authors to submit the problem of the solubility of collagen to systematic studies. Harkness et al. (1954) prepared three different collagen fractions from the rabbit's skin: one was soluble in alkali phosphate, another in acid and the third was insoluble. Based on radioisotope experiments they suggest that the fraction soluble in phosphate buffer is much more consistent with a presumed collagen precursor, i.e. precollagen than the acid-soluble fraction. Gross et al. (1954) as well as Jackson and Fessler (1955) used neutral or weak alkaline salt solutions to prepare soluble collagen. These authors succeeded in

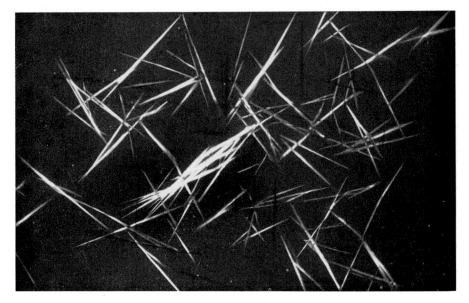

FIG. 37. Procollagen crystals from the collagen of the rat-tail tendon

obtaining fibrils from such solutions by salt precipitation or dialysis. The description of citrate-soluble procollagen and of collagen soluble in solutions of neutral salts caused confusion initially. It was questionable, first of all, which of these forms might be considered as collagen precursor. On the basis of the experiments of Harkness et al. (1954) and the extensive investigations of Jackson (1957) concerning the production of carragenin-inducible collagen it can be concluded that first the collagen extractable with neutral salts is produced by the fibroblasts and this is followed by the production of the acid-soluble collagen. It has been shown that the former is not uniform in its physicochemical character. It contains a fraction soluble in 0·14 M NaCl and another requiring higher salt concentrations (0·45 M) to be dissolved (Kühn 1962). It is thought that the citrate-soluble procollagen arises from these precollagens by a higher degree of organization. The soluble forms of collagen convert into insoluble, mature collagen *in vivo*. The knowledge of this conversion and the bonds bringing about the conversion is still poor. The relevant results will be described in the following chapters.

120

It is owed first of all to the discovery of the soluble collagens that the problem of the molecular construction of Tc. has been more or less solved, and the Cambridge (Mass.) school has been able to demonstrate the different macromolecular collagen aggregates.

Tustanovsky et al. (1954) put forward a new theory concerning the soluble and insoluble fractions of collagen. Accordingly, the soluble procollagen and the insoluble fraction represent two phases which are different in some other characteristics, too. These authors have proved by histological, X-ray diffraction and electron-microscopic investigations that the two collagen fractions are not identical, although both show a complex structure. They consider procollagen to be one phase of collagen and call the insoluble fraction collastromin. The latter serves as a basal phase on which procollagen takes place. Collagen is identical with procollagen in all its histological, X-ray diffraction and electron-microscopic characteristics. In contrast to this, collastromin is different from collagen in its histological staining, in particular in its metachromatic and argyrophilic stainings. Its X-ray diffraction and electron-microscopic pictures are also different from those of the collagen. Periodical cross-striation cannot be demonstrated in the collastromin. However, in the collastromin preparation of the above authors denaturation might have played a role, for from the skin procollagen cannot be extracted totally without heating the citrate-extracted residuum with water at 50 °C for 90 minutes. It is well-known that above 35 °C collagen is slowly denatured under certain circumstances (acid or alkaline pH, non-physiological ionic strength, etc.). Consequently, heating at 50 °C may give rise to structural alterations even in the collastromin that make it different from the native collagen. In the next chapter it will be pointed out that during the so-called heat-denaturation certain mucoproteins are dissolved from the collagen tissue, and the same substances are removed from the collastromin while heated at 50 °C. On the other hand, some acid MPS-s and certain other heteropolysaccharides remain in the collastromin fraction, and the reactions of these substances will become more pronounced after the removal of the procollagen. This fact can explain why collastromin gives stronger metachromasia and PAS reaction than does collagen. Even these experiments provide evidence of the complex structure of the collagen tissue and of the strong fixation of some acid and neutral MPS-s in the structure. The alteration of the X-ray diffraction patterns and the loss of the periodical cross-striation demonstrable under the electron microscope are consistent with the supposed heat denaturation.

Several protein fractions play a part in the formation of collagen fibres. Some of these fractions (mucoids) are incorporated directly as components of the fibre and others influence the composition of the fibre only indirectly. This view is supported by the investigations of Németh-Csóka (1960, 1961, 1963) who studied the fibril formation by chemical and polarization and electron-microscopic methods in the presence of various MPS-s and non-collagen proteins (plasma proteins). He found that besides the chemical composition also the thickness and meta-chromasia (measurable by polarization optics) of the collagen are greatly influenced by both the acid MPS-s and the plasma proteins. In addition to these examples a number of further data in the literature support the complex structure of the collagen fibre.

In the course of experiments with isolated collagen fibres we have also been able to separate the soluble and insoluble fractions of collagen from each other. Initially Banga et al. (1954) called the fibre after citrate extraction also metacollagen, but later they reserved this name for the chemically relaxed fibre (Chapter XIII, p.151). In the following the citrate-extracted fibre will be called procollagen-free fibre. Although the basic concept of Tustanovsky et al. (1954) is correct, i.e. the soluble and insoluble collagens are undoubtedly distinct in their physicochemical character, yet the technique of these authors led to the denaturation of collagen. Consequently, the differences demonstrated in other properties than solubility are more characteristic of a partially denatured collagen than of the true, mature, insoluble one. In our opinion this problem cannot be studied on collagen of skin origin because in the skin the collagen fibres do not run parallel and so are inadequate for functional investigations. According to our experiments, on the other hand, only functional studies are adequate for the clarification of the native state of collagen and the verification of its complex nature.

Soluble and insoluble collagen can be separated and their components can be studied only in collagen tissues like the tendon, in which, exactly because of their special function, the fibres are parallel-arranged. In the tendon tissue the well-developed and histologically well-distinguishable individual collagen fibres are embedded in the loose connective tissue, and in the part containing the ground substance. From these, single fibres can be separated easily. For this purpose Verzár (1955a,b) drew out single collagen fibres with a forceps from rat tail. Banga et al. (1956b) and Baló et al. (1956), after peeling off the skin of the rat's tail, removed the ligaments from the cartilage and isolated single fibres from the ligaments. These were cleansed mechanically to remove the attached ground substance, and from some thicker fibres the smallest physical units were separated to avoid any disturbance by other soluble proteins or the MPS-s of the ground substance during analysis. Naturally, the fibres so isolated might still have contained some contamination. Yet, it seems reasonable to suppose that this is an appropriate method of obtaining collagen fibres being able to function and practically free of foreign materials.

STUDY OF THE NATIVE STATE AND OF THE WORKING
CAPACITY (FUNCTION) OF FIBRES

In our opinion investigation of the function of the native fibre, as far as it is in connection with its chemical structure, may provide valuable information on the chemical structure of the whole fibre. For this reason we made efforts to evolve reactions and methods by which the changes associated with the function of the fibres can be followed.

It is an old experience that the collagen tissue becomes shortened or even shrunk at a well-defined temperature. This temperature (T_S), however, varies for different sorts of collagen. T_S for the collagen of vertebrates is 67 °C as measured in water. Thermal shrinkage has been thoroughly studied (Gustavson 1956, Chapter 9). Unlike the collagen-containing tissues which show no ordered arrangement at the beginning of the shrunken state, (e.g. cutaneous collagen), the fibres isolated from fascicles of the rodent's (mouse, rat) tail or the kangaroo's tail display interesting structural changes, particularly when they are examined in a loaded,

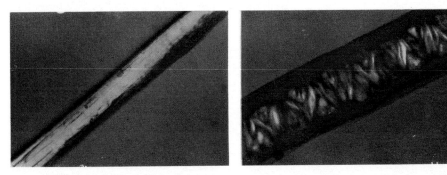

FIG. 38. Polarization-optical picture of the native collagen fibre (the green colour indicates a high-order positive birefringence)

FIG. 39. Polarization-optical picture of the contracted collagen fibre

i.e. extended state in a perpendicular position. In water, saline, Ringer solution or dilute acetic acid the fibres spring together as the special T_S is reached. This phenomenon is connected with a very characteristic change in the internal, submicroscopic structure. We call this change contraction and, since it is brought about by heat, we use the term thermal contraction. Similar phenomena proceed also at room temperature in the presence of some substances called lyotropic by Gustavson (1956). The contraction induced by chemical substances is called chemical contraction by us (Banga et al. 1954). In the experiments to be described in this chapter, 40% solution of KI was used as lyotropic substance. The contraction induced either by heat or chemicals is spiral in nature. While thermal contraction proceeds very quickly (in 10 to 40 sec), chemical contraction needs 1 to 5 minutes, depending on the animal's age.

The submicroscopic structural alterations associated with the thermal and chemical contraction can be followed excellently under the polarization microscope. The native collagen fibre shows a strong positive birefringence measurable by the compensator. When a membrane made of plaster of Paris is inserted, the high-degree birefringence will appear in a bluish-green colour as shown in Fig. 38. According to our data obtained by Ehringhaus' compensator the positive birefringence of these native fibres ranges, without imbibition, from 100 mμ to 400 mμ as

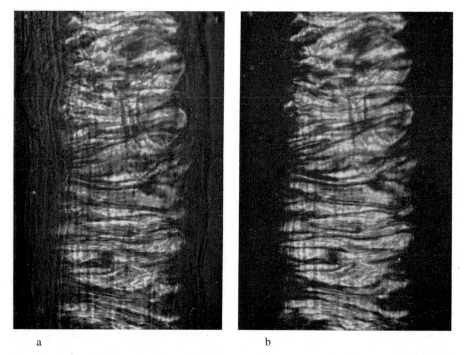

a   b

FIG. 40. Contracted fibre in cedar oil (a); the same between completely crossed Nicols (b)

expressed in retardation. The fibre is homogeneous and shows no internal arrangement even by great-power magnification.

During contraction, on the other hand, two phases are separated inside the
fibre. At the beginning a narrow stripe of weak birefringence (isotropic) appears

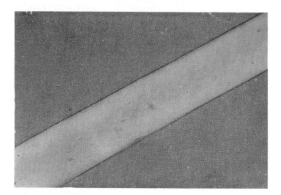

FIG. 41. Polarization-optical picture of the metacollagen fibre (owing to a stretch a pale blue-green colour is visible)

at the edge of the fibre; this
grows until full contraction is
reached which comes to about
30% of the fibre. At the same
time the inner part shows a
well-arranged spiral structure,
in which the helices crossing
one another show blue and yellow colours when examined under the polarization microscope
(Fig. 39). When measured by
the compensator quantitatively,
the birefringence of the outer
part of the fibre is found to be
weak compared with that of
the inner part, and in cedar oil

124

(refraction index, approximately 1·5) the outer part shows no birefringence as shown in Fig. 40. In Fig. 40a the outer part which is already isotropic in cedar oil, is still well visible; it contains longitudinal fibrils. In Fig. 40b this part is invisible between Nicols set exactly across. As heating or the chemical effect has ceased, i.e. the fibres have been removed from the warm water or from the lyotropic salt solution and washed with cold water, a rubber-like, extensible elastic fibre will be obtained. In case this is extended to its initial length and dried in this state, it can be used in further experiments.

If the thermally contracted fibre is left in 67 °C water or the chemically contracted fibre in the lyotropic solution, the contraction converts slowly into relaxation, i.e. the fibre will extend to its original length. This phenomenon is called thermal and chemical relaxation, respectively. The former ensues during 120 to 300 sec, whereas the latter needs 60 to 120 minutes, depending on the animal's age. (The course of the age-dependent relaxation is discussed in this

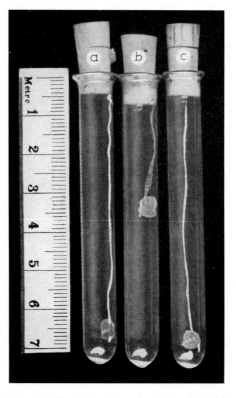

FIG. 42. Chemical contraction-relaxation; (a) native; (b) contracted; (c) relaxed fibre

chapter, p. 132.) In the course of relaxation the inner helical structure of the collagen fibre disappears; the outer part keeps growing until the whole fibre becomes homogeneous. Under such conditions the fibre is almost isotropic, i.e. it shows only weak birefringence (10 to 50 mμ). This birefringence can be further reduced by imbibition in media with a refraction index of about 1·5, but cannot be ceased completely. Accordingly, fibres have, in addition to the formal birefringence, an intrinsic one. The chemically relaxed fibre was termed metacollagen by us (Banga et al. 1954, 1956a,b,c,d). It is shown in Fig. 41, where the light-blue colour represents a very low birefringence. This can be increased by extension. In an extended state retardation reaches 20 to 80 mμ.

The contraction-relaxation phenomenon is only shown by the fibre that has retained its working capacity; strictly speaking this is the function that can be used for analyses when the reactions taking place or being induced in the collagen are studied. The most simple experiment for studying the work performed in association with contraction-relaxation is demonstrable in Fig. 42. The fibre adjacent to the centimetre-graduated ribbon is the native fibre, it is followed by

125

the contracted fibre and the third is the relaxed one. The fibres which are placed in 40% solution of KI are loaded by 80 mg lead shot. Using such an equipment we can decide by a preliminary experiment whether or not certain chemical effects (e.g. concentrate inorganic salt solutions, concentrate urea) have altered the working capacity of the fibre under study.

In a quantitative function test, the greatest weight is measured which the fibre is able to raise when contracted. Verzár (1955a, 1956) showed the age-related changes in collagen fibres in similar experiments. The temperature of contraction, the length of the contracted fibre, contraction time, the length of the relaxed fibre and the relaxation time can also be measured in such experiments. Extensibility, tensile strength and elasticity of fibres can also be determined. The latter tests can be performed most favourably with fibres previously contracted chemically by 50%.

The nature of the linkages whose fission, and of the chemically-definable substances whose solubilization, brings about the contraction and the subsequent relaxation were studied in separate experiments. These will be discussed in a separate chapter.

THE ROLE OF PROCOLLAGEN IN THE FUNCTION OF THE FIBRE

COMPARATIVE STUDIES WITH NATIVE AND PROCOLLAGEN-FREE FIBRES

In one of our earlier reports (Banga et al. 1956a) the substance obtained by extracting the procollagen from native collagen with citrate buffer of pH 4 was, erroneously, also called metacollagen. This was because we found the fibre completely freed from procollagen to be different in certain chemical properties from the starting substance, and believed that the former was identical with the relaxed fibre, i.e. metacollagen. At present, however, the term metacollagen is reserved for the chemically relaxed fibre, whereas the fibre extracted several times with a citrate buffer of pH 4 is termed procollagen-free fibre.

Procollagen-free fibre was prepared from isolated fibres of the rat's tail tendon by extraction at 16 °C with 0·1 N citrate buffer of pH 4. The extracting fluid was changed every day until all soluble protein had been solubilized, i.e. for 4 or 5 days, in general. Subsequently, the fibres to be freed from the residual citrate were washed with water. The fibres so treated were dried in the air and stored.

The quantity of the extracted procollagen, as estimated from the total N or Hypro content of the extract ranged from 15 to 25% and from 3 to 5% in the fibres of young (4 to 6 months) and old (12 to 24 months) animals respectively.

In citrate buffer of pH 4 both native and procollagen-free fibres show only minimal swelling. In water, however, there is a striking difference in the behaviour between native and procollagen-free fibres. The former show only moderate swelling, whereas the swelling of the latter is rather pronounced (Fig. 43). Swelling in water is called neutral swelling. Figure 43 shows that, as a result of the pronounced neutral swelling, the fibrils will become visible in the initially homogeneous-looking fibre. This type of disintegration is most pronounced when the fibre is

126

squashed by pressing with a glass rod (Fig. 44). This observation may suggest that an adhesive substance holding the fibrils together is also extracted by the citrate buffer. However, it may alternatively be supposed that in the collagen fibre the procollagen itself, particularly its MPS content, may be the cohesive, stabilizing substance. The data to be presented in the following support the view that procollagen contains carbohydrates (Grassmann et al. 1957) which appear to be bound covalently in the molecule. We assume that procollagen and the insoluble collagen are bound together by these carbohydrates, but, as revealed by our more recent studies, also electrostatical forces play a part in this linkage.

The difference in stability between native fibres and procollagen-free fibres is most clearly shown by the different contraction temperatures and the qualitative structural differences observable during thermal effect. Banga et al.

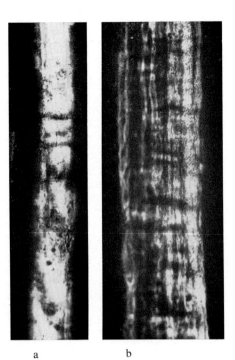

a   b

FIG. 43. Neutral swelling of the native (a) and procollagen-free (b) fibre

(1956a) constructed a heatable electric apparatus to study the thermal contraction of collagen fibres under the microscope. In this apparatus native and procollagen-free fibres were examined adjacent to each other. To prepare such fibres a collagen fibre was cut in two pieces. One piece (control) was kept in distilled water while the other (procollagen-free fibre) was extracted with citrate. Thermal contraction ensued at 55 °C in the procollagen-free fibre, whereas only at 67 °C in the native fibre. Accordingly, the removal of procollagen made the fibre less stable.

The microscopic examination of the fibres displayed another interesting phenomenon. The native fibres while shortened to about one-third of their original length grew three-fold in thickness. This is a true contraction and not associated with any change in the volume of the fibre (fibres in Figs 45a and b). Unlike this, the "thermally-contracted" procollagen-free fibre did not show the well-known helical structure and failed to become thicker; instead, it showed a shrinkage in every direction, i.e. loss in volume (Fig. 46). This phenomenon is termed thermal shrinkage (Hitzeschrumpfung) or syneresis. In the literature the term "thermal shrinkage" is used exclusively. It was first observed in this Institute (Banga et al. 1954, 1956c, d) that the response of the native fibres to thermal effect is a true contraction, whereas the removal of certain components (procollagen and mucoids) leads to an altered structure which will shrink instead of being contracted on the

127

effect of heat. We consider this phenomenon to be highly important as regards the functional study of the fibre.

The difference between native and procollagen-free fibres was also pronounced in functional studies. In lyotropic solutions (we generally used 40% KI solution)

FIG. 44. Procollagen-free fibre disintegrated into fibrils

chemical contraction of the native fibres ensues, and this is followed by chemical relaxation. The procollagen-free fibre, however, shows no contraction; instead, it breaks within several minutes after it was loaded. (In our experiments a dried fibre 60 mm in length and 1·2 mg in weight was loaded with 80 mg lead shot.)

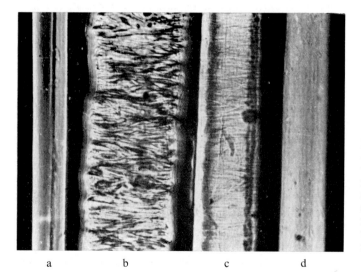

FIG. 45. Polarization-optical picture of the native (a); thermally-contracted (b); contracted and then extended to the original length (c) and thermally-relaxed (d) fibre

a   b   c   d

Accordingly, in the procollagen-free fibre certain stabilizing linkages had weakened or split, resulting in a loss of the working capacity of the fibre and consequent breaking up. However, the split linkages can be substituted by new electrostatical linkages restituting the stability of the fibre. Procollagen-free fibres, after having been removed from the citrate buffer and placed into a 0.1 N Na_2CO_3/HCl buffer of pH 9.5 to 10.5 for a short time (e.g. one hour), will show thermal contraction again. The fact that at a higher pH, i.e. in the presence of cations, the stability

a   b

FIG. 46. Procollagen-free fibre (a); the same after thermal shrinking (b). The black spots are air bubbles

of the fibre is restituted proves that electrostatical linkages were also split in the citrate solution at pH 4. However, the stable structure cannot be restituted in the fibre from which the total amount of procollagen has been extracted. Fibres extracted for a very long time with pH 4 citrate solution will not regenerate any longer, suggesting that a prolonged extraction leads to a fission of the linkages which are not restituted in the presence of cations.

During these experiments we made a very interesting observation concerning the relationship between the pH of the buffer solution used for extraction and its effect on the chemical contraction. Extraction with a citrate solution of pH < 4 did not lead to a complete loss of the contraction capacity in 40% KI. The lower the pH the more pronounced was the residual contraction capacity as shown in Table 28. The fibres extracted at pH values between 1 and 4 showed contraction,

TABLE 28

Contraction-relaxation study of collagen fibres obtained from the tail of a 5-month-old rat and extracted with citrate buffer of various pH at 20 °C for five days

Composition of buffer			Contraction time		Relaxation or breaking time	
0·1 N citrate (ml)	0·1 N HCl (ml)	pH	(sec)	(%)	(sec)	(%)
0·0	10·0	1·038	77	27	132	20 Broke
2·0	8·0	1·418	120	23	132	— Did not
3·0	7·0	1·925	85	22	132	— relax
4·5	5·5	3·364	120	12	132	— but
6·0	4.0	4·158	No contraction		360	— broke

but this was not followed by relaxation; they broke immediately after contraction had ensued (at pH 1 even relaxation was observable). Raising of the pH of the citrate solution resulted in a decline in the working capacity, i.e. contraction ability of the fibre. At pH 4 it disappeared completely. We attempted to cease the contraction capacity by raising the concentration of the citrate solution used for extraction at pH < 4. However, citrate concentration failed to influence the result, suggesting that the working capacity is a function of pH rather than of the citrate concentration. The peptization effect depends on the dissociation of the organic acids, the latter being determined by the pH of the milieu (Buzágh 1960, Becker 1962). Low pH appears to prevent procollagen from passing into solution. This is striking because low pH greatly favours protein hydrolysis or the fission of electrostatical linkages, for as long as procollagen is present in the fibre the latter does not lose its working capacity. The same has been proved by the experiments in which the swelling of fibres was studied under varying conditions. The fibres showed swelling at acid pH until they lost their procollagen. Between pH 1 and 3·3 the swelling was 10-fold compared with the volume of the untreated fibre, whereas at pH 4 where the procollagen passed mostly into solution, the procollagen-free fibre showed no swelling. On the other hand, the procollagen-free fibre shows an enormous swelling in water (neutral swelling) while the fibrils become visible (Figs 43 and 44), indicating that linkages of high hydration capacity were split during the solubilization of procollagen. However, these linkages are not identical with those playing a part in the acid swelling.

Our theory suggesting that the functioning collagen is built up of two main protein components, viz. procollagen and the insoluble collagen, has been based on these experiments. If either of the two components is lacking, functional disturbances and alterations in the physical and physicochemical characteristics of the fibre will ensue (Banga 1954; Szabó and Banga 1954; Banga et al. 1956a,b, c,d; Banga 1957).

Procollagen can thus be defined not only as the soluble form of collagen, but also as a component of the native fibre. This appears to be homogeneous under the microscope, but disintegrates into a great number of fibrils when procollagen has been removed. Accordingly, the significance and function of procollagen are different from, and more than what was learned from earlier X-ray and electron-microscopic studies. The fact that extraction with NaCl, irrespective of the salt concentration, never results in fibres eliciting the characteristics of the procollagen-free ones proves that tropocollagen, i.e. the factor soluble in neutral salt solutions, though it may be a collagen precursor, cannot substitute for procollagen either physicochemically or morphologically. Besides the data presented in Table 28 numerous experiments support the evidence that it is not exclusively the procollagen that is solubilized during the swelling induced by 0·1 M acetic acid at pH 3·0 to 3·3. It is much more likely that some other electrostatical linkages are loosened. But only very dilute solutions of acetic acid (0·01 M to 0·0025 M) may split the linkages between procollagen and the insoluble collagen. After such an extraction the residual fibres behave like the procollagen-free fibres produced by citrate extraction.

If it is true that procollagen is one of the components of the collagen fibre, it may also be supposed that procollagen-free fibre occurs in nature. The existence of such fibres is supported by the morphological observations of Kovács and Romhányi (1962). These authors when studying the submicroscopic structure of the connective tissue succeeded in distinguishing two types of collagen fibre. The differentiation was based on the anisotropic toluidine-blue staining reaction (Chapter VI, p. 71). The first type of the collagen fibre showed positive dichroism, an enhanced positive birefringence in monochromatic red light and a compact structure. This type of collagen which corresponds to the mature native fibre has been termed stenocollagen by Romhányi. The second type of fibre displayed opposite anomal colours, negative dichroism and negative birefringence in red light. This has been termed porocollagen. The latter type shows a loosened submicroscopic structure which allows a transversal orientation for toluidine-blue molecules on the fibrillar structure of collagen. In its morphological aspect this type of fibre may be regarded as the procollagen-free fibre. Because of the compactness of stenocollagen or some other steric conditions the molecules of the dye can only be arranged parallel on the fibre surface. In *in vivo* experiments Kovács and Romhányi (1962) observed structure diastasis in cutaneous collagen fibres on the effect of dilute organic acids, histamine or some pharmaceutics. In these cases stenocollagen converted into porocollagen. In our opinion this *in vivo* phenomenon was the same as that occurring *in vitro* when procollagen-free fibre is prepared from native collagen fibre. On the effect of dilute acid the mature, insoluble stenocollagen converted into the loose, fibrillar porocollagen which is morphologically similar to the procollagen-free fibre. It can therefore be concluded that a special fibre corresponding to the procollagen-free fibre may arise even *in vivo* and the submicroscopic structure of this fibre becomes demonstrable by the anisotropic toluidine-blue staining reaction evolved by Romhányi.

In this chapter experiments and conclusions concerning the functional manifestation of senescence of the collagen fibre are discussed. It is an old observation that the collagen fibres become more and more mature, i.e. less soluble with advancing age. The component soluble in neutral salt solutions (tropocollagen) and that

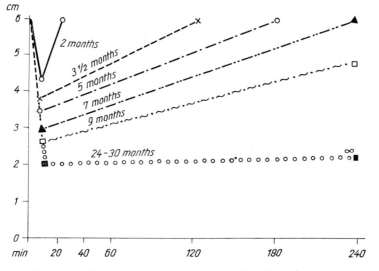

FIG. 47. Chemical contraction-relaxation as a function of age

soluble in dilute organic acids, strictly speaking, in buffers containing organic acids (procollagen) are always diminishing. In the preceding chapter numerous experiments proving that procollagen is one of the components of the native fibre were reviewed. Lack of this component leads to alterations in the structure and function of the fibre. In the following the significance of procollagen will be discussed in relation to the functional changes accompanying old age.

Verzár (1955a, 1956) was the first to demonstrate that the thermocontraction of the collagen fibres of the rat's tail is age-dependent. Thermocontraction had been studied earlier by a number of authors (Roy 1880; Gottschlich 1893; Wöhlisch 1931; Partridge 1948). Partridge, like Verzár and ourselves, used rat-tail tendon in his experiments. Verzár demonstrated a well-measurable difference between young and old animals in the load (g) preventing thermocontraction. While a 50% shortening of the fibres of two to three-month-old rats can be inhibited by 0·5 g, a similar shortening of the fibres of 33 or 34-month-old rats needs 8 to 10 times this load (about 5 g). A similar correlation was found between the temperature inducing thermocontraction and the animal's age. To demonstrate correlation between the function of the fibre and the age of the animal, the chemical contraction-relaxation can also be used with success. As set forth in the foregoing in detail, the collagen fibre shows contraction in solutions of lyotropic substances even at temperatures lower than that of the thermocontraction, and thermo-contraction is followed by relaxation, i.e. extension to a degree depending on the animal's age. The results of our systematic studies on this subject are shown in Fig. 47 (Banga et al. 1956 b). In these experiments 40% solution of KI was used as lyotropic solution. The length of the fibre is given on the ordinate in cm while the abscissa shows the time. It is seen that the fibres of the two-month-old animal relax, i.e. regain their original length immediately, after a relatively slight contrac-tion, while the relaxation of the fibres of animals aged three and a half months or more is considerably protracted. While the degree of contraction is growing with age that of relaxation shows a continuous decline. Fibres obtained from ani-mals 24 to 30 months of age show practically no relaxation.

Since measurable amounts of procollagen can only be dissolved from the fibres of young animals, we have put forward the hypothesis that the strength and the quality of the linkages of this component may be responsible for the changes characteristic of old age. Another observation of ours (Banga 1956a,b), namely that both thermal and chemical relaxation are associated with the dissolu-tion of significant amounts of protein and the amount of the dissolved protein is also age-dependent, supports the above hypothesis. While as much as 45 to 55% of the total protein is dissolved until the end of relaxation from fibres of rats 2 to 6 months of age, this percentage falls to 25 to 30% when fibres of animals 26 to 30 months old are used. (These are not true procollagen values, for thermal denatura-tion is accompanied by an increased proteolysis.) The protein passing into solution during relaxation is, therefore, the collagen fraction that is fixed less strongly in the collagen fibre; it would resemble procollagen if it were not in a denatured state. The residual, chemically-relaxed fibre, on the other hand, is identical with that term-ed metacollagen by us. In the thermally relaxed fibre, however, one part of the collagen has been gelatinized, thus cannot be regarded as true metacollagen. Table 29

TABLE 29

Protein solubilization during heat contraction and relaxation from the native collagen fibre

Native collagen fibre (mg)	H₂O (ml)	Temp. °C	Contraction, i.e. relaxation time (sec)	State	Solubilization of collagen protein (%)
20	2	20	0	No change	0·0
27	2	67	40	Contraction starts	1·1
20	2	67	80	Strong contraction	10·0
20	2	67	120	Relaxation starts	15·0
20	2	67	300	Full extension	43·0
20	2	67	600	Full extension	73·0

shows the amounts of protein that passed into solution during thermal contraction
and relaxation from a fibre of a six-month-old rat. Since a great amount of protein
is dissolved during the period from the start of relaxation till the time of the maximal
extension and the solubilization is continuous even thereafter, the thermally-
relaxed fibre cannot be regarded as a well-defined type of fibre. In spite of this,
we have studied the phenomenon of thermal contraction and relaxation as well
as the related physicochemical changes and the lability of the thermally-contracted
and relaxed fibre in the presence of proteolytic enzymes, just like the similar phenomena occurring during chemical contraction relaxation. In the following we shall
refer to the type of contraction-relaxation induction by heat or by treatment with
40% KI solution.

It is well-demonstrable morphologically that neither the thermally-contracted
nor the chemically-contracted fibre can be dissolved completely by proteolytic
enzymes. The contracted fibre is characterized by a strongly birefracting spiral
inner structure in which no linkages attackable by the enzyme have yet been liberated. However, one part of these fibres have already converted into a structure
readily soluble in the elastase-enzyme complex. Figure 48 shows the contracted
fibre before (a) and after (b) enzyme digestion. It is well-visible that the helices
are still unaffected, while in the contracted fibre of the altered part their structure
has disappeared because of the dissolution of a substance from the interhelical
material.

In order to check our hypothesis, it seemed most important to study the linkages
whose fission starts the proteolysis during thermal and chemical relaxation. While
thermal relaxation can uniformly be observed in young and old animals, chemical
relaxation is in close correlation with age. According to the data of Fig. 47 the
relaxation shown by the fibres of young animals (up to 2 to 5 months of age)
is quick, whereas that of the fibres of nine-month-old animals is considerably
protracted and the fibres of 12 to 16 months old show practically no relaxation.
It appeared reasonable to study the above problem on the basis of these observations.

In this relation we have studied the role of mucoid$_1$ and searched for substances
converting the fibres capable of chemical contraction and relaxation into non-
relaxing, i.e. "old" fibres. On the other hand, we have made efforts to convert
old fibres into those capable of relaxing, i.e. fibres showing the characteristics of
the young fibre. It was found that at acid pH (about pH 3) certain substances,
mainly reducing agents were capable of transforming non-relaxing old fibres (Banga
et al. 1956 d) into relaxing ones. Most of the reducing substances applied in the
photography were more or less effective. Ascorbic acid proved to be the most
effective, even in concentrations from 0·0025 M to 0·001 M. Acetic acid and citric
acid had to be used in about 100 times higher concentrations (0·1 M) to achieve
the same effect. It was interesting to see that the effect of ascorbic acid could be
enhanced by keeping the fibres in a Na_2CO_3-HCl buffer of pH 8 for 30 minutes
after 30 minutes incubation in 0·0025 M ascorbic acid. This phenomenon indicates
that besides the linkages split off by reduction also electrostatical linkages become

labile. The latter can be stabilized by placing the fibres in an alkaline salt solution.

While non-relaxing fibres can be converted into relaxing ones at moderately acid pH in the presence of reducing substances, oxidizing agents exert an inverse effect at neutral or mild alkaline pH (Banga et al. 1956d). To demonstrate the latter effect, potassium permanganate has proved to be suitable. By ascorbic acid and potassium permanganate mutually reversible alterations could be brought

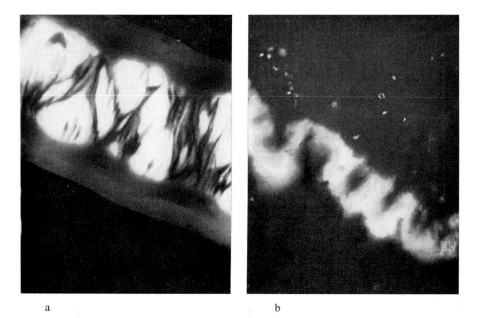

a   b

FIG. 48. Contracted fibre (a); fibre digested with elastase after contraction (b)

about in the relaxation capacity of the fibres. Young fibres capable of relaxing lost this capacity while incubated in 0.001 M $KMnO_4$ for 30 minutes. The fibres so treated regained their original relaxation capacity by a treatment with ascorbic acid at pH 3 and subsequent stabilization in dilute alkali. Inversely, non-relaxing fibres converted into relaxing ones by ascorbic-acid treatment and subsequent stabilization, (Fig. 49). and the resulting fibres could be retransformed by permanganate treatment. Naturally, the reducing and oxidizing agents cannot be applied for long periods without causing irreversible alterations.

We assume that the number of certain cross linkages which play a part in the stabilization of the collagen fibre — in the sense of our hypothesis, the number of linkages between mucoids and collagen — grows with age; the new, more stable linkages are not attacked by lyotropic substances. Consequently, chemical relaxation and the associated solubilization of procollagen will not ensue. These linkages are more sensitive to heat than to lyotropic substances. The fact that stabilization can be achieved by oxidizing agents, and the stabilized linkages can be loosened again by reducing substances suggests that carbohydrates must play a part in this reaction.

Differences between the fibres of old and young animals were demonstrated by other reactions as well (Banga 1957). Fibres shortened by 50% in 40% KI solution

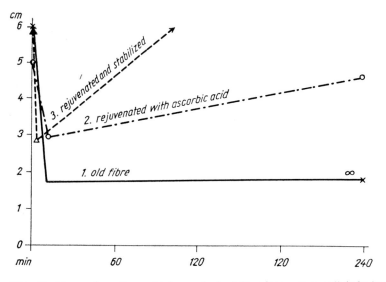

FIG. 49. Conversion of an old (non-relaxing) fibre into a "young" (relaxing) one

and then washed with water can favourably be tested for the following characteristics: tensibility in water, excess extension, tensile strength and elasticity. In these characteristics great differences are demonstrable between young and old fibres as shown in Table 30. Tensibility is expressed in the load (in g) extending the con-

TABLE 30

Physical characteristics of chemically-contracted fibres of young and old animals

Age of animals (months)	Tensibility (g)	Excess extension (%)	Tensile strength (g)	Elasticity (mm)
4	2 ± 0·5	—	9 ± 5	10 ± 1
5	14 ± 4	115 ± 10	35 ± 8	8 ± 1
6	16 ± 5	115 ± 10	65 ± 15	8 ± 1
19	19 ± 10	120 ± 10	134 ± 14	7 ± 0·8
21	32 ± 10	122 ± 15	175 + 30	6 ± 0·8
28	42 ± 10	125 ± 10	200 ± 40	5 ± 0·5

tracted fibre to its original length. Excess extension, i.e. the extension shown by the maximally loaded fibre before breaking is given in per cent of the original length. Tensile strength is expressed in the smallest load in g capable of breaking the fibre. Elasticity is given in the shortening (in mm) after removal of the load. Significant differences were demonstrated in each of these properties between young and old fibres. Old, mature fibres need greater force to be extended. Elasticity continuously decreases as age advances. The differences demonstrable in these physical characteristics are good indicators of the structural changes that ensue while the collagen fibre is growing older. According to our theory all these phenomena are in relation to the fact that in the fibres of old animals mucoid$_1$ is not released during chemical contraction. Consequently, the same degree of extension needs greater force and the fibre already extended is less elastic, if it is elastic at all.

Since ascorbic acid exerted an enormous effect on the working capacity of the fibres, it appeared to be of interest to investigate the possible influence of other organic acids on the above listed physical characteristics of fibres (Banga 1957). The effects of 0·0025 N solutions of six organic acids, such as acetic acid, lactic acid, succinic acid, citric acid, oxalic acid and ascorbic acid were tested at pH values from 3·5 to 4·2. Fibres were incubated in the acid solution at 20 °C for ten minutes, rinsed quickly with distilled water, hung up and dried in the air. The fibres of young animals showed enormous swelling and, up to four months of age, the fibres converted into gel state. For this reason the physical constants under study could only be measured in the old fibres. Table 31 shows the results obtained with collagen fibres taken from animals 22 and 24 months of age. Every experiment was carried out with four fibres. The results were sufficiently consistent. The contraction time was shortened after treatment with either of the six acids; in the case of the old fibres the average period shortened from 360 sec to 150 sec, the latter time being approximately identical with the contraction time of young fibres. While shortening of the contraction time is independent of the quality of the organic acid, the effect of different organic acids on the tensibility, excess extension, tensile strength and elasticity was, to some extent, inconsistent. With regard to these characteristics the organic acids may be divided into two groups. Acetic acid, lactic acid and succinic acid belong in the first group, citric acid, oxalic acid and ascorbic acid in the second group. The acids in the first group do not significantly alter the physical constants of the fibre contracted by 50% of its original length, whereas those in the second group do. Thus, for the latter fibres the load expressing tensibility falls from 20 to 25 g to 10 to 14 g; excess extension grows; the weight expressing tensile strength falls from 150 to 180 g to 50 to 70 g; elasticity grows. Ascorbic acid was the most effective in increasing elasticity.

The effects of organic acids on the physical characteristics of the fibres of young animals can only be examined if 0·1 N NaCl is added to the solution of the organic acid. In this case fibres will not convert into the gel state or, if gel formation has already ensued, the gel will release the bound water which amounts to about 80 to 100 times the weight of the fibre. Under such circumstances we compared

TABLE 31

Alterations in the physical constants of the fibres of old animals on the effect of organic acids

Age of animals (months)	Treatment	pH	Contraction time (sec)	Tensibility (g)	Excess extension	Tensile strength (g)	Elasticity (mm)
22	Control	—	360 ± 20	20 ± 5	122 ± 10	150 ± 30	7 ± 1
24		—	380 ± 25	25 ± 6	122 ± 10	180 ± 30	6 ± 1
22	Acetic acid	3·5	150 ± 15	17 ± 5	122 ± 10	140 ± 20	7 ± 1
24			175 ± 20	17 ± 5	122 ± 10	140 ± 25	6 ± 1
22	Lactic acid	4·2	150 ± 15	20 ± 5	122 ± 10	140 ± 30	6 ± 1
24			175 ± 20	20 ± 5	122 ± 10	140 ± 25	6 ± 1
22	Succinic acid	4·2	150 ± 15	17 ± 5	122 ± 10	130 ± 25	7 ± 1
24			175 ± 20	17 ± 5	122 ± 10	140 ± 25	6 ± 1
22	Citric acid	4·0	150 ± 15	14 ± 4	135 ± 10	55 ± 15	12 ± 2
24			160 ± 20	15 ± 5	135 ± 10	70 ± 17	12 ± 2
22	Oxalic acid	4·0	150 ± 15	14 ± 5	130 ± 20	50 ± 15	11 ± 2
24			150 ± 15	14 ± 5	130 ± 5	50 ± 15	11 ± 2
22	Ascorbic acid	4·0	150 ± 15	10 ± 3	150 ± 10	65 ± 20	13 ± 2
24			150 ± 15	10 ± 3	140 ± 10	72 ± 21	13 ± 2

the characteristics of the fibres of young and old animals. As regards the physical characteristics, considerable differences were demonstrable. In KI solution 50% contraction of young fibres required 400 to 500 sec instead of 140 to 200 sec, whereas old fibres needed 900 to 1000 sec to be contracted. In the latter case contraction failed to reach 50% even during such a prolonged period. Accordingly, organic acids shorten the contraction of the fibres when applied alone, whereas in the presence of 0·1 N NaCl they protract or, in the case of old fibres, prevent it. Since the fibres are highly breakable their tensibility can hardly be examined. Fibres obtained from young animals broke at a 1 to 2 g load, those of old animals at 10 to 15 g. From these experiments it can be concluded that although the presence of NaCl counteracts the swelling effect of organic acids, an organic acid together with NaCl exerts a significantly greater destructive effect on the fibres than the organic acid alone. At present we cannot explain this phenomenon exactly; yet it seems likely that besides solubilization of procollagen tropocollagen is dissolved and the loss of the latter substance may account for the profound alterations.

CHAPTER XII

LYOTROPIC SUBSTANCES

GUSTAVSON (1956) in his book "The Chemistry and Reactivity of Collagen" extensively deals with the effect of the so-called lyotropic substances on collagen. He classifies compounds of different types, such as concentrate solutions of neutral salts, concentrate acetic acid, urea, weak organic acids, phenols and aromatic sulphonic acids, among lyotropic substances.

According to Gustavson the effect exerted by lyotropic substances had been considered hydrolysis. However, the phenomenon does not cover the term hydrolysis, for it is brought about by fission of weaker valence-bonds, probably hydrogen bonds or electrostatical cross-linkages (van der Waals forces) and not by the fission of primary bonds. The lyotropic effect is associated with two phenomena, viz. a high-degree peptization (solvatation) of the collagen and a permanent swelling. The term "peptization" has been used by colloid-chemists; it is acceptable from the etymological point of view, and at present it is the most generally used term expressing the destruction accompanying the solubilization of collagen. In Gustavson's (1956) book a separate chapter deals with the effect of concentrate solutions of neutral salts whose greatest part, such as the bromides, iodides and chlorides of alkali metals and alkali earth metals, cause peptization of different degree on powders prepared from the animal skin. This solubilization, strictly speaking peptization, is termed lyotropic effect by Gustavson. In his opinion this is not an ionic effect, but it is manifested in conversion of the protein of the

TABLE 32

Peptization of cutaneous collagen by concentrate neutral salt solutions

Solution tested	Protein solubilized during 20 days (%)	Solution tested	Protein solubilized during 20 days (%)
KI	26	$CaCl_2$	28
NaI	26	$MgCl_2$	26
NaBr	25	$MgSO_4$	2
NaCl	10	Na_2SO_4	2
KCl	10	Control: (H_2O)	5
LiCl	16		

cutaneous collagen into a soluble form. The statement that the effect is non-ionic is based on the fact that the assumption of tanning substances, such as cationic chrome sulphate and chrome chloride, is not changed after treatment with neutral lyotropic substances, whereas that of the non-ionic sulphito-chrome sulphate grows proportional with the lyotropic effect of neutral salts. Table 32 taken from the corresponding figure of Gustavson's book (p. 174) presents the amount of protein solubilized by different lyotropic substances during a period of 20 days. In this figure Gustavson did not present the data for KI but he (1926) found a very pronounced peptization effect by this salt, too, as presented in Table 32. It is seen that the bromides and iodides of the alkali metals are considerably more active than their chlorides. Cutaneous collagen is solubilized to a significantly higher extent by the chlorides of bivalent earth metals than by the chlorides of alkali metals.

Interrelation between Chemical Contraction-relaxation, Peptization, Submicroscopic Structure and Conversion into Metacollagen

The function of the collagen fibre in relation to the chemical contraction-relaxation was examined with KI, i.e. the same lyotropic substance that was used in the experiments (Chapter XI, p. 123); KI is a neutral salt. It appeared to be of interest to see whether the activity in inducing chemical contraction-relaxation of other inorganic salts, in the same high concentration as examined by Gustavson for peptization activity, shows a close correlation with their latter activity. On the other hand, we wished to know whether the effects of other substances, beside the inorganic salts accepted by Gustavson as lyotropic, are similar to those exerted by KI. Chemical contraction-relaxation is accompanied by very characteristic polarization-optical phenomena as discussed in Chapter XI (p. 128). The questions have arisen whether the change in the polarization-optical picture of the collagen fibre is independent of the quality of the lyotropic substance used and whether the lyotropic effect may be considered uniform also morphologically.

In the first part of these experiments we examined the effects of eleven neutral salts available to us and that of urea. First, we wished to know whether the contraction of the collagen isolated from the tail-tendons of rats of the same age will ensue at the same temperature in concentrate solutions of different lyotropic substances. Since the peptization effect of different lyotropic substances varies, it seemed possible that in bringing about chemical contraction the effect of the different substances may run parallel with their peptization effect. Since, according to the literature, chemical contraction in KI solution ensues at 20 to 22 °C, in contrast to thermal contraction which needs 60 to 67 °C, we examined the temperatures characteristic of the chemical contraction induced by different lyotropic substances (Banga and Szabó 1964). The results are summarized in Table 33. (In our apparatus temperatures over 70 °C could not be examined.) It is shown in the table

TABLE 33

Contraction temperature of collagen fibres in different lyotropic salt solutions

Solution tested	Observation of collagen fibres	Solution tested	Observation of collagen fibres
40% KI	Contraction at 22 °C	40% NaClO₄	Contraction at 22 °C
40% KSCN	Contraction at 22 °C	40% CaCl₂	Contraction at 22 °C
40% KBr	Contraction at 51 °C	40% BaCl₂	Contraction at 45 °C
30% KCl★	No contraction at 70 °C	40% MgCl₂	No contraction at 70 °C
40% NaI	Contraction at 22 °C	40% Urea	Contraction at 32 °C
40% NaBr	Contraction at 51 °C	H₂O control	Contraction at 63 °C
30% NaCl★	Slow contraction at 70 °C		

Note: ★ = these 30% solutions were already saturated at 22 °C

that out of the eleven neutral inorganic salts five induced contraction at 22 °C. These were the iodides of alkali metals and KSCN, NaClO₄ and CaCl₂. The bromides and chlorides of alkali metals induced contraction only at 51 °C and 70 °C, respectively. Certain chlorides (KCl and MgCl₂) were even ineffective or induced a slow, protracted contraction. The fact that in water contraction ensued at 63 °C suggests that KCl and MgCl₂, in the presence of which contraction fails to ensue even at 70 °C, inhibit the contraction. Thus, it appears to be reasonable to qualify the latter salts as lyotropic substances of negative effect, in contrast to the others whose effect is termed positive.

In further experiments the effect of the same neutral salts was examined as a function of contraction and relaxation time, degree of shortening and degree of extension (Table 34). Rapid contraction and relaxation ensued only in the presence of KI or KSCN. In the case of the remaining three salts that induce contraction not only the contraction was slower but, and this is of importance, the relaxation was protracted and the fibres failed to reach their original length even after prolonged incubation. (In urea the fibre broke during prolonged relaxation.) As regards contraction, NaClO₄ and CaCl₂ are the salts, besides KI and KSCN, in which a high degree of contraction ensued within a relatively short period. However, the relaxation was much slower in these cases, too, than in the presence of KI or KSCN.

A comparison of these data with those of Gustavson presented in Table 32 makes it clear that there is no close correlation between the high peptization effect of the compounds under study and their capacity to induce chemical contraction and relaxation. If in its peptization effect NaI is considered to be equivalent to KI and CaCl₂, some correlation appears to exist. However, MgCl₂ is highly effective in peptization, yet inactive in inducing contraction. The bromides and chlorides of alkali metals exert very strong and moderate peptization effects, respectively, without being able to induce contraction of collagen fibres. Accordingly, the

TABLE 34

The process of contraction-relaxation at 22 °C in different salt solutions

Solution tested	Initial length (cm)	Collagen fibre			
		Contraction		Relaxation	
		time (min)	length (cm)	time (min)	length (cm)
40% KI	6	1·5	3·5	10	6
40% KSCN	6	1·5	3·5	10	6
40% KBr	6	120	6·0	—	—
30% KCl*	6	120	6·0	—	—
40% NaI	6	30	3·7	90	5·5
40% NaBr	6	120	6·2	—	—
30% NaCl*	6	120	6·2	—	—
40% NaClO₄	6	4	2·6	60	6
40% CaCl₂	6	5	2·3	90	5·8
40% BaCl₂	6	120	6·2	—	—
40% MgCl₂	6	120	6·2	—	—
40% Urea	6	120	3·3	960	4·5 (broken)
H₂O control	6	—	—	—	—

Note: * = these 30% solutions were already saturated at 22 °C

chemical, physical and physicochemical alterations accompanying contraction and relaxation cannot be attributed to the peptization effect observed in powders prepared from animal skin. Gustavson considers the permanent swelling and solubilization effect induced in the collagen by neutral salts to be a molecular effect, suggesting that specific effects are brought about by the molecular form of these substances and not by ionized forms (ions and ion-pairs). Anyhow, the alterations brought about by different salts are not uniform. The fact that the I^- and SCN^- ions, both lying at the end of the Hofmeister row, appear to be most active in contraction-relaxation suggests that the role of the anion is much more significant in this reaction than that of the cation. Chvapil and Zahradnik (1960) conducted systematic investigations to show which of the cations and anions might account for the chemical contraction and relaxation. They found that besides KI several other salts exert a similar effect. The pseudo-halides (thiocyanate, xanthogenate) and the perchlorate proved to be highly effective. The effect might be in relation with the Hofmeister row:

$$SO_4^{--}, \ C_2H_3O_2^-, \ Cl^-, \ Br^-, \ NO_3^-, \ ClO_3^-, \ I^-, \ SCN^-$$

The first few members of the row are ineffective, whereas the anions most effective in inducing contraction-relaxations lay at the end of the row. The above authors extended their investigations to further salt solutions, such as sodium cyanate, ammonium acetate, lithium chloride, sodium bromide, potassium nitrate, potassium chloride, sodium nitrate and sodium chloride. None of these salts induced any alteration within 180 minutes when applied in 2·5 M concentration. They examined all the effective iodides from LiI to CsI and found that the effect was independent of the cation.

Chvapil and Zahradnik (1960) who studied the kinetics of relaxation in $NaClO_4$ solution confirmed the findings published from this Institute (Banga et al. 1954, 1956 a, b, d) about the chemical changes ensuing in the course of contraction-relaxation. This question is discussed in Chapter XIV (p. 166) in connection with the role of mucoid$_1$. As to the submicroscopic alterations accompanying contraction we have found that alkali iodides, KSCN and $NaClO_4$ bring about the same contraction and relaxation structure. In the presence of these salts metacollagen is formed which, as pointed out in Chapter XIII (p. 153), gives very characteristic reactions. In contrast to this, in the concentrate solutions of other inorganic salts, i.e. those causing neither contraction nor the characteristic submiscroscopic structural changes, metacollagen was not formed.

Elden (1959) and Elden and Boucek (1959) investigated the effect of formaldehyde and concentrate acetic acid on the contraction-relaxation of collagen fibres. According to these authors the ε-amino group of the lysine might be responsible for the cross-linkages occurring during formaldehyde treatment. They suggest that this alteration is similar to those accompanying senescence. The effect is manifested in an accelerated and increased contraction and a reduced relaxation.

The submicroscopic structural changes occurring in the course of thermal and chemical contraction-relaxation are very similar and the associated functional changes are also consistent. Consequently, thermal and chemical contractions might be considered to be identical phenomena. It has been mentioned that certain authors consider the thermal effect as a denaturation process. We were also unable to induce thermal relaxation without a significant degree of peptization. It is another question whether the effect of the substances inducing chemical contraction-relaxation must also be considered denaturation. The fact that chemical contraction-relaxation can be induced by the concentrate solution of only few closely-related neutral salts might suggest that the phenomenon is not necessarily accompanied by a denaturation like that responsible for the solubilization of collagen protein. In our opinion the special reaction that is proceeding during chemical contraction-relaxation is related to the fission of the cross-linkages between collagen and mucoid$_1$, and we attribute the shortening of the collagen fibres to these fissions which are followed, during relaxation, by dissolution of the denatured procollagen.

According to our observations CaCl$_2$ exerts a very characteristic effect on the submicroscopic structure of the collagen fibre. However, this effect is different from the effect of the 40% solution of KI, the phenomenon investigated most thoroughly by us. The effect of the iodides and sulphocyanates of alkali metals and that of NaClO$_4$ was uniform not only in the temporal course of contraction and in inducing relaxation, but the submicroscopic spiral structure, the characteristic reduction in birefringence during relaxation and the development of the metacollagen structure were also identical. The relaxed fibres obtained corresponded to the real metacollagen fibre, and showed all the characteristics of metacollagen

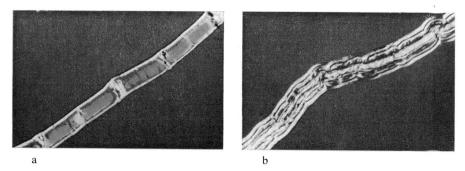

a   b

FIG. 50. Positive birefringence in Canada balsam (a); and negative birefringence in phenol (b) of fibres pretreated in 24% CaCl$_2$ at 22 °C for two minutes

(see Chapter XIII). CaCl$_2$, as presented in Tables 32, 33 and 34 exerted a peptization effect resembling that shown by the above salts and also induced contraction followed by a considerably slower relaxation. However, the resultant submicroscopic structure was not identical with the well-known picture and the relaxed fibre did not agree with metacollagen. For this reason we investigated the effect of CaCl$_2$ as a function of the degree of contraction and a function of time (Banga and Szabó 1964). The fibres were pretreated with CaCl$_2$ and rinsed amply with water for five minutes three times. The fibres were then examined for birefringence under Canada balsam and for the phenol reaction in xylol-dissolved 30% phenol. The collagen fibres were prepared from the tail-tendon of Wistar rats 4 to 6 months old. After an incubation for 20 minutes in 12% solution of CaCl$_2$ at a temperature of 22 °C the fibres showed almost the same picture as the native fibres. They showed an intensive positive birefringence in Canada balsam but in phenol dark stripes were observable among birefracting fibrils. In 24% CaCl$_2$ solution the fibres displayed a weak contraction even after two minutes and at the same time a slight (about 30%) reduction in their positive birefringence was observed (Fig. 50 a). Such fibres still give the phenol reaction, but the dark stripes are visible here, too (Fig. 50b). In 36 to 40% solutions of CaCl$_2$, at 22 °C the fibres show a peculiar picture after two minutes of incubation. Spike-like formations appear on their

144

surfaces at regular distances (Fig. 51). The continuity of the dark stripe running along each fibre fascicle breaks in the spikes. The fibres give the phenol reaction. After ten minutes in 40% $CaCl_2$ solution the fibres become more swollen, the spike-like formations flatten down, the positive birefringence weakens and no phenol reaction is observable. Continuing this treatment for two hours will cease both the birefringence under Canada balsam and the phenol reaction, and the fibres will become extremely swollen (Fig. 52). Only the fibre-fixed $CaCl_2$ shows birefringence. This is well-observable in photographs taken at a crossed position of the polarization filters without insertion of a compensator (Fig. 53). The picture proves that, although the fibres had been amply rinsed with water, $CaCl_2$ penetrated

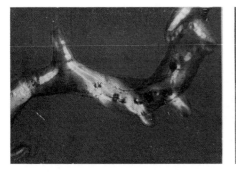

Fig. 51. Positive birefringence in Canada balsam of fibres pretreated in 40% $CaCl_2$ at 22 °C for two minutes

Fig. 52. Fibre pretreated in 40% $CaCl_2$ for two hours; the fibre is swollen but shows neither positive birefringence nor phenol reaction

the fibres and was deposited irregularly inside them during drying. The fibres were dried in the air and covered with, and examined, under Canada balsam.

The fibres that have been treated with $CaCl_2$ for a longer period, though in the relaxed state (Table 34), cannot be solubilized either by the elastase-enzyme complex or by trypsin-containing collagenmucoproteinase, although solubilization by these enzymes is characteristic of metacollagen. If loss of resistance to proteolytic enzymes is accepted as a criterion of denaturation, the $CaCl_2$-treated fibre cannot be considered denatured, for it is not digestible by proteolytic enzymes. However, as shown experimentally, $CaCl_2$ treatment converted the native fibre into a fibre which can be regarded a denatured fibre both in its submicroscopic structure and physicochemical characteristics. Its properties are markedly different from those of the native fibre, e.g. it shows a very pronounced neutral swelling (see Fig. 52).

The dissimilarity between $CaCl_2$ and KI in the effect on the submicroscopic structure developing during contraction-relaxation is explainable by the fact that in the case of alkali iodides and sulphocyanate the univalent anion is active, whereas in the $CaCl_2$ molecule the effect is bound to the bivalent Ca ion. The mode of action of the univalent anions is hitherto unknown; we assume that they act by loosening the linkages of mucoid[1].

The effect of $CaCl_2$ was first studied by Loeb (1922) and Loeb and Kunitz (1923), later by Thomas and his school. In his book Gustavson (1956) attributes the fission of the secondary, i.e. hydrogen bonds to the $CaCl_2$. After splitting of these bonds $CaCl_2$ forms a coordination component, so-called molecular component, with smaller units of the collagen molecule. This initial reaction is followed by formation of soluble fragments. As Gustavson had assumed and our investigations have

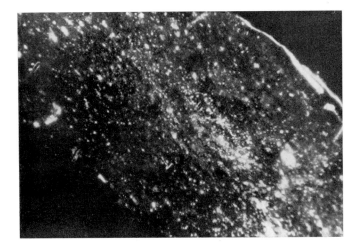

FIG. 53. Incorporation of $CaCl_2$ crystals in the collagen fibre

proved, after splitting of certain bonds, $CaCl_2$ itself enters the molecule and, consequently, submicroscopic crystals become demonstrable by submicroscopic-polarization optics (Fig. 53). Presumably $CaCl_2$ is bound together with its crystal water.

THE EFFECT OF UREA

It has been known for a long time that concentrate urea solutions may split hydrogen bonds in proteins (Burk and Greenberg 1930). In 6·6 M (about 40%) urea solution the globular protein molecules are decomposed into a great number of well-defined subunits. In Gustavson's (1942, 1956) opinion the effect of urea is similar to that of the neutral salt solutions; from many respects it is also a molecular effect. For this reason the examination of the effect of concentrate urea solutions appeared to be of interest. In this regard three questions deserved interest: a) how is the submicroscopic structure altered by the loosening of the secondary structure due to fission of hydrogen bonds?; b) does urea treatment influence the working capacity of the fibre?; c) does it lead to metacollagen formation? Our experiments concerning this subject have thrown light on another problem, viz. whether the fibres while being denatured by urea retain or lose their resistance to proteolytic enzymes. We are looking for an answer to a further question, viz.

146

whether thermal and chemical contraction is the same kind of denaturation as that induced by urea. As shown in Tables 32 and 33, shortening of fibres by urea needs a rather long (120 minutes) incubation at 22 °C. In 40% KI solution the same degree of shortening ensues after one and a half minutes. According to our

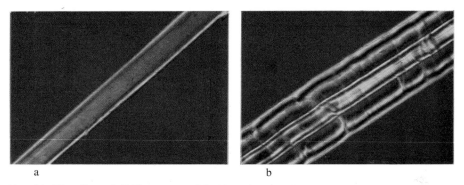

a   b

FIG. 54. The effect of 40% urea at 22 °C; fibre after 10-minute treatment in Canada balsam (a); in phenol (b)

observations on a heatable objective table (Banga and Szabó 1964) urea does induce shortening of the fibres at 32 °C, but this shortening is not followed by a significant relaxation; after 960 minutes the fibre shows a slight extension and then breaks. Accordingly, urea does not induce chemical contraction-relaxation in

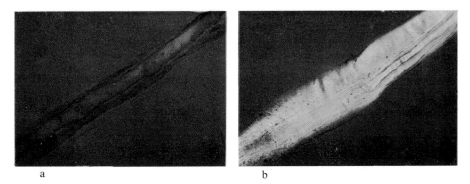

a   b

FIG. 55. The effect of 40% urea at 22 °C; fibre after 16-hour treatment in Canada balsam (a); in phenol (b). Swollen, structureless fibre

contrast to the positive lyotropic salt solutions discussed in the preceding chapter. Gustavson emphasized that at room temperature swelling, peptization and shrinkage were hardly demonstrable in urea. All these ensued only at about 35 °C.

The difference in function between the fibres treated with concentrate urea solution and concentrate KI appears still more pronounced when the fibres are

147

examined under the polarization microscope. In fibres kept in urea solution at 22 °C for ten minutes a slight weakening of the positive birefringence is observable (Fig. 54a), but the fibres retain their reactivity with phenol (Fig. 54 b) in spite of having lost their homogeneity, showing fibrillar disintegration on the effect of

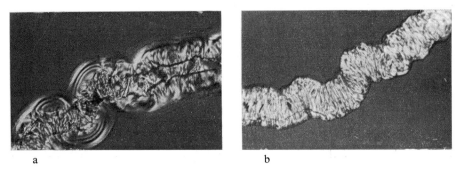

a   b

FIG. 56. The effect of 40% urea at 37 °C; fibre after 10-minute treatment in Canada balsam (a); in phenol (b)

phenol. If fibres are kept in urea solution at 22 °C for a long period (16 hours) their positive birefringence will considerably weaken (Fig. 55a), but the phenol reaction is still performable (Fig. 55b). Raising the temperature increases the urea effect. At 37 °C urea treatment for a period longer than 5 to 10 minutes results in

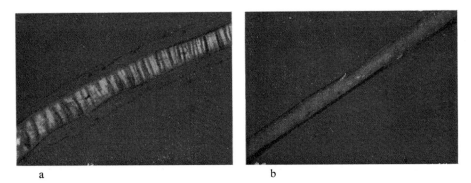

a   b

FIG. 57. The effect of 40% urea at 37 °C; fibre after 20-minute treatment in Canada balsam (a); in phenol (b)

a reduced birefringence and shortening of the fibre. However, the resulting submicroscopic structure is strikingly different from that of the chemically-contracted fibre (Fig. 56). Separation of the fibre into two phases is lacking, i.e. the peripheral, slightly birefringent stripe and the inner stripe showing very strong birefringence fail to appear. Instead a shrunk, slightly swollen picture appears

148

without any arrangement. The positive birefringence is reduced (Fig. 56a), whereas the phenol reaction is retained (Fig. 56b). If this treatment is continued at 37 °C for 20 minutes, the birefringence of the shrunk fibres will considerably weaken and, simultaneously, a transversal, periodical arrangement will appear. The latter may correspond to the optical effect of the wavy course of fibrils (Fig. 57a). The fibres so pretreated do not give the phenol reaction (Fig. 57b). In several cases 30 minute incubation led to a very pronounced swelling of the fibres and a reduction in birefringence by 90% (Fig. 58). Disappearance of the positive birefringence of collagen fibres on urea effect was also found by Neumark (1964). The structure so obtained resembles that of metacollagen, except that it cannot be digested either by the elastase enzyme complex or by a mixture of trypsin and collagenmucoproteinase. This is, therefore, another denatured fibre resembling metacollagen

FIG. 58. The effect of 40% urea at 37 °C for 30 minutes; total disappearance of the birefringence in Canada balsam

in its every reaction, except resistance to proteolytic enzymes. In this case one might think that urea having split the secondary bonds occupies the site of the former hydrogen bonds, i.e. it becomes imbibed. In this way linkages stronger than hydrogen bonds come about and prevent proteolytic enzymes from attacking the peptide bonds for which they are specific. Iodides, sulphocyanates and the perchlorate, even if they are imbibed and bring about certain cross-linkages, do not prevent the proteolytic enzymes from exerting their solubilizing, digesting effect. Metacollagen structure digestible by proteolytic enzymes is not induced by $CaCl_2$ either; possibly because the $CaCl_2$ molecule is bound to two polypeptide side chains in such a way that it can prevent proteolysis. In this case we succeeded in demonstrating by the submicroscopic technique the incorporation of $CaCl_2$ crystals in the collagen molecule and so we have proved our theory on the resistance to proteolytic enzymes. After simple incubation in urea we failed to demonstrate incorporation of urea in the collagen fibres. If, however, the fibres had been converted into the contracted state by sulphatation and then were treated with urea, we observed a very interesting phenomenon under the microscope. Urea was slowly diffusing into the fibres, causing a reduction in the birefringence, proceeding from the edges into the fibres; at the same time the fibres were swelling and converted into a metacollagen-like structure. If such a fibre was dried it showed crystals at the middle of the fibre. (The crystals were not attached to the surface of the fibre. The urea solution had been washed off from the surface of the fibre. Only the urea incorporated in the fibres might have crystallized inside the fibre.) The most concentrate urea solution used by us was 6·6 M. In this solution the relaxation of fibres did not ensue. Elden and Webb (1961) and Elden and Cassac

(1962) reported that in the presence of 10 M urea solution at 37 °C the effect of urea could be divided into five periods: 1. lag period; 2. contracion; 3. the period of maximal contraction; 4. relaxation; 5. breaking. In the sense of their earlier conception these authors attempted to relate the process of contraction-relaxation to the degree of swelling. However, they came to the conclusion that the process limiting the degree of periods 2. to 4. would be explainable by a reaction between the crystalline region of collagen and urea. Accordingly, "melting" of the crystalline region of the collagen-mucopolysaccharide structure would give rise to the process of contraction-relaxation·

CHAPTER XIII

CHARACTERIZATION OF METACOLLAGEN

As DESCRIBED in the previous chapters, the metacollagen fibre, i.e. the fibre obtainable by treatment with lyotropic substances is a special form of the insoluble collagen. It shows fibrillar structure without having lost its integrity. Its characteristics are different from those of the native fibre from which it originates and in many respects similar to those of the elastic fibre. In our opinion, like collastromin, metacollagen is also different in its chemical composition and, consequently, in its physicochemical characteristics both from the native and the procollagen-free fibre.

Metacollagen shows no molecular birefringence, but in an extended state it shows a slight formal one. Its birefringence becomes negative in water because of a marked neutral swelling. It is digestible without residuum with either of the proteolytic enzymes, provided these contain also ribo- or deoxyribonuclease. In the absence of both of the latter enzymes a cell-containing residuum is left behind. As to its histological staining, metacollagen has retained the positive van Gieson reaction of the native fibre and, in addition, fixes orcein and resorcin. It fails to give the phenol reaction.

DIFFERENCES BETWEEN HEATED COLLAGEN AND COLLASTROMIN

In the following we are going to discuss: 1. whether heated collagen which is in many respects similar to metacollagen might be considered to be identical with the collastromin described by Tustanovsky et al. (1954), and 2. to what extent metacollagen can be regarded as an elastin-like substance.

Recently Tustanovsky et al. (1960) showed that the collagen derivative originally called collastromin can only be obtained from cutaneous tissues. The preparation obtained from the Achilles tendon by a method almost the same as that employed in the preparation of collastromin elicited different characteristics. The collastromin isolated from the skin retains its characteristics, such as the filamentar structure and the lack of the layer line at 2·9 Å in the X-ray pattern (characteristic of the absence of procollagen) and of the electron-microscopic cross-striation of 640 Å periodicity. The collastromin prepared from the tendon tissue shows these characteristics less definitely; transitory forms between the native fibre and the fibre partially freed from procollagen occur. The structure of these fibres is not uniform. Beside fibres without cross-striation those still showing the cross-striation of

640 Å periodicity are also present. The layer line at 2·9 Å is not consistently absent in the X-ray diffraction patterns. Accordingly, the collagen fibres lying in the loose structure of the cutaneous tissue which are not oriented to form fibre fascicles (in contrast to those in the tendon tissue) can easily be converted into collastromin. Thus, procollagen can pass into solution from small fibre fascicles during citrate extraction, but not from the tendon tissue consisting of compact, dense and thick collagen fibres. Some solubilization from the thinner fascicles may occur, but even if some dissociation of procollagen and insoluble collagen does come about, the former, as a large molecule, cannot pass over the envelope substance surrounding the fibre fascicles in the tendon tissue. Zaides (1956) pointed out that the electron micrographs of the tendon tissue were the most suggestive of the presence of a special sheath-like envelope in the collagen tissue. This means that preparations equivalent to the collastromin of the skin cannot be produced from the Achilles tendon.

The collastromin-like preparation obtained from tendon tissue was not the only preparation that Tustanovsky et al. (1960) compared with the collastromin of the skin. Another preparation obtained from powdered Achilles tendon by heating at 70 °C for ten minutes was also compared. The amorphous collagen so obtained was ground to a fine powder prior to the experiment. This preparation, too, was called metacollagen by Tustanovsky et al. (1960). In the following we shall call it heat-treated collagen. It was demonstrated by X-ray diffraction and electron-microscopic studies that under such circumstances thermal shrinkage, i.e. isodiametric contraction or syneresis occurs in the Achilles tendon; as shown above this is substantially different from the true contraction. It leads to the complete disappearance of the cross-striated fibrils and to an X-ray diffraction pattern characteristic of an amorphous material. The so-called metacollagen obtained from the Achilles tendon cannot be considered completely equivalent to the relaxed fibres obtainable from separate, single fibres of the rat's tail. The most pronounced difference is that the Achilles tendon cannot be brought into chemical relaxation, only into chemical contraction. Although from the compact, thick collagen-fibre fascicles of the Achilles tendon preparations equivalent either to the collastromin of the skin or to the relaxed fibre of the rat's tail cannot be obtained, yet the resulting fibre is different from the starting material in its physicochemical character. Of the dissimilar characteristics the differences between neutral (in water) and acid swelling are those which most markedly distinguish the collastromin and the heat-treated collagen of the Achilles tendon

TABLE 35

Neutral and acid swelling of collastromin and heated collagen prepared from Achilles tendon

	Swelling, H_2O fixed in g per collagen g	
	in water	in 0·01 N acetic acid
1. Control, powdered Achilles tendon	8·7 ± 1	25 ± 2
2. Collastromin	25·0 ± 2	25 ± 2
3. Heated collagen	6·8 ± 1	10 ± 1

from the native control preparation (Banga and Baló 1959). The differences are shown in Table 35. In addition to these, substantial differences in silver-fixation (Chapter XIV, p. 165) and in solubilization by elastase are demonstrable. The results of the latter types of experiments are summarized in Table 36. On the basis of the data in Tables 35 and 36 it is reasonable to make a distinction between collastromin and heat-treated collagen. Furthermore, the experiments have also shown that the collastromin of the Achilles tendon, not identical with the collastromin of the skin, is significantly different also from the native Achilles tendon in its physicochemical, chemical and enzyme-digestion characteristics.

TABLE 36

Silver fixation by, and digestibility of, collastromin and heated collagen

	Ag fixed in mg per g collagen	Solubilization by elastase during 24 hours (%)
Control, Achilles tendon	8·6 ± 1	15
Collastromin	20·0 ± 4	4
Heated collagen	4·0 ± 1	100

Similar experiments with the rat-tail collagen have led to identical results. Such investigations are preferable because also functional and submicroscopic changes can be observed in the resulting fibre.

SIMILARITY BETWEEN METACOLLAGEN AND ELASTIN

When investigating the characteristics of the metacollagen obtained from the rat-tail tendon, Banga et al. (1956c) found these similar to those of the elastin in many respects.

According to our theory (Banga 1954; Banga et al. 1956a,b,c,d) the steps included in the arisal of metacollagen during contraction-relaxation are as follows. During contraction a mucoprotein, the so-called $mucoid_1$ is split off; this substance holds procollagen and metacollagen together. Subsequently, relaxation starts and this is associated with the solubilization of denatured procollagen. During this reaction variable amounts of procollagen pass into solution and as a result the weight of the residual collagen as related to the native fibre will also be variable. We consider metacollagen to be an intermediary form between collagen and gelatin. The conversion of collagen fibres into gelatin is always preceded by the arisal of a metacollagen structure. In the chemical sense metacollagen is the fibre being devoid of $mucoid_1$ and procollagen, but still containing a mucoid, namely $mucoid_2$ whose linkages in the native fibre can be split specifically by the collagenmucoproteinase (CMPase) enzyme. The conversion of metacollagen into gelatin requires long-term boiling because $mucoid_2$ is greatly resistant to heat, in contrast to $mucoid_1$ which splits off very rapidly.

153

In the following the common characteristics in the metacollagen fibre and in the elastic fibre are discussed.

1. *Elasticity*. In the presence of water, like the elastic fibre, the metacollagen fibre elicits a high degree of elasticity. If it is dried in the extended state, it retains its extended form, but it springs together in water.

2. *Birefringence*. Unlike the native fibre, the metacollagen fibre shows no birefringence unless it is extended in water. In lipid solvents (xylol, toluol) and in oils (olive oil, cedar oil) the birefringence of the extended and dried metacollagen

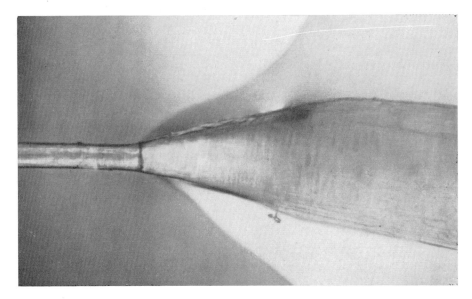

FIG. 59. Digestion of the metacollagen fibre with the elastase-enzyme complex

remains high, like that of elastic fibres. On the other hand, the native fibre behaves differently; due to its well-known imbibition curve its birefringence is the lowest in the above substances having refraction indices between 1·5 and 1·6. Like elastin, metacollagen elicits a low birefringence on the effect of water or aqueous solutions. Swelling to a high degree frequently makes the fibres negatively birefringent. Weak birefringence in water is one of the characteristics of the native elastic fibre. However, the fact that the extended fibre is birefringent proves that it also consists of regularly arranged micelles.

3. *Digestibility by proteolytic enzymes*. Metacollagen is digestible to a great extent by trypsin, elastase and CMPase. It is digested by the elastase-enzyme complex to a rate ten times exceeding the digestion rate of the isolated elastin. Figure 59 shows the mechanism of solubilization. The metacollagen fibre when dried in an extended state swells showing broom-like fibril formations and then will be dissolved.

154

4. *Acid swelling.* Unlike the native fibre, metacollagen shows no swelling in the presence of dilute acid. In acetic acid it neither swells nor passes into solutions. It agrees with the elastic fibre in this characteristic, too.

5. *The metacollagen fibre*, in contrast to the native collagen fibre, reacts with Weigert's resorcin-fuchsin which is a specific elastica stain (Fig. 60). Parallel with histological investigations we examined the fixation of resorcin-fuchsin with

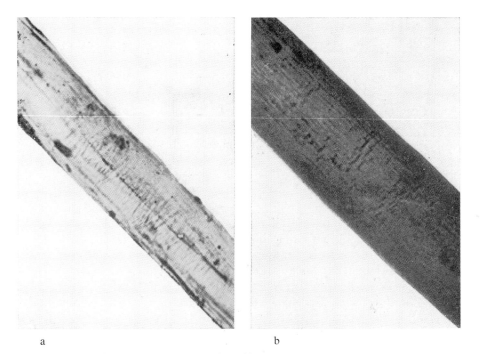

a   b

FIG. 60. Resorcin-fuchsin-stained native fibre (a); metacollagen fibre (b)

quantitative chemical methods; 170 g of the metacollagen fibre is able to fix 9 mg resorcin-fuchsin (about 5·5%). Unlike this, the native fibre does not fix resorcin-fuchsin in demonstrable quantities.

METACOLLAGEN FIBRE AND PHENOL REACTION

The phenol reaction was first described by Ebner (1894). In the presence of well-defined concentrations of phenol the positive birefringence of the collagen fibres converts into negative. The metacollagen fibre does not show the phenol reaction which is characteristic of the native collagen fibre. Nor does the isolated elastic fibre give the phenol reaction after their mucoid and collagen components have been removed by boiling. However, the elastic fibres of the vascular wall do give the phenol reaction (see Chapter VI), but this reaction is morphologically distinguishable from the phenol reaction of the collagen fibre. Figure 61 shows both the native collagen fibre and the metacollagen fibre in phenol solution. Accordingly, an interesting analogy exists between the native elastin and the collagen, and the isolated (purified) elastin and the metacollagen. While the phenol reaction is characteristic of the native fibres, neither the isolated elastin nor the metacollagen fibre gives this reaction. The isolation procedure for elastin includes an alkali effect (N NaOH) associated with a thermal effect (100 °C; Lansing et al. 1953) or a long-term boiling in the autoclave (Lowry et al. 1941). Both of these procedures lead to preparations that have lost their capacity to react with phenol. Similarly, in the course of the preparation of metacollagen the thermal effect or the lyotropic substances inducing chemical contraction-relaxation give rise to a chemical reaction that deprives the metacollagen fibre of its reactivity with phenol. In the case of metacollagen we have demonstrated (see pp. 126, 143 and Chapter XIV for a detailed discussion) that the dissolution of both mucoid$_1$ and the denatured procollagen leads to the arisal of this sort of collagen. Based on these findings we assume that in the course of the isolation, the same two substances pass into solution and the "purified" elastin being deprived of these substances shows properties different from those of the native fibre. The lack of the phenol reaction is the most characteristic of these differences.

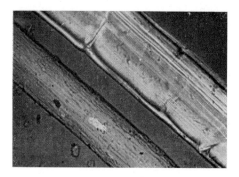

FIG. 61. Native (yellow, swollen) and metacollagen (blue) fibre in phenol. The yellow colour indicates negative birefringence

We made attempts to prove that native elastic fibres also contain a mucoid which is solubilized during a thermal effect (Banga 1956a). For this purpose we determined

TABLE 37

Analysis of the two mucoids of lig. nuchae

Isolation method	Mucoid (%)	Carbohydrate (%)	Hexosamine (%)	N (%)	Carbohydrate hexosamine ratio
1. Fraction solubilized from native lig. nuchae during heat denaturation	3·0	4	4	12	1 : 1
2. Same as 1. after alcohol extraction	1·5	4	4	12	1 : 1
3. Mucoid obtained in 0·1 N NaOH from lig. nuchae freed from collagen by boiling with acetic acid	1·6	3	1·5	—	2 : 1

the chemical composition of the substance passing into solution from the native lig. nuchae during thermal denaturation. As shown in Table 37 this substance should be considered a mucoid. Furthermore, we found that when all the alcohol-soluble substances were extracted with alcohol, one half of the mucoid substances dissolvable on thermal effect was removed from the fibre. When, on the other hand, the collagen had been removed from the lig. nuchae by boiling with acetic acid, a subsequent extraction with 0.1 N NaOH removed another mucoid in which the ratio of carbohydrate to hexosamine was different from that of the other mucoid. We have concluded that the native lig. nuchae contains two mucoid substances; one of these is identical with $mucoid_1$ which can be dissolved on the effect of heat, whereas the other is alkali-labile, but does not pass into solution when heated; it is only removed when the fibres are boiled with alkali. Consequently, the native elastic fibres of the lig. nuchae lose their $mucoid_1$ during the purification procedure.

Principally the collagen passing into solution from the lig. nuchae on the effect of boiling may be either denatured procollagen or gelatinized collagen. Since the collagen content of lig. nuchae fibres is not more than 16%, it cannot be proved that only procollagen is dissolved on the thermal effect. It cannot be demonstrated either whether the collagen-containing protein which is dissolved from the fibre when boiled in acetic acid is procollagen or gelatinized collagen. Furthermore, since the process of contraction-relaxation cannot be observed in the lig. nuchae, the associated protein solubilization cannot be examined either. However, the solubility of procollagen in a 0.1 M citrate buffer of pH 4 has supplied a method for the demonstration of procollagen in the native lig. nuchae. With this buffer a sort of collagen with a Hypro content of 13 to 14% was dissolved. This was insoluble in elastase (therefore it is not elastin) and when heated to 40 °C it showed swelling and became gelatinized. In these characteristics this substance was similar to the procollagen. From the lig. nuchae of young cattle 4 to 5% of the dry matter can be isolated as procollagen. Considering the 16% collagen content of these fibres, the isolated procollagen made 25 to 30% of the collagen.

We consider these experiments and evidence very important as regards our theory. The native elastic and collagen fibres capable of functioning represent substances of complex structure. Both contain mucoids, and the collagen consists of procollagen and metacollagen. The fact that neither the isolated (i.e. boiled) elastic fibre nor the metacollagen fibre reacts with phenol suggests that this reaction is attributable to the presence of $mucoid_1$ alone or of $mucoid_1$ + procollagen, both of which are absent in these isolated materials.

DOES COLLAGEN CONVERT INTO ELASTIN?

Concerning the conversion of collagen fibres into elastin Hall et al. (1955) proposed a theory. This was based on the experiments of these authors and of Burton (Burton et al. 1955) which have shown that the collagen fibres isolated from the cutaneous tissue or those present in the cutaneous tissue become elastin-like on the effect

157

of alkaline borate buffer of pH 8 to 9 or sodium periodate (pH 5). According to the above authors the resemblance can be demonstrated histologically, viz. the collagen fibres so obtained become stainable with the Weigert stain modified by Hart, or by electron microscopy. In the electron micrographs the cross-striated collagen fibres are continued in structureless, elastin-like, branching fibres, among which a great amount of an amorphous substance is visible. This finding would suggest that the conversion of collagen is accompanied by an increase both in the elastic fibres and the amorphous substance. Borate buffer extracted a protein with a Hypro content higher than that of the collagen (Hall et al. 1955). Based on these evidences the authors concluded that in these experiments collagen converted into elastin. According to their hypothesis a special secretion of polypeptides and polysaccharides, due to fibroblast activity, gives rise to both the elastic and collagen fibres. This would be the physiological way. Under pathological conditions elastic fibres might arise even from the products of the partial hydrolysis of collagen.

There are, however, contradictory data as well. One of these is the amino-acid composition of different fibres. At our request Dr. B. Keil* (1955) kindly determined the amino-acid composition of both the native fibre and the metacollagen by his quantitative paper-chromatographic method and found no significant difference. Since collagen is significantly different from elastin in its amino-acid composition, a conversion of metacollagen into elastin would be manifested in an altered amino-acid composition as well.

We have examined whether the method applied by Hall et al. (1955) leads to metacollagen production. It has been mentioned that the latter has a number of characteristic reactions. We have succeeded in demonstrating that in alkaline borate buffer the mucoid$_1$ is extracted from the collagen fibre and the resulting fibre is different from the native one in some characteristics. Yet, it is also different from metacollagen in some essential characteristics.

The effect of sodium periodate is similar to, but not identical with, that of the borate buffer. According to our experiments, unlike the organic buffers of pH 4 to 5 (acetate, citrate, etc.) (Chapter XI, p. 138) which split the bonds between metacollagen and procollagen, periodate, although it oxidizes mucoid$_1$ (Chapter XIV), even fixes the linkages between procollagen and metacollagen. This means that periodate gave rise to a pseudoelastic fibre similar to elastin in being elastic and incapable of acid-swelling. This fibre has retained its thermal and chemical-contraction capacity, but does not show relaxation any longer. According to our theory the lack of relaxation suggests that though mucoid$_1$ was oxidized by the periodate, the latter gave rise to linkages more stable than the original ones. The new linkages do not allow the so-called denatured collagen to be dissolved from the fibre and so prevent the fibre from being relaxed.

Therefore, in our opinion the collagen fibre having been treated with either borate buffer or periodate still contains procollagen, indicating that metacollagen, the type of fibre which is most similar to elastin, cannot be brought about by these

* We are greatly indebted to Dr. B. Keil (Prague) for these investigations.

reagents. The most convincing evidence of the lack of elastin or metacollagen production is the insolubility of the product in elastase.

Although metacollagen agrees with the elastic fibre in several characteristics the view that the two substances are not identical is supported, in our opinion, by some other arguments in addition to their different amino-acid composition. One of these arguments is that the elastic fibres are different from both the native and the metacollagen fibres in their mucoid components as well. Each type of fibre contains at least two mucoid components, out of which $mucoid_1$ may be an essential component of both the functioning elastic and collagen fibre, but the second mucoid corresponding to the $mucoid_2$ of the collagen must be different in the elastic fibre. We are still unable to differentiate them and so we are compelled to establish hypotheses.

CHAPTER XIV

THE ROLE OF POLYSACCHARIDES IN THE CONSTRUCTION OF THE COLLAGEN FIBRE

GRASSMANN and Schleich (1935) were the first to find a carbohydrate component in the cutaneous collagen. On the spectrophotometric evaluation of the orcein reaction (Sørensen and Haugaard 1933) it was suggested that in the 1% carbohydrate content of the collagen galactose and glucose take equal parts. The same amount of carbohydrate was demonstrated in the histologically homogeneous collagen fibre as in the highly-purified collagen. Based on these data the so-called "lactose" was considered to be a real component of the fibres. Schneider (1949) believed that in the collagen the polypeptide chains were separated by short sugar bridges which form ester-like bonds with carboxyl groups, and N-glycosidic bonds with the amino groups of peptide chains. Pahlke (1954) brought convincing evidence that during maturation the collagen fibres incorporate carbohydrates. Experiments carried out with borohydride and Na periodate by Grassmann et al. (1953, 1955) and Grassmann and Kühn (1955) provided indirect evidence that the collagen molecule contains carbohydrates as integral components.

Several arguments support the presence of carbohydrate components in the collagen molecule in the form of large molecules. Konno and Altman (1958) succeeded in isolating carbohydrate-containing peptides from the rat-tail collagen by means of carboxypeptidase digestion. According to Oreson and Zacchariades (1960) the isolation of oligosaccharides from the partially hydrolyzed collagen clearly shows that the carbohydrates are present as polysaccharides (not as monosaccharides) in the collagen chain. Schuldtz-Haudt and Eeg-Larsen (1961) reported on the presence of a glycoprotein soluble in 5% solution of trichloroacetic acid in the skin of the guinea-pig. This substance incorporated the radioactive proline that had been injected in the animal. Hörmann (1962) searched for the reactive groups which play a part in the conversion of procollagen into insoluble, mature collagen. Thus, he examined the ε-amino groups (lysine and hydroxylysine), the hydroxylamine-sensitive linkages (e.g. ester bonds) and the hexoses in both the procollagen and the collagen. He found practically all the ε-amino groups in the free state, thus being unable to play a part in substitution reactions.

EXPERIMENTS WITH HYDROXYLAMINE

In the thermally denatured procollagen and in the gelatin Gallop et al. (1959) found linkages reacting with hydroxylamine and hydrazide under the circumstances most suitable for the fission of ester bonds. During these reactions peptide bonds are not split, and the products of the reaction are non-dialysable proteins with a molecular weight of 20 000. Further experiments revealed six ester bonds and 20 to 30 gamma-glutamyl peptide bonds in the collagen of 10^5 g molecular weight (Gallop et al. 1962). The authors assume that in the ester bonds the carbohydrate components of the collagen play a role.

According to Hörmann (1960) who carried out experiments with hydroxylamine at pH 8·5, thermally denatured procollagen produces 0·64 Mol hydroxamic acid as calculated for 100 Mol amino acid during a relatively short time. When mature collagen reacted with hydroxylamine in the presence of 4 M LiCl or any other agent that splits hydrogen bonds, the collagen was solubilized within one or two days. Only 15% of the solubilized product was dialysable, whereas the residuum contained 1·05 Mol hydroxamic acid as calculated for 100 Mol amino acid. The molecular weight dropped from 300 000 to 20 000, indicating that the procollagen molecule was separated into about 15 components. These components are held together by the hydroxylamine-sensitive ester bonds which, according to present concepts should be intramolecular. The cross-linkages in the mature collagen are attributed to the 0·4 Mol excess hydroxamic acid per 100 Mol amino acid. The hydroxylamine-sensitive bonds in the mature collagen are different from those in the procollagen not only in quantity but also in reactivity. While in the procollagen these bonds are free and so readily accessible, in the mature collagen they are in a masked form and react only when the protein has already been denatured. At room temperature the native collagen apparently does not react with hydroxylamine, it remains insoluble and its shrinkage temperature does not change. The native collagen cannot be solubilized by adding 4 M LiCl after hydroxylamine treatment; solubilization only occurs if LiCl and hydroxylamine are added simultaneously. In our opinion the hydroxamic acid produced in the native collagen by hydroxylamine remains in the collagen molecule and gives rise to new, strong cross-linkages which will prevent the solubilizing effect of LiCl or similar lyotropic agents. On the other hand, when the two agents act simultaneously, the solubilizing, strictly speaking, disintegrating effect of the lyotropic substance will prevent the arising hydroxamic acid from giving rise to cross-linkages.

The number and the reactivity of the ester bonds in the procollagen are different from those in the insoluble collagen. The excess in the latter corresponds to the intermolecular cross-linkages between the collagen monomers. A fission of these linkages results in the dissolution of collagen in the macromolecular form.

There is a fair quantitative agreement between the number of the hydroxylamine-sensitive bonds and the carbohydrate content of the mature collagen. Based on this correlation Hörmann (1960) suggests that the hexose component of the collagen plays a part in the ester bonds which are responsible for the steric intermolecular- and intramolecular-network formation. The same author exposed heat-denatured collagen to trypsin effect. In this case the collagen passed into solution only partially and in the insoluble fraction an accumulation of carbohydrates was observed. The quantity of the insoluble protein depended on the degree of denaturation. Its carbohydrate content attained even 15 to 30%. It is thought that in the mature collagen molecule the stabilizing cross-linkages are due to certain carbohydrates that do not split off during thermal denaturation. Trypsin, on the other hand, exerts its digestive effect at sites lying farther from the stabilizing linkages, thus in the insoluble residuum the hexose-containing polypeptide fragments will accumulate.

The experiments in which partially denatured collagen was subjected to elastase digestion produced similar results. In these cases, too, carbohydrates accumulated in the less easily denaturable areas. After collagenase degradation of the native collagen even a little enzyme-resistant residuum is left behind, in which the concentration of the neutral sugars (3·5%) exceeds the initial level. In this residuum every amino acid of the collagen, including hydroxyproline (Hypro), is present in the same proportion as in the collagen (13 to 14% Hypro content). Consequently, this is a substance identical with collagen except for its higher carbohydrate content.

EXPERIMENTS WITH PERIODIC ACID

The demonstration of carbohydrates and their presence in cross-linkages is mainly inhibited by the fact that their reducing groups are not in a free state. Free reducing groups and N-glycosidic bonds would be demonstrable by osazones formed with phenylhydrazine. However, this reaction is negative for the procollagen as well as for the collagen. Consequently, reducing groups cannot be present except in O-glycosidic bonds. Thus, the presence of polysaccharides, more exactly carbohydrates, in the cross-linkages of collagen could only be evidenced when more abundant information of their chemical nature became available from periodic-acid oxidation experiments. Gustavson (1958) was the first to observe that oxidation of the collagen dropped its shrinkage temperature by 10 °C. When thermally denatured collagen dissolved in acetic acid or native collagen was oxidized with periodate in the presence of 8 M urea, the collagen passed slowly into solution (Hörmann 1960, 1962). Like the soluble product of the hydroxylamine treatment, the soluble collagen protein resulting from the oxidative reaction in the presence of urea contains only large molecules, consequently it is non-dialysable. The Grassmann school applied the procedure of Hörmann and Fries (1958) in which sugars are decomposed more or less selectively. During periodate oxidation of acetic-acid solutions of the procollagen 60 to 65% of the neutral carbohydrate is decomposed within two hours, whereas the residuum remains unchanged even after 182 hours. This experiment as well as most of the experiments carried out in the laboratories of Prof. Grassmann on carbohydrates confirm our concept of the presence of the two mucoids in the native collagen fibre.

The finding of the Grassmann school, viz. no change ensues in the amino-acid composition during the first two hours of periodic-acid treatment, is of great interest. An alteration, namely in the side-groups of hydroxylysine, tyrosine, methionine and, to a low degree, of histidine requires very long (5 to 150 hours)

162

treatments with periodate. This alteration does not affect the peptide chain itself, and dialysable fragments of molecular weight are not produced. It is an important observation that, provided the oxidation has proceeded in highly-diluted acetic acid, during the subsequent dialysis some fibril formation with "native" periodicity still occurred. However, the cross-striation of the resulting fibrils became unclear during the long-term reaction with periodate. In spite of this observation the authors denied any role of mucoids in the electron-microscopic cross-striation. They based their negative view on certain adequate preparations and electron-microscopic staining procedures. In contrast to this, we insist on the role of the mucoids in the formation of the cross-striation both in the FLS form and the SLS form. This role is not a simple inductive one as supposed by others. Only the present methods are not adequate, not sufficiently sensitive, to evidence this role. Naturally, incorporation of 1 to 2% neutral and acid mucopolysaccharide in a structure containing 98 to 99% amino acid needs new discoveries resulting in an improvement in the accuracy of present analytical methods by two or three orders of magnitude. Until such a discovery the view of certain illustrious laboratories (Schmitt, the Gross−Highberger school, the Grassmann school) will be predominant. According to this view the mucoids do not form covalent bonds in the collagen, but only induce the formation of different collagen structures by their mere presence.

In the present work the results of our investigations concerning the submicroscopic structure, function, physicochemical characteristics and chemical structure of the fibres are arranged according to the concept that the mucoids are integral components of the functioning collagen (and elastic) fibre. We suggest that even in the large group of collagen diseases the close connection of these substances with the collagen has ceased. The observed morphological alterations, the arisal of amorphous collagen and the changes in the swelling characteristics (e.g. oedema formation) all result from changes in the chemical characteristics and linkages of the mucoids.

According to Grassmann and Kühn (1955) mature, insoluble collagen (obtained from the skin of adult cattle) when oxidized at 40 °C with periodic acid will slowly be dissolved. The same phenomenon does not ensue at 16 to 18 °C as shown by the same authors and also by us. The results were similar when collagen prepared from bovine Achilles tendon was examined (Baló et al., unpublished data). When, however, the oxidation with periodic acid proceeds in an acetic-acid solution of higher concentration in the presence of urea, 99% of the collagen passes into solution at room temperature, although this process needs a period of at least 5 to 7 days. Similar experiments can be carried out in the presence of 40% KI, KSCN or NaClO$_4$, suggesting that lyotropic agents alone do not dissolve the mature collagen completely, but do so in the presence of periodic acid and 10% acetic acid. For an explanation of these experiments an assumption of the Grassmann school may be accepted, viz. in the collagen bonds of primary valences responsible for the steric network formation of collagen had to be split during the above experiments. Namely the network formation (Vernetzung) of the mature collagen inhibits the solubilization of the collagen in concentrate phenol solutions or in urea solution both being able to split hydrogen bridges.

The difference between mature collagen and procollagen is manifested in the insolubility of the former in the above solvents. Its insolubility distinguishes collagen also from such stable proteins as, e.g. silk. Procollagen is considerably different from the mature collagen also in its denaturation temperature; it is already denatured at temperatures exceeding 38 °C, whereas the mature collagen, in water, only at 67 °C. This is another argument for the presence in the collagen of primary valences which are essential in giving rise to the steric network formation and consequent insolubility. The attractive forces existing between the polar groups of collagen are, even in the opinion of certain members of the Grassmann school (Hörmann 1960, 1962), insufficient for the explanation of the differences between the procollagen and the mature collagen. The concept suggesting the existence of groups possessing primary valences is also supported by the fact that the two kinds of collagen are identical in their amino-acid composition and, according to present knowledge, their amino-acid sequence is not different to such an extent that would provide a satisfactory basis for the supposition of differences in the molecular structure between procollagen and insoluble collagen. If, however, the electrostatical attractive forces are identical, there is nothing to explain the differences between soluble and insoluble collagen.

As covalently bound periodate-sensitive groups only neutral sugars may come into consideration. The coupling of peptide chains by means of carbohydrates can be explained either by glycosidic bonds between OH groups of the carbohydrates and amino groups of the peptide chain or by ester bonds between carboxyl groups of the peptide chains and one or two hydroxyl groups of the carbohydrates. As a result of oxidation with periodic acid the 1 to 2 glycol groups are split off. In the presence of acetic acid the residual sugar hydroxyls are acetylated and so stimulate the fission of further cross-linkages after oxidation. These reactions lead to the solubilization of the collagen.

In the mature collagen hexoses may form bifunctional or trifunctional intermolecular linkages. In the bifunctional linkage one of the bonds is an O-glycosidic bond, the other is ester-like (Hörmann 1960, 1962). In the trifunctional linkage two ester bonds should be assumed. Besides these bonds there may remain two neighbouring C atoms with free OH groups (1 to 2 glycol group) in each hexose molecule. This is the prerequisite of the oxidation of hexose by periodate. According to our investigations splitting of the 1 to 2 glycol bond is a secondary process, as solubilization of the mature collagen with periodate does not ensue without the simultaneous effect of heat or lyotropic agents. During thermal contraction or chemical contraction brought about by lyotropic substances mucoid$_1$ is released as shown by our experiments. Before the oxidizing effect of periodic acid is exerted on the mature collagen, in our opinion through the release of mucoid$_1$, all the oxidizable groups must have become free. Thus, periodic acid can exert its further effect

164

both on the separated mucoid$_1$ and the 1 to 2 glycol groups of the residual collagen which still contains a mucoid, the mucoid$_2$. In the closely-packed mature collagen these groups are inaccessible to both periodic acid and hydroxylamine. The loosening associated with the thermal or chemical contraction renders the masked specific groups of the polysaccharides reactive. As Hörmann (1962) calculated, 0·35 Mol hexose falls to every 100 Mol amino acid, indicating that within a 640 Å period two steric network-forming valence bonds (Vernetzungsvalenzen) should be assumed. From the extension reaction of the thermally denatured collagen it can be calculated that these network-forming groups take place at a given site of the identity period. This means that starting from every triple helix two network-forming valences must be present in every 640 Å period.

SILVER-FIXATION EXPERIMENTS

In our laboratory the carbohydrate content of the procollagen was determined by the Rimington (1940) method in addition to the Anthron method. In general it was found to be about 1 to 1·2%. The fact that in the procollagen the carbohydrate groups (in contrast to the opinion displayed above) may exert a reducing effect was experienced in the course of so-called silver-fixation experiments. Grassmann and Kusch (1952) evolved a procedure for the quantitative assay of the silver-fixing capacity of collagen. These authors thought that it was the histidine content of the collagen that was indicated by the silver fixation. However, our experiments have shown that the silver is fixed by the polysaccharides in the collagen, and it is mainly the procollagen in which silver is reduced by these polysaccharides.

Silver impregnation is an old histological method for the demonstration of reticular and procollagen fibres. The fibres take up silver from the ammoniacal-silver solution and so are stained black. Dettmer et al. (1951) used the silver-fixing capacity of connective-tissue fibres also in electron-microscopic studies. They found that silver was deposited inside the fibrils in the so-called D part of the cross-striation.

In our own experiments the silver-fixing capacity of the native rat-tail collagen and of procollagen samples prepared from the former was comparatively determined (Table 38).

TABLE 38

Silver-fixing capacity of native collagen and procollagen

Material tested	Age of animal (months)	mg Ag/g collagen
Collagen from the rat-tail tendon	4	13·4
Collagen from the rat-tail tendon	6	12·8
Collagen from the rat-tail tendon	10	12·0
Collagen from the rat-tail tendon	12	11·0
Procollagen No. 1	4	16·0
Procollagen No. 2	6	15·0
Procollagen No. 3	6	13·0

12 S.F.E.C.

In procollagen the fixed silver is reduced to a higher degree than in collagen. The former becomes darker when allowed to stand. Figure 62 shows native collagen (a) and procollagen (b) after silver fixation.

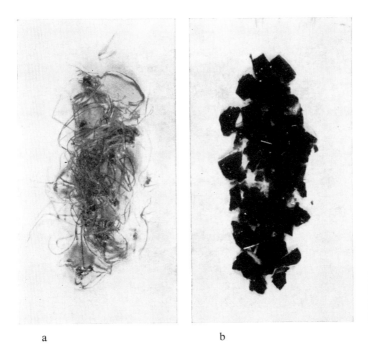

FIG. 62. Native collagen fibres (a), and procollagen (b) after silver treatment

a   b

THE ROLE OF MUCOID₁ IN THE FUNCTION OF FIBRES

In connection with the thermal and chemical contraction of collagen we have mentioned several times that according to our hypothesis the shortening of the fibres is a result of a loosening of certain linkages having held the fibre in the extended state. These linkages holding procollagen and metacollagen together are identical with the ester bonds whose existence has been evidenced by several literary data (Gallop et al. 1962; Grassmann et al. 1953, 1955; Hörmann 1960, 1962) and discussed on pp. 160–165.

Owing to an accidental observation we were able to ascertain that a very short heat effect makes the native, elastase-resistant fibres elastase-soluble (Banga 1953). When investigating the chemical changes we found that a mucoprotein, the mucoid₁ was released; the polysaccharide content of this protein was found to be higher than that of the original collagen (Banga 1953; Banga and Baló 1954). While the native collagen fibres contain 0·5 to 0·7% polysaccharide according to the Grassmann school and 1% according to our data obtained by Rimington's (1940) method, the material dissolved during thermal contraction contained 4 to 10%, and

166

this percentage was age-dependent. From the results of several hundreds of experiments we have concluded that the shorter the heat effect the purer the liberated mucoid$_1$. In the collagen fibres of the rat's tail 1% of the dry matter of the fibres passes into solution during a thermal contraction of 10 to 40 sec duration. The dissolved substance contains 12 to 14% nitrogen as determined by the micro-Kjeldahl method or according to Folin. Its carbohydrate content was found to fluctuate from 8 to 10% in animals 3 to 6 months of age and from 4 to 5% in 24-month-old animals. These values have been confirmed by different assays (Rimington 1940; Anthron method; Park-Johnson 1949). Considering that only little amounts of collagen can be isolated from the rat-tail tendon, in the material obtained from a single animal only one substance can be analysed, i.e. in addition to the polysaccharide analysis tests for hexosamine and hexuronic acid cannot be performed.

The same substance is released during the chemical contraction in 40% KI solution. The experiments of Chvapil and Zahradnik (1960) who used $NaClO_4$ as lyotropic agent confirmed that during the first three minutes of a very rapid reaction a substance was liberated which showed maximum absorption at 275 mμ, but did not contain Hypro. During the relaxation following contraction a Hypro-containing protein passed into solution. However, the latter reaction is slow in contrast to the dissolution of mucoid$_1$ which ensues very rapidly. Because of the high speed of the reaction and the little amount of the dissolved substance the isolation and the analysis of mucoid$_1$ encounters great difficulties. For this reason our supposition and argument on the existence of mucoid$_1$ and on its functional role have never been checked, except in the experiments of Chvapil and Zahradnik (1960).

Since the collagen fibres of the rat's tail yield such a little amount of mucoid$_1$ that in each series of experiments only one kind of analysis could be performed, experiments were initiated with fibres obtained from bovine Achilles tendons (Banga and Baló 1954). First of all it was demonstrated that the appearance of this substance is not necessarily associated with the conversion of collagen into gelatin, although it always precedes the latter phenomenon. It is well-known that the conversion of the collagen of the bovine Achilles tendon into gelatin requires boiling for several hours or even several days, whereas the substance under study passes into solution within 10 to 40 sec from the rat's tail, and within 5 to 10 minutes from the Achilles tendon at 70 °C. The solubilization is associated with a great "spontaneous" swelling of the collagen fibres. This ensues in water already at 50 to 55 °C, and in dilute acetic acid even at lower temperatures. The presence, strictly speaking, the loosening of mucoid$_1$ is a prerequisite of the so-called neutral or spontaneous swelling of the collagen. As the latter has passed into solution at 60 to 70 °C, the fibres show no neutral swelling any longer. The acid-swelling of the fibres is also related to mucoid$_1$. The fibre loses 70 to 75% of its swelling capacity in dilute acetic acid, while its mucoid$_1$ passes into solution. According to Gross (1958) and Gross and Kirk (1958) precipitate formation at 30 to 35 °C depending on pH and ion concentration is a highly a characteristic reaction of tropocollagen solutions. This is the so-called "gelation". At a lower temperature the precipitated collagen will be dissolved again. According to our view and experimental results this characteristic of the tropocollagen is due to its mucoid$_1$ content. This means that the gelation-forming capacity is characteristic of the tropocollagen-mucoid$_1$ complex. If a tropocollagen solution is heated to 40 to 55 °C in dependence of pH, it will lose its gelation-forming capacity, owing to the fission of the linkages between mucoid$_1$ and tropocollagen and the consequent dissapearance of the characteristics of the complex.

According to chemical analyses the carbohydrate of mucoid$_1$ is a neutral polysaccharide containing glucose, mannose, galactose and fucose in a non-dialysable form. Some of our mucoid$_1$ preparations also contained minimal amounts of hexosamine, hexuronic acid and neuramic acid, but these are considered to be contamination. We consider mucoid$_1$ to be a mucoprotein because the neutral mucopolysaccharides migrate in the electrical field together with the protein fraction. If it is prepared from the Achilles tendon (by dissolution in water at 70 °C for 10 minutes), 1 g powdered tendon yields 30 to 60 mg dry matter. However, this powder frequently contains, in addition to mucoid$_1$, a collagen protein as shown by its Hypro content. This protein makes the isolation of mucoid$_1$ still more difficult.

Verzár and Huber (1958) studied several substances influencing thermal contraction and found some of them (e.g. formaldehyde) to strengthen the crosslinkages loosening during contraction and others to weaken these linkages (e.g. urea and urethan). They call in question Gustavson's hypothesis about the chemical nature of these cross-linkages. They suggest that the linkages may be crosslinkages of ionic nature between glutamic acid and lysine (10 to 100 Å); van der Waals forces (50 to 60 Å); hydrogen bonds occurring mainly between neighbouring amino-acid residues and the keto-imide group of the Hypro. Such intermolecular hydrogen bonds might bridge over distances of 2 to 3 Å. According to Gustavson (1956) the hydrothermal stability is markedly influenced by hydrogen bonds. The latter statement has been confirmed by our experiments carried out with urea (Chapter XII, p. 146). These experiments have shown that contraction can be produced by urea, but only at a slightly raised temperature. The process does not lead to the formation of metacollagen fibre, i.e. mucoid$_1$ does not pass into solution. The effect of ethanol and glycerine (Verzár and Huber 1958) is also explainable by the assumption that mucoid$_1$ is solubilized only in the hydrolytic way and these hygroscopic substances hinder the fission of the linkages of mucoid$_1$.

Meyer and Verzár (1959) thoroughly investigated the quantity of the released Hypro and the temporal course of the reaction. They make a distinction between the release of the so-called free Hypro and the Hypro which can only be determined after acid hydrolysis. Their most interesting observation was that Hypro could only be demonstrated if the fibres had been allowed to convert into the contracted state. If contraction was prevented by an adequate loading, detectable amounts of Hypro did not appear in the outer fluid. As loading ceased, the contraction came about and the liberated Hypro became demonstrable. The authors suppose two alternative reasons: a) Hypro is not split off from the collagen when contraction

168

is being inhibited; b) Hypro is split off on the thermal effect even in the extended fibre but cannot diffuse out of the fibre until contraction has ensued. Young and old animals differ from each other in the quantity of both the easily releasable Hypro and the Hypro-containing polypeptide. The former passed into solution completely from the fibres of rats 2 to 4 months of age within 50 minutes, whereas in old animals the solubilization was protracted and incomplete. The residual, so-called elastoid contained the more Hypro the older the animal was. These experiments confirm our results. In Verzár's experiments the easily released Hypro was determined, i.e. the component whose quantity in the collagen fibre and sensitivity to splitting effects is age-dependent. According to our theory mucoid$_1$ holds together procollagen and metacollagen, and the ester bonds of this linkage are split during contraction, resulting in the diffusion of procollagen as soluble component out of the fibre. In the insoluble, residual metacollagen a mucoid substance, namely mucoid$_2$ still remains. This is responsible for the insolubility of the metacollagen fibre. The thermal and chemical contraction-relaxation induces the solubilization of mucoid$_1$ and this is followed by the solubilization of the denatured collagen on the thermal effect. For this reason it seems to be impossible to draw the line between the heat-relaxed fibre and the metacollagen fibre. In the case of chemical relaxation the metacollagen fibre is easier separable, but the residual metacollagen fibre will pass into solution on the effect of the CMPase enzyme in both cases, for this enzyme is specific for mucoid$_2$ (Chapter XII). However, as seen in the course of the experiments performed with urea and $CaCl_2$ (Chapter XII), the resulting fibre will not be digested by CMPase since presumably incorporation of these substances have given rise to new stabilizing linkages.

CHAPTER XV

EFFECT OF COLLAGENMUCOPROTEINASE ON THE COLLAGEN FIBRE AND COLLAGEN-CONTAINING TISSUE

FUNCTIONAL AND SUBMICROSCOPIC ALTERATIONS IN THE COLLAGEN FIBRE WHEN TREATED WITH COLLAGENMUCOPROTEINASE

THE COLLAGENMUCOPROTEINASE (CMPase) enzyme was first isolated by us, using the paper electrophoresis method (Chapter III). The effect of the elastase enzyme complex was observed earlier (Banga and Baló 1956), but a specific and homogeneous enzyme could not be isolated until the individual fractions of the elastase-enzyme complex were separated. As shown in Fig. 11 (Chapter III) the spot No. 1 (CMPase) migrated most rapidly and the same fraction was the most effective on collagen. The differences in migration velocity among the three enzyme components of the elastase-enzyme complex made the isolation of these enzymes possible. Greater amounts of CMPase were prepared by starch electrophoresis from trypsin preparations of high CMPase content (Chapter XVII p. 196).

FUNCTIONAL STUDIES

On the effect of CMPase the fibres lose their capacity of performing work during chemical or thermal contraction. Their stability disappears and in 40% solution of KI the CMPase-treated fibres break without contraction when loaded with a small weight. In the neutral salt solutions (KI, NaI, KSCN, NaClO$_4$) inducing chemical contraction-relaxation the CMPase-treated fibres behave uniformly; they disintegrate and pass slowly into solution instead of becoming contracted. The velocity of the process depends on the concentration of the enzyme, the time of incubation and the temperature. Table 39 shows the dependence of the effect on the CMPase concentration. If the fibres are incubated for 10 to 30 minutes instead of 16 hours, disintegration ensues only at an enzyme concentration as high as 1000 μg per ml.

TABLE 39

Functional changes in 40% KI solution of CMPase-treated collagen fibres obtained from the tail tendon of 6-month-old rats

CMPase concentration μg/ml	Contraction-relaxation	Disintegration and solubilization time (min)
0	ensued	none
40	none	65
100	none	48
200	none	38
500	none	21
1000	none	12

Note: Enzyme-treatment at pH 7·6 in Tris-buffer-dissolved CMPase at 38 °C for 16 hours

170

The morphological changes which ensue continuously until complete degeneration in the CMPase-treated fibre when incubated in 40% KI solution are well observable under the polarization microscope (Baló et al.1960, Baló and Banga 1961). The difference manifested in this reaction between native and CMPase-treated fibres has proved that the enzyme splits linkages and so separates a component whose lack altered the submicroscopic arrangement of the collagen molecule. This component has been termed $mucoid_2$ to distinguish it from $mucoid_1$ the component passing into solution during thermal and chemical contraction-relaxation, together with the procollagen. Like $mucoid_1$ $mucoid_2$ may be considered to be a stabilizing factor of the collagen fibre. However, loosening of the linkages of $mucoid_1$ does not lead to a total loss of the working capacity in the initial phase of the treatment. This can be restituted by new, electrostatical bonds, whereas the liberation of $mucoid_2$ always results in total disintegration. In the following the polarization-optical and dark-field microscopic pictures observed after CMPase treatment will be described.

The positive birefringence of the fibres remains high after CMPase treatment, as high as that of the native fibre, whereas the phenol-induced negative birefringence definitely weakens. Table 40 shows the results of polarization-optical studies in relation to enzyme concentration. On the effect of 200 to 1000 μg per ml enzyme the phenol reaction weakened by 75 to 80%, indicating that the component reacting in the native fibre with phenol had been removed. Comparing the meta-collagen fibre with the fibre pretreated with CMPase makes clear that in the former both the positive and the phenol-inducible negative birefringence disappears while the latter fibre retains its crystalline arrangement which is characteristic of the positive birefringence, and even a weakening of the phenol reaction needs long-term incubation with a high CMPase concentration. The usefulness of polarization optics in pathological studies was proven by Jobst's (1954) experiments. To differentiate fibrin from collagen, this author utilized the observation that pyridine converts only the collagen's birefringence into negative, while that of the fibrin remains unchanged. On this basis he could demonstrate that the placentar fibrinoid and the fibrin in the goitres represent pure fibrin, whereas the fibrinous inhibitions of the articular capsules, ganglia and the vascular wall contain precipitated fibrin. In rheumatic zones connected

TABLE 40

Polarization-optical studies on CMPase-treated collagen fibres

CMPase concentration (μg/ml)	Retardation in mμ	
	in Canada balsam	in 30% phenol
0	+ 601	− 740
40	+ 596	− 740
100	+ 653	− 720
200	+ 600	− 225
500	+ 522	− 225
1000	+ 526	− 225

Note: Enzyme-treatment at pH 7·6 in Tris-buffer dissolved CMPase at 37 °C for 16 hours

171

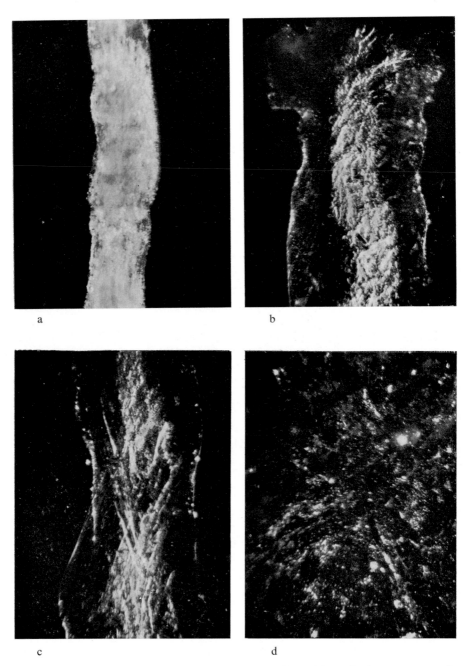

FIG. 63. Collagenmucoproteinase- (CMPase-) treated fibre; (a) no further treatment; the same after incubation in 40% KI for 15 to 20 seconds (b); five minutes (c); and several hours (d). Dark-field microphotographs

172

with impairment of the connective tissue and in ulcers, however, fibrin could not be detected i.e. in these cases some other substance is deposited.

By dark-field microscopy the CMPase-treated fibre fascicle shows a nearly homogeneous picture, except for some unevenness on its surface (Fig. 63a). On a depressed slide in 40 % KI solution at 20 °C an extremely rapid and intensive contraction, more exactly, shrinkage of the fibres is observable as soon as after 15 to 20 sec (Fig. 63b). The use of the word shrinkage is more appropriate in this case because, in contrast to the contracted native fibre (Fig. 39), the shrunk fibre in Fig. 63b does not show the well-known, arranged helical structure. Instead, fine ravelled

FIG. 64. Shrinkage of the fibrils of the CMP-ase-treated fibre in 40 % KI; the fibres are loaded with 20 g

fibrils form the part separating the outer, homogeneous phase. The solubilization of the outer part starts immediately after the fibre has been placed in the KI solution. The shortening, strictly speaking, shrinkage of the fibre is not followed by relaxation; instead, the inner fibre fascicle disintegrates into fibrils (Fig. 63c) before relaxation could ensue. In addition to the fibrillar disintegration, a fragmentation of the fibrils is also visible (Fig. 63d) and finally disintegration becomes complete.

In another series of experiments (Baló et al. 1960) a fibre fascicle was placed on a slide, several drops of 40 % KI were added, the preparation was covered with a cover-slip and the latter was loaded with 20 g. Contraction, more exactly, shrinkage ensued in such cases as well (Fig. 64). The fibrils passed into solution from both sides in the direction of the lowest resistance and the fascicle stretched out like a flower. As a result of shrinkage the fibrils became thicker. Finally a total dissolution ensued in this case, too. For taking the photograph shown in Fig. 64 a condenser giving slant illumination was used, for the relief-like picture so obtained reflects the phenomenon most clearly.

In the following, CMPase-treated fibres were loaded under a cover-slip with 75 g and the ends of the fibrils were fixed with a silk thread. In this way we applied

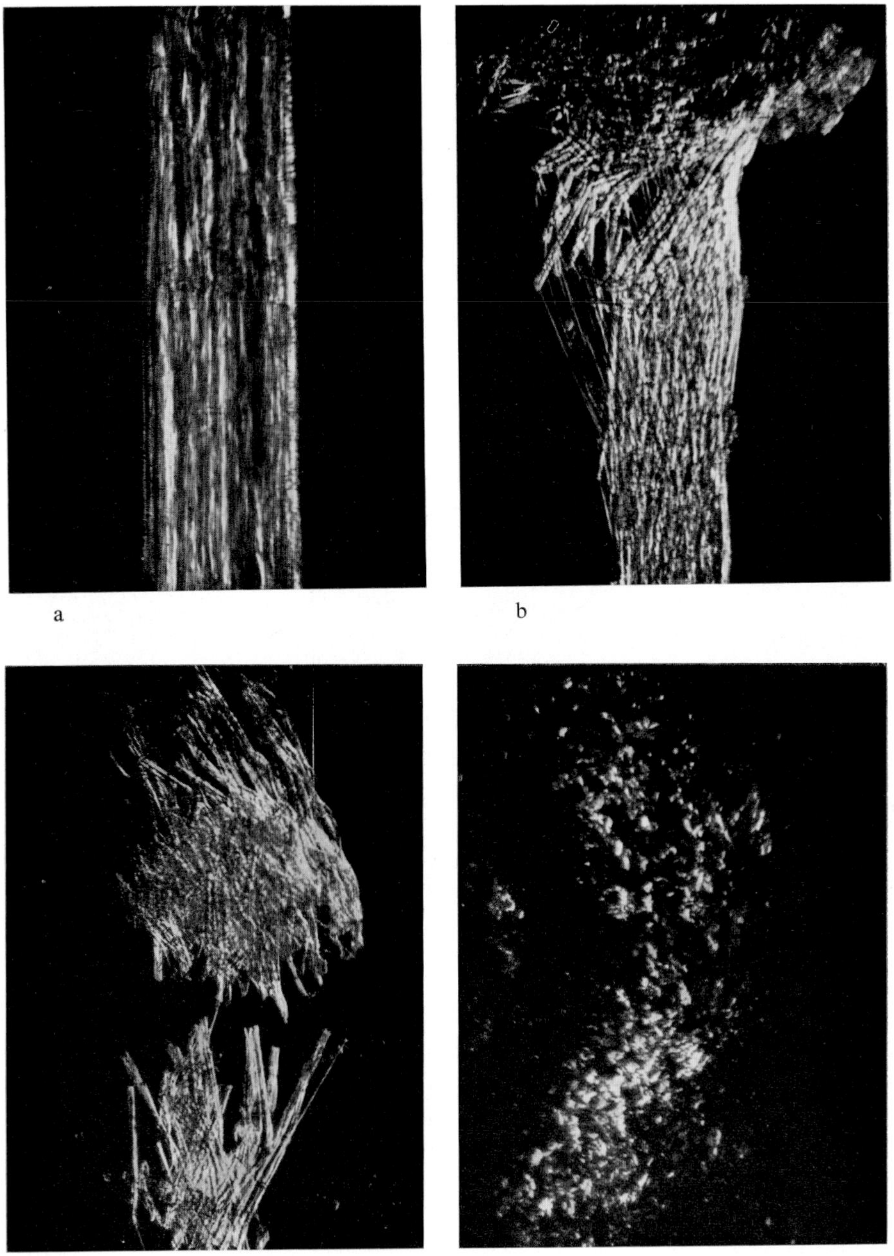

FIG. 65. Temporal course of shrinkage in 40% KI of CMPase-treated fibres. The fibres are loaded with 75 g; 60 seconds after addition of solution KI (a); incomplete shrinkage (b); 5 to 10 minutes after addition of solution KI (c); 20 minutes after addition of solution KI (d)

some force against contraction. Sixty seconds after adding the 40% solution of KI a high degree of separation of fibrils was observable (Fig. 65a). Shrinkage did start, but it was incomplete at the ends of the fibres because of their fixation (Fig. 65b). After 5 to 10 minutes the fibres broke off (Fig. 65c). Twenty minutes after adding the KI solution solubilization of the fibrils started (Fig. 65d) just like in the unloaded fibres. It seemed to be of interest to see whether similar phenomena would ensue in formalin-fixed fibres when these are submitted to the same procedures which were applied on unfixed, native ones. The fibres fixed in a 4 to 8% solution of neutral formaldehyde showed neither shrinkage nor separation of fibrils, nor passed into solution. The result was the same whether formalin-fixation preceded or followed the CMPase treatment. Formaldehyde prevents the chemical contraction-relaxation of the native fibre as well. It can, therefore, be concluded that CMPase treatment does not destroy the groups reacting with formaldehyde. As a result of such reactions formaldehyde is still able to give rise in the CMPase-treated fibre to cross-linkages which resist the lyotropic solutions able to induce chemical contraction.

Pretreatment with CMPase changes the behaviour of the collagen fibre in dilute organic acids as well. It can be seen with the naked eye that compared with the native fibres the CMPase-treated ones swell to a considerably greater extent in dilute solutions of almost every organic acid. The fibres of young animals show disintegration after swelling (Banga 1957). Without enzymatic pretreatment the fibres of old animals show only moderate swelling in organic acids, but the enzyme-treated fibres convert into the gel state, indicating that they may assume unrestricted amounts of the organic acid and, at last, become dispersed in the latter. In the foregoing it was pointed out that gelatinization is characteristic of the young fibre. In the present experiment, however, the enzyme made the fibres of old animals similar to young fibres in this respect.

For morphological examination CMPase-treated fibres were placed in dilute (0·005 N) acetic acid. The fibres swelled to three times their initial volume (Figs 66a and 66b). Figure 66b shows that the swollen fibres are separated by lines of nuclei. In this experiment 7·5 g load on the cover-slip led to destruction of the fibrils and disintegration of the fibre fascicles (Fig. 66c). In native fibres which also swell strongly in dilute acid, such a disintegration never ensues. Accordingly, besides the KI-induced disintegration a disintegration into fibrils in dilute organic acids is another characteristic reaction of the CMPase effect. The native collagen fibre having swollen in dilute organic acid reconverts into normal fibre in 5 to 10% solution of NaCl. In contrast to this, the CMPase-treated fibre disintegrates into filaments, passes into solution from which fibres cannot be restituted by adding NaCl. Consequently, the so-called fibre-formation reaction of Nageotte (1927) (the same reaction was applied also by Huzella 1941) cannot be performed with a fibre from which the mucoid$_2$ has been dissolved by CMPase.

Experiments resembling those described in the foregoing were carried out with hyaluronidase (hyase) to clarify whether CMPase is able or not to exert a hyase-like effect and vice versa. Native collagen fibres were incubated at 37 °C

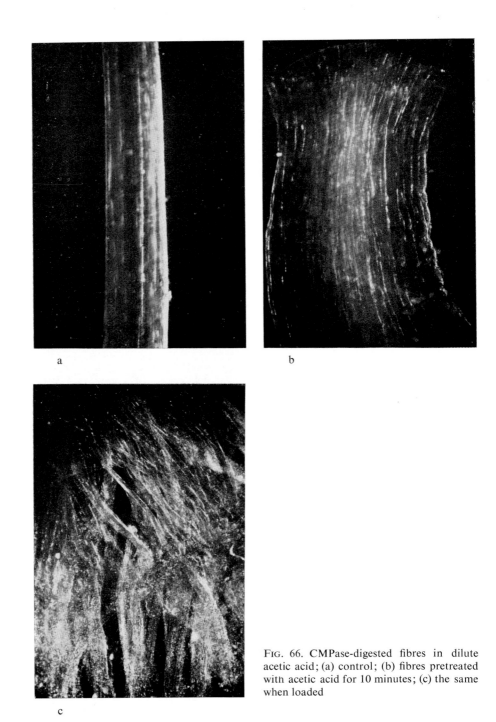

a

b

c

FIG. 66. CMPase-digested fibres in dilute acetic acid; (a) control; (b) fibres pretreated with acetic acid for 10 minutes; (c) the same when loaded

176

in 5 ml saline containing 150 TRU of hyase (Wyeth Institute, Philadelphia) for 24 hours. To avoid solubilization of the procollagen, the pH was not adjusted to the optimum for hyase (pH 5·5). (In our opinion hyase should be active also in saline.) The fibres so treated were different from the CMPase-treated ones. The hyase-treated fibres showed normal contraction and relaxation in 40% KI, indicating that the factors responsible for the stabilization of the fibres, i.e. for their normal function are not the hyase-sensitive acid mucopolysaccharides. It looks likely that, besides mucoid$_1$ and procollagen, mucoid$_2$ plays an equivalent part in the stabilized and regularly-oriented (crystalline) structure of the fibre.

CHAPTER XVI

THE MECHANISM OF COLLAGENMUCOPROTEINASE ACTION

OUR VIEW that mucoid$_1$ and mucoid$_2$ represent two different mucopolysaccharides is supported by the following observations (Baló and Banga 1961c) already mentioned above. When during thermal or chemical contraction mucoid$_1$ has passed into solution, about one half of the total polysaccharide content of the collagen still remains in the residual insoluble metacollagen which, however, passes into solution completely and very rapidly when incubated with CMPase. To explain the rapid dissolution of metacollagen we have assumed that the mucoid$_2$ component of the metacollagen fibre is specifically split off by CMPase and the removal of this component which plays a part in holding the collagen molecule together longitudinally, leads to a disintegration of the collagen into smaller polypeptide molecules.

CMPase liberates mucoid$_2$ also from the native fibre, and in this case a fibre dissolvable by any effect able to split off mucoid$_1$ is left behind. Thus, the mucoid$_2$-free fibre, originated either from the rat-tail tendon or the bovine Achilles tendon, will pass into solution in water at 70 °C or in lyotropic salt solutions which induce chemical contraction-relaxation by dissolving the mucoid$_1$. Accordingly, neither the removal of mucoid$_1$ or mucoid$_2$ leads to rapid dissolution of the collagen in water; this phenomenon will only ensue if both mucoids are removed regardless of the sequential order.

When fibre fascicles isolated either from the rat-tail tendon or from the bovine Achilles tendon are treated with CMPase, significant quantities of mucoid$_2$-containing protein cannot be detected in the medium (see pp. 188 and 192). If, however, the dehydrated fibres have been ground into powder, CMPase liberated mucoid$_2$ in quantities sufficient to be purified and isolated. (Dehydration can be carried out either by drying in the air or with acetone or alcohol.)

ISOLATION OF MUCOID$_2$ FROM THE ACHILLES TENDON
AND FROM INTERVERTEBRAL DISCS

Considering that the isolation of mucoid$_2$ requires a relatively great amount of starting material, mainly the collagen of the Achilles tendon was taken into account. In addition, isolation experiments were carried out in which smaller amounts of the anulus fibrosus of the intervertebral disc were used.

Dissolution of mucoid$_2$ from the powdered Achilles tendon by CMPase was usually performed as follows (Banga and Baló 1960a). Fifty g Achilles tendon was dried with acetone and ground to obtain a fine powder. This was suspended in 450 ml 0·025 M barbiturate-acetate buffer of pH 7·4 (in later experiments in Tris or Na$_2$CO$_3$-HCl buffer) and preheated at 37 °C for 15 minutes before its use as substrate. Then 50 mg CMPase dissolved in 50 ml of the same buffer was added to the reaction mixture and the incubation at 37 °C was continued for another 15 minutes. After subsequent cooling and centrifugation the supernatant which contained mucoid$_2$ was filtered through a filter paper. The control experiment was performed in the same way, but enzyme was not added. In the supernatant the protein was assayed by the Folin-phenol method, and the polysaccharides by the Anthron reaction. As calculated from numerous experiments, on average 16% of the Achilles tendon passed into solution. The total carbohydrate content of the dissolved material was 1·8% as computed from the standard curves for glucose, mannose and galactose. Mucoid$_2$ was precipitated from the obtained extract with 2·5 volumes of acetone. (From this step on the reaction was performed at 0 °C.) The precipitation with acetone served only for the concentration of the material in a small volume to facilitate the subsequent processes of purification. The supernatant was allowed to stand with acetone for two hours. Then the precipitate was removed by centrifugation and dissolved in 50 ml water. The subsequent step was precipitation with trichloroacetic acid. An equal amount of a 50% solution of trichloroacetic acid was added to the mucoid$_2$-containing solution, and after two hours a yellow oil could be centrifuged. The mucoid$_2$ remained in the supernatant, showing that it contained protein fragments unprecipitable by the 25% trichloroacetic acid as final concentration. The mucoid$_2$ was separated from the supernatant by precipitation using 2·5 volumes of acetone. An oily precipitate resulted. This was washed with acetone and dissolved, in general, in 50 ml water. For electrophoresis and chromatography, however, the precipitate was dissolved in 10 ml water. To make the precipitate soluble, several drops of N NaOH had to be added. Further purification included adsorption to IRC resin at pH 5·5 from the 1 : 2 diluted solution. Twenty g Amberlite IRC resin was added to 50 ml of the fluid. The resin had been treated with hydrochloric acid to be converted into the hydrogen form. (The excess HCl was removed from the resin by washing with water.) After shaking for two hours the IRC was filtered. During the short treatment the contaminating substances had been adsorbed by the IRC, while the mucoid$_2$ remained in the solution in a purified state. However, during longer agitation with IRC or repeated treatment mucoid$_2$ was also adsorbed and could not be regained by elution in a purified state. For this reason the IRC adsorption was, in general, not repeated.

In the course of the isolation the following chemical procedures were carried out: protein N and Hypro were determined; in the acid-hydrolysed fractions amino-acid analysis was performed by paper chromatography; the neutral polysaccharides were determined by the Anthron reagent and a modified Molisch-Szára reaction (Banga and Baló 1960a); the hexosamine and hexuronic-acid

179

components of the mucopolysaccharides were analysed by Elson and Morgan's (1935) method modified by Blix (1948) and by Dische's method, respectively. The yields of the different fractions, the losses and the percentage carbohydrate content as calculated for the protein are shown in Table 41. It is seen that 99·5%

TABLE 41

The mucoid$_2$ yield of powdered Achilles tendon during isolation (yields from 100 g tendon; averages from 20 experiments)

Fractions obtained during isolation	Yield		Loss		Carbo-hydrate/protein (%)
	Protein (g)	Carbo-hydrate (mg)	Protein (g)	Carbo-hydrate (mg)	
1. First extract	16·0	300	—	—	1·8
2. Acetone precipitation	8·0	200	8·0	100	2·6
3. Trichloroacetic-acid extract	0·4	100	7·6	100	25·0
4. After IRC treatment	0·08	50	0·32	50	62·5
Total loss			15·92	250	
Total loss (%)			99·50	81·3	

of the protein and 81·3% of the carbohydrates had been lost, indicating that the first protein extract still contained a carbohydrate-free component. The fact that we followed the fraction containing the mucopolysaccharide that is fixed to the Hypro-containing protein makes the results of our analysis comprehensible. The Hypro content of the fractions are summarized in Table 42. Table 43 contain the quantitative data for the different carbohydrates obtained in the course of the isolation of mucoid$_2$. The results in Tables 41, 42 and 43 show that the isolation of mucoid$_2$ led to a substance in which carbohydrate and mucopolysaccharide components were bound to protein. The protein component of mucoid$_2$ may be considered to be a true protein, for its Hypro content was consistent during the isolation procedure. The lower Hypro content after IRC treatment may be attributed to a hydrolysis in the trichloroacetic-acid-treated fractions. This hydrolysis gave rise to a polypeptide-split product of high Hypro content which was, however, free of the polysaccharide-containing fraction. Consequently, the mucoid$_2$ fragment contained less Hypro. Mandl (1958) using pure collagen-

TABLE 42

Hydroxyproline content of the fractions obtained during the isolation of mucoid$_2$ (calculated from six experiments)

Fractions obtained during isolation	Hydroxy-proline/protein (%)
1. First extract	9·75 ± 0·3
2. Acetone precipitation	9·90 ± 0·3
3. Trichloroacetic acid extract	10·0 ± 0·2
4. After IRC treatment	5·5 − 6·0

180

TABLE 43

Carbohydrate content of the fractions obtained during the isolation of mucoid$_2$ (gram/100 g protein)

Fractions obtained during isolation	Carbohydrate	Hexosamine	Hexuronic acid
1. First extract	1·8 ± 0·25 (20)	0·5 ± 0·1 (5)	0·0*
2. Acetone precipitation	2·5 ± 0·4 (20)	3·0 ± 0·2 (5)	1·0 ± 0·2 (5)
3. Trichloroacetic acid extract	25 ± 10 (20)	25 ± 5·0 (5)	13 ± 5·0 (5)
4. After IRC treatment	70 ± 10 (10)	70 ± 10·0 (6)	35 ± 5·0 (3)

Note: The numbers in brackets give the experiments from which the averages were calculated.
* = The fluid was opalescent and colourless

ase prepared from *Clostridium histolyticum* demonstrated that some of the soluble peptides occurring in the course of the digestion of collagen fractions do, and others do not, contain Hypro. It is, therefore, possible that similar peptides are liberated from the soluble collagen-mucoid complex.

To clarify the relationship of the protein to the carbohydrate components in the mucoid$_2$, various experiments were carried out (Banga et al. 1961b; Banga and Baló 1961c). Although the analysis of the fractions obtained during the isolation procedures brought satisfactory evidence for the existence of strong covalent bonds between the carbohydrate components and the collagen protein, yet it appeared reasonable to confirm this statement from other sides. Such experiments were necessary because the existence of a polysaccharide-containing collagen protein in which carbohydrate is bound to the protein component covalently has not yet been accepted. Only several indirect data and some experiments of the Grassmann school (Chapter XIV, p. 162) seem to support this view.

The diffusibility of the fractions was examined by dialysis using tubes made in England and in Germany. The dialyser tubes produced in Germany (Kalle and Co., Wiesbaden) permit the components below a molecular weight of 20 000 to pass through. In these tubes 30% of the proteins and 12% of the carbohydrates of the mucoid$_2$ fractions proved to be diffusible. On the other hand, when the English dialyser tubes were used (Visking Tubing, Hudes Merchandising Corp., London) no dialysable fraction was obtained from mucoid$_2$.

According to our studies CMPase fails to liberate any polysaccharide component from the collagen molecule, nor splits glycoside bonds in the polysaccharide chain, but liberates a mucoprotein complex in the protein component of which Hypro, the amino acid characteristic of the collagen, is present.

On the homogeneity and more detailed composition of mucoid$_2$ paper-electrophoresis experiments have provided characteristic data (Banga and Baló 1960a). These threw light on the nature of mucoid$_2$ from another side, viz. on the question whether it is a mucopolysaccharide (MPS) belonging to the acid MPS-s, the so-called polyuronides, or whether it is a substance in which neutral hexoses are bound to protein. It might have been supposed that the Achilles tendon, as the connective tissue in general, contains acid MPS-s in its ground substance and these, although in a non-specific way, might pass into solution on the proteolytic effect of the enzyme. By chance even the isolation procedure might have led to an enrichment in these substances in some fractions. If so, mainly the hexosamine content might have been due primarily to an accumulation of acid polyuronides. However, this

FIG. 67. Electrophoretic separation of mucoid$_2$ into protein (red) and metachromatic (lilac-blue) components

assumption has been opposed by the fact that the percentage hexosamine content was higher (at least twice) than the hexuronic-acid content in every fraction. In most of the acid MPS-s, on the other hand, equal amounts of hexosamine and hexuronic acid are present (hyaluronic acid and chondroitin sulphates may come into account). It was, therefore, more likely that the acid polyuronides as non-specific substances were present beside mucoid$_2$. Consequently, mucoid$_2$ is a mucoprotein complex in which neutral heteropolysaccharides are bound by covalent bonds to the collagen protein.

To prove the complex nature of mucoid$_2$, paper-electrophoretic experiments were carried out (Banga and Baló 1960a) with the fluid obtained after trichloro-acetic-acid precipitation. One and a half hours at 300 V and pH 8·6 was sufficient to obtain two separate stripes. One of these, a scarcely-moving component, strictly speaking migrating slowly towards the cathode, gave a very strong protein staining, whereas the other which migrated fast towards the anode showed a strong metachromasia with toluidine blue, but failed to give the protein reaction with acid fuchsin (Fig. 67). The more than 2 cm distance between the protein and the metachromatic stripe allowed a satisfactory analysis of the two substances. The separated stripes were eluted in water and their polysaccharide and protein contents were analysed (Table 44). Although the metachromatic spot gave no protein reaction with acid fuchsin, yet some protein was detected with the Folin-phenol reagent in the eluate. However, this protein, just like the little amount of hexuronic acid in the protein spot, may be considered to be contamination. Neither of them may be taken into account as a component of the separated substances. The hexosamine analysis is lacking in Table 44 because the eluate used in its assay was not enough to provide accurate data by our method. For this reason we tried the chromatographic procedure recommended by Kirk

FIG. 68. Native (red) and CMPase digested (pale) collagen fibres; PAS stain

and Dyrbye (1957). The experiments suggested that the same amount of hexosamine was present in the two spots, but even these data are not satisfactorily accurate.

When the electrophorized paper strips were treated with the PAS reagent a very weak red colouration was obtained near the protein spot. The metachromatic spot showed no colouration with the PAS reagent. It is well-known that the PAS reaction is given by the carbohydrates or polysaccharides in which each of two vicinal C atoms has an OH group in identical stereochemical position. When these C atoms are split off, aldehyde groups arise which oxidize the reduced Schiff reagent and so bring about the red colour. The collagen fibres of the young rat's tail give a red colour with PAS. However, if these fibres are pretreated with CMPase, colouration does not ensue as seen in Fig. 68. From the data of the analysis it is

TABLE 44

Analysis of the protein and metachromatic components separated from mucoid$_2$ by paper electrophoresis

Substance tested	Protein spot	Metachromatic spot
Protein (%)	85—90	11—15
Carbohydrate (%)	70—75	20—27
Hexuronic acid (%)	10—15	80—85

Note: Starting material: trichloroacetic-acid extract containining 14·3 mg protein, 3·55 mg Anthron-positive substance, 3·42 mg hexosamine and 1·81 mg hexuronic acid per 1·0 ml

13*

concluded that the greatest part of the carbohydrates and about one half of the hexosamine are bound to the protein. In the electrical field both of these migrate together with the latter. It would be reasonable to confirm this evidence by ultra-centrifugation, but we have not yet had the opportunity to carry out such an analysis. The individual carbohydrate components could not be separated from the mucoid$_2$ even by paper chromatography, indicating that the carbohydrates are bound to the protein by strong covalent bonds. We made attempts with hydrochloric-acid hydrolysis (N HCl, two hours at 110 °C) to throw light on the chemical nature of the carbohydrates present in the protein-polysaccharide component separated by paper electrophoresis. The chromatogram of the hydrolysate was developed with aniline-hydrogen-phthalate (Block et al. 1956). Of the eight spots recognizable in the chromatogram five were identified with known carbohydrates, namely glucose, galactose, mannose, fucose and glucosamine. The other three remained unidentified. According to the data in Table 44 an Anthron-positive substance was detected also in the metachromatic spot. As the presence of Anthron-positive neutral carbohydrates in this spot was unexpected, we tested the known mucopolysaccharide components for colour reaction with the Anthron reagent. As shown in Table 45 the known mucopolysaccharides, except keratosulphate, give only very faint colouration. (We are grateful to Prof. K. Meyer, Columbia University, for the mucopolysaccharides.) Since the migration velocity of the keratosulphate scarcely differs from that of the chondroitin sulphate, it may be supposed that keratosulphate is also present in the metachromatic spot, among the acid mucopolysaccharides of the ground substance.

TABLE 45

Anthron reaction of known acid mucopolysaccharides; the extinction by the substance 1 mg per ml in 0·5 ml cuvette was read in a Pulfrich photometer at 610 mμ

Acid mucopolysaccharides	Extinction	Acid mucopolysaccharides	Extinction
Chondroitin sulphate A	0·06	Hyaluronic acid	0·05
Chondroitin sulphate B	0·09	Heparin	0·07
Chondroitin sulphate C	0·12	Keratosulphate	0·28

Further experiments with hyaluronidase (hyase) supported this supposition. In these experiments two hyase preparations were used, an Organon preparation and a preparation of the Wyeth Laboratories (Philadelphia, Pa. U.S.A.). Both of these were used at a concentration of 75 turbidity-reducing units per ml, at pH 6; I=0·1; the incubation period was 16 hours. The effectiveness of the preparations was controlled on chondroitin sulphate C as substrate. The greatest part of the chondroitin sulphate was decomposed into diffusible hexosamine and hexuronic-acid components, whereas such components were not liberated from the metachromatic substance by hyase. Its mobility changed on the effect of hyase but did not disappear. In the light of tnis experimental result we believe that in the metachromatic spot chondroitin sulphate B and keratosulphate were predominant, for both of these are resistant to hyase. It can, therefore, be suggested that the hyase-resistant Anthron-positive component of mucoid$_2$, showing metachromasia with toluidine blue, consists of two components, such as heparin or heparitin sulphate and keratosulphate. It is not yet known whether these substances are integrant components of the mucoid$_2$ complex or not. It is well-known that in the Achilles tendon these substances are present among numerous other mucopolysaccharides (MPS) as components of the ground substance, but it is uncertain whether they were solubilized directly by the enzyme or indirectly, due to a loosening of the connective tissue.

Besides the Achilles tendon, the anulus fibrosus of the intervertebral disc was used as starting material to prepare mucoid$_2$ with CMPase (Banga and Horváth 1960). The anulus fibrosus appeared to be very suitable because it contains a great amount of acid MPS (Sylven 1951; Sylven et al. 1951; Malmgren and Sylven 1952). Considering this quantitative difference, it was of interest to investigate the possible differences in the MPS composition of the mucoid$_2$ dissolvable from the anulus fibrosus, in comparison with that prepared from the Achilles tendon. Some further questions were also to be answered. Is there any neutral-MPS-containing component in the anulus fibrosus, and if there exists such a component, is it dissolvable by the enzyme? or only the well-known acid MPS-s will appear in the mucoid$_2$ fraction? Does the enrichment in the different neutral and acid MPS components run parallel when anulus fibrosus and Achilles tendon are submitted to the same fractionation procedure? In the corresponding experiments the fractionation procedures were the same as described above. Since the collagen-protein content of the anulus fibrosus is significantly lower than that of the Achilles tendon, it was of great interest to determine the amino-acid composition and the Hypro content of the protein component of the mucoid$_2$ dissolvable from the anulus fibrosus. These data were necessary to decide whether this protein may be regarded a collagen protein or not. Experiments were carried out with both human and bovine anulus fibrosus. The results unequivocally prove that the enrichment in the Anthron-positive substance, in hexosamine and hexuronic acid, ran parallel whether anulus fibrosus or Achilles tendon was used as starting material. In the first extract of the mucoid$_2$ obtained by enzyme digestion from the anulus fibrosus the starting material for further fractionations was a component with a relatively high carbohydrate content (5 to 7% carbohydrate as calculated for the protein). It is, therefore, comprehensible that the loss in carbohydrate was significantly less than in the course of the isolation of mucoid$_2$ from the Achilles tendon. The Hypro content continuously increased during purification, and in the trichloroacetic acid fraction of the bovine anulus fibrosus it reached 12·6% of the protein, indicating that the protein present in this fraction was pure collagen protein. In contrast to this, the purest preparation obtained from the human anulus fibrosus contained only 7·2% Hypro. To explain the difference, it should be noted that the human material has originated from old arteriosclerotic cadavers in which severe patho-morphological lesions were present. In the paper electrophoretograms, like in those of the mucoid$_2$ obtained from the Achilles tendon, two separate spots were present, viz. the so-called protein spot that gave the protein reaction and the metachromatic spot giving lilac metachromasia with toluidine blue. The latter spot, like the corresponding spot of the Achilles tendon, failed to give the protein reaction with acid fuchsin; yet in the eluate protein was demonstrable by the Folin-phenol method. Nevertheless, this protein as well as the 13% hexuronic acid in the protein spot should be considered contamination. The separation of the two spots was, however, incomplete. Thus, mutual contamination with the components of the other spot is unavoidable. Considering the differences in the composition of both spots obtained by paper chromatography of the mucoid$_2$ preparations derived from the bovine anulus fibrosus and the Achilles tendon, the data for the anulus fibrosus are also presented (Table 46). The table shows

TABLE 46

Paper-electrophoretic analysis of the mucoid$_2$ obtained from the anulus fibrosus of cattle (percentage distribution of the substance in the two spots)

Substance tested	Protein spot	Metachromatic spot	Substance tested	Protein spot	Metachromatic spot
Protein	80	20	Hexuronic acid	13	87
Carbohydrate	33	67	Hydroxyproline	96	4
Hexosamine	29	71			

that two-third of the carbohydrates analysed as Anthron-positive substance and the hexosamine appeared in the metachromatic spot, whereas in the Achilles tendon, inversely, two-third of the carbohydrates appeared in the protein component. Hyase digestion of the metachromatic spot increased the amount of the reducing sugars, while the quantity of the Anthron-positive substance remained unchanged. Since according to Table 45, in the meta-chromatic spot keratosulphate is the only component that gives the Anthron reaction and is, to our best knowledge, resistant to hyase, the relative amount of this substance to other neutral MPS-s is presumably higher in the mucoid$_2$ of the anulus fibrosus than in that of the Achilles tendon. In the intervertebral disc Hall et al. (1957) found keratosulphate in the nucleus pulposus. Prior to our experiments keratosulphate had not been detected in the anulus fibrosus. Thus, the present data are the first quantitative values in this respect. The fact that highly pronounced metachromasia remained (Fig. 69) after hyase treatment also supports the view that the isolated product contains kerato-sulphate and heparitin sulphate and/or heparin besides hyaluronic acid and chondroitin sulphate.

In the light of these results it was of interest to study the solubility of the total polysaccharide and polyuronide content of the human and bovine anulus fibrosus by CMPase digestion. According to our results 30 to 40% of the polysaccharides and 50 to 60% of the polyuronides were released and passed into solution. Two-third of the polysaccharides consist of acid MPS, mainly keratosulphate and heparin-sulphate. These are bound to the little-known protein of the anulus fibrosus probably by polar bonds and, according to the nomenclature recommended by Meyer (1953), they may be considered to be mucoproteides. The neutral part consists of heteropolysaccharides in which there are covalent bonds between the carbohydrate component and the protein. In this substance, which is identical with the neutral-polysaccharide-containing component of the mucoid$_2$ of the Achilles tendon, 96% of the protein appearing in the electrophoretically separated protein spot proved to be collagen protein as calculated from its Hypro content (Table 46). The analysis of other amino acids (Gly, Pro and Ala) is also consistent with the composition of the collagen protein. The existence of covalent bonds between the heteropolysaccharides and the collagen protein is supported by the stability of the substance in the presence of trichloroacetic acid and by the fact

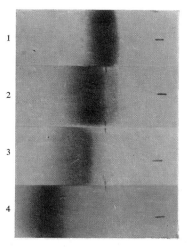

FIG. 69. Effect of hyase on the mobility of mucoid$_2$. The protein spot is red, the metachromatic one is lilac-blue; 1 and 3 after hyase treatment; 2 and 4 control

that in the electrical field the polysaccharides migrate together with the protein.

These data support, from the biochemical point of view, our theory (see Chapter XV, p. 170) proposing that CMPase liberates a stabilizing factor from the collagen molecule, while the residual fibre loses its normal function, i.e. its working capacity. The substance split off by the enzyme is a mucoprotein complex consisting of two parts as expounded in the foregoing. It is still uncertain whether all the analysed acid MPS and the neutral heteropolysaccharide-protein complex are present in the stabilizing factor and play a part in its function. Considering the successful extraction of mucoid$_2$ from the human vascular wall (aorta, carotids) with CMPase we consider the concept that all fibres of the connective tissue contain mucoid$_2$ to be reasonable. However, the quantity of mucoid$_2$ is variable according to the function of the fibre. In this relation a publication of Dische et al. (1958) deserves interest. According to these authors in the connective tissue of the vitreous body of the eyes there is a mucoid containing neutral heteropolysaccharides in covalent bonds. This mucoid may be identical either with mucoid$_1$ or with mucoid$_2$. Richter (1959) also found neutral polysaccharides in the anulus fibrosus of the intervertebral discs, but did not study their separation from the acid MPS-s and their relationship to the protein component.

187

An examination of the mechanism of CMPase action encounters extraordinary difficulties because, due to the close-packing of the fibre fascicles, only little amounts, if any, of the enzymatically liberated mucoid$_2$ can diffuse into the incubation medium.

In order to study the mucoid$_2$ passing into solution, great amounts of hair's-breadth thin fibre fascicles were prepared from the Achilles tendon of a young calf. From these we succeeded in obtaining sufficient amounts of mucoid$_2$. The fibres whose surfaces were naturally large were incubated in a solution containing 0·1 mg CMPase per ml at 25 °C (to avoid thermal denaturation) and pH 7·4 for 3 to 6 hours. The results in Table 47 represent averages from five experiments. Accordingly, in the initial phase of incubation a protein of very low Hypro content passed into solution . In the same fluid neutral and acid MPS-s were predominant. The great spreading of the results suggest that the percentage dry-matter content of the dissolved mucoid depended on the ratio of thick fibres to thin ones and the ratio of fibres to ground substance in the 100 mg Achilles tendon used as starting material. The data in Table 47 show that a protein with high (8 to 10%) Hypro content like that dissolved from the pulverized Achilles tendon or the anulus fibrosus within 15 minutes failed to pass into solution from the fibres even during the long period of incubation; however, little amounts of a mucopolysaccharide-containing material appeared in the supernatant. The nature of the protein with low Hypro content is still unknown. The protein component of the mucoid$_2$ isolated from powdered preparations of either the Achilles tendon or the anulus fibrosus always contained large quantities of Hypro, suggesting that it mainly consisted of collagen protein.

TABLE 47

Analysis of mucoid$_2$ obtained by CMPase from hair's-breadth-thin fibres of the Achilles tendon

Incubation with enzyme (hours)	Dissolved mucoid (%)	Hypro (%)	Hexose (%)	Hexuronic acid (%)	Neuramic acid (%)
			In the protein of mucoid$_2$		
3	3	2—3	8—23	3—8	3—6
6	4	3—4	5—18	2—6	2—6

The collagenolytic effect of the enzyme cannot be proved biochemically except by promoting the diffusion of the split products with a polypeptide character. This can be achieved by destroying the close packedness of the collagen fibres by grinding them into powder. The more perfect the pulverization the easier the polypeptides diffuse out of the fibres. As a result of pulverization the membranes

188

surrounding the fibres and the filaments inside the fibres lose their continuity and so cease to function as barrier systems. The same is valid for the electron-microscopically invisible ground substance which is, according to Romhányi (1962), structurally arranged in the connective tissue and forms a separate barrier system outside the membranes. Pulverization ceases the barrier system in a physical way and so enables the mucoid$_2$ + polypeptide, which have already been released inside the native fibre as a result of an enzymic effect, to diffuse into the outer fluid. Consequently, an intensive dissolution of the collagen protein takes place.

CMPase, as it will be evidenced in the following, is closely related to trypsin both chemically and physicochemically; even its identity with one of the active groups of trypsin would not be surprising. Therefore, in the case of the CMPase the fission of peptide bonds is associated with, or results from, the specific muco-proteolytic effect of the enzyme. Considering that the CMPase effect is accompanied by some solubilization of the collagen protein, the enzyme may be regarded as true collagenase concerning its mechanism of action.

Even the existence of the CMPase is a strongly disputed problem. Does the human (and animal) organism contain an enzyme capable of decomposing the native collagen? The investigators belonging to the great collagen schools still answer this question negatively, in spite of the growing number of observations suggesting that proteolytic-enzyme preparations obtained from the human (or animal) pancreas may account for the digestion of collagen. It would be almost inconceivable even from the biochemical point of view if the organism possessed no enzyme or enzyme system capable of synthesizing and decomposing the protein-like collagen which represents 25 to 35% of the total protein content of the human (and animal) organism. Nevertheless, Mandl et al. (1958) stated that the mammalian tissue does not contain any enzyme capable of digesting native collagen. Based on his earlier experiments Grassmann (1936) did not accept the digestibility of collagen by trypsin. The more recent work of the Grassmann school (Kühn et al. 1961) also tended to prove that only associated accessory substances are removed during trypsin digestion, whereas the collagen protein is not attackable by trypsin. However, the same authors firmly state that electron-microscopic structures identical with the native collagen fibres in being contrast-rich and thick and having sharp periodicity do not occur in the absence of certain trypsin and pepsin-sensitive "accompanying accessory substances".

According to the experiments of Orekhovich and Tustanovsky (1948) 15% of the procollagen is digestible by trypsin. Ziffren and Hosie (1955) reported on a collagenase present in the dog's pancreas secrete, but in the same laboratory Straumfjord and Hummel (1957) could not confirm this observation. According to the data published by Neumann and Tytell (1950) 60% of the powdered animal skin, but only 5 to 8% of the Achilles tendon is digestible with crystalline trypsin within a period of 24 hours. Houck and Patch (1959) prepared from porcine pancreas an activated preparation, named bridase, which is able to reduce the viscosity of procollagen solutions. Accordingly, the data in the literature on the existence of CMPase of animal origin are still uncertain and contradictory. In contrast to this, experiments carried out in our laboratory since 1956 have unequivocally confirmed the existence of CMPase whose true collagenase effect has also been proved.

RELATIONSHIP BETWEEN DENATURATION OF COLLAGEN AND CMPASE EFFECT

As regards the collagenolytic activity of CMPase several authors including Mandl (personal communication) suggest that during dehydration, drying and grinding collagen is denatured and this denaturation accounts for its digestibility by CMPase. To clarify this question we initiated experiments. Collagen was exposed to various physical, physicochemical and chemical effects in order to reveal a possible relationship between the so-called denaturation and the digestibility by CMPase. The first experiments have shown that powdered preparations of the acetone-dehydrated tissues are consistently digestible by CMPase (Banga et al. 1961a, b) (Table 48).

In further experiments fibres of the Achilles tendon were treated with hygroscopic agents to show whether dehydration and drying, without grinding into powder, will or will not make the fibres able to deliver soluble collagen to the supernatant on the effect of the enzyme. Furthermore, dehydrated collagen fibres were exposed to high temperature to be denatured. The digestibility of these fibres was examined in an unground state. Neither of these effects brought about the so-called "denaturation" of the collagen (Banga 1963a). Consequently, the resulting fibres failed to become digestible by the enzyme, even if the enzyme treatment was prolonged to 24 hours. On the other hand, if either of these preparations had been ground into powder after dehydration, or before or after heating, the subsequent enzyme treatment resulted in the dissolution of 20 to 30% of the collagen protein within 15 to 30 minutes. Even when the collagen fibres were dehydrated very carefully (in vacuum at low temperature) pulverization of the fibres led to their enzymatic solubilization. It could, therefore, be concluded that

TABLE 48

Collagenmucoproteinase activity in the presence of various substrates

Substrate	Collagen solubilized by the enzyme	
	(mg)	(%)
Powdered Achilles tendon	12·5	25
Collagen powder from rat-tail tendon (6-month-old rats)	11·5	23
Powdered human aorta (young)	10·0	20
Powdered human aorta (old)	5·0	10
Powdered calf aorta	10·0	20
Powdered human skin (young)	8·5	17
Powdered human skin (old)	8·0	16

Note: Experimental conditions: 50 mg powdered tissue; $Na_2CO_3 - HCl$ buffer of pH 7·6; enzyme 0·1 mg/ml; volume 5 ml; incubation period 30 min; temperature 25 °C. Enzyme effect was determined: a) by gravimetrical weighing of the insoluble residue of the substrate, and b) from the dissolved collagen calculated from the Hypro content of the supernatant

190

among the interventions under study disintegration by grinding was the only one that made fibres sensitive to enzymatic digestion.

The collagen fibres isolated from the rat-tail tendon were very suitable for denaturation experiments with chemical substances. One of such chemical procedures is sulphatation. As sulphatizing fluid a mixture composed of 50 ml sulphuric acid, and 15 ml ether was used. Fibres were placed in this solution for variable periods. Then the fibres were washed amply in water for one minute three times. The fibres showed contraction and became elastic even after two and a half minutes of sulphatation, and the contraction was very intensive after 6 to 7 minutes. The contracted fibres showed a fibrillar internal structure. The fibrils which had run parallel with the axis of the fibres, were converted into a transversal arrangement. As a result of this rearrangement a negative birefringence predominated in the fibres. In the extended state the fibrils regained their original position and the positive birefringence was restituted. The sulphatized fibres do not give the phenol reaction, indicating that sulphatation destroys the phenol-reacting groups. Although the sulphatized fibre must be considered to be a denatured fibre, it does not pass into solution on CMPase effect. On the basis of our theory we suggest that sulphate groups are incorporated in the molecule and form sulphate esters both with $mucoid_1$ and $mucoid_2$. These ester bonds bring about new cross-linkages and so inhibit the dissolution of the two mucoids. However, procollagen cannot be liberated and thus the metacollagen structure is not formed when $mucoid_1$ is present in the collagen molecule; CMPase is not effective on $mucoid_2$ either. Consequently, the concept of denaturation should neither be generalized in the case of the collagen nor identified with CMPase sensitivity.

Urea denaturation does not lead to CMPase-digestible so-called metacollagen, as shown in Chapter XII, p. 146. Exposure to 6·6 M urea at 37 °C ceases birefringence of the fibres, indicating that fission of hydrogen bridges accounts for the structural decomposition, and the resulting fibres are denatured morphologically. Nevertheless, these fibres are undigestible by CMPase. It is, therefore, obvious that only the metacollagen-forming "denaturing" effects make the fibres completely digestible by CMPase. Dissolution of the powdered collagen in acetic acid or alkali and subsequent neutralization and precipitation with salt or alcohol also result in enzyme-resistant fibres. Even pretreatment with hyase fails to make fibres enzyme-sensitive. As pointed out in the foregoing, digestibility by CMPase is fixed to the metacollagen structure which results from the chemical contraction-relaxation. Heating also produces an enzyme-soluble structure, but in this structure the heat-induced gelatinization cannot be separated from metacollagen formation.

Naturally, the CMPase-induced collagenolysis of the pulverized tissues should be sharply distinguished from the total enzymatic digestion of the metacollagen. The collagen-containing tissues pass into solution with CMPase only to 20 to 30 %, and even 70 % of the collagen remains insoluble if all the metacollagen-forming denaturing effects (high temperature, lyotropic agents) are excluded in connection with the enzyme effect. Based on certain experiments (Chapter XVII p. 202) we assume the existence of a distinct enzyme of metacollagenase activity

However, the CMPase effect on the native fibres and on the pulverized collagen tissue should be sharply distinguished from the metacollagenase activity. The aim of the denaturation experiments with sulphatation and urea was to prove that the effect leading to the true denaturation of the collagen is in no relationship to enzymatic digestibility. On the other hand, the physical disintegration due to grinding into powder cannot be considered denaturation. This process only promotes the diffusion of mucoid$_2$ and the polypeptide component. Numerous experiments were carried out to clarify whether the denaturation or the diffusion is responsible for the phenomenon that CMPase dissolves only several (3 to 6) per cent of the mucoid$_2$ from the native fibres, whereas under the same circumstances from the powdered fibres a material containing 25 to 30% collagen protein passes into the supernatant of the incubation medium. We supposed that if the collagenolysis is due only to the diffusion, it must be reversible, whereas if denaturation had occurred in the course of the pulverization, it must have been an irreversible process. To elucidate this question, further experiments were carried out. We studied whether the enzyme-treated fibres from which the enzyme had been washed off can be solubilized by simple powdering. Solubilization would indicate that the enzyme exerts its effect in the fibres and powdering accounts only for the diffusion into the supernatant of the mucoid$_2$ that has been split off inside the fibres. As shown in Table 49, only little amounts of protein (as assayed by the Folin-phenol method) had passed into solution from the fibre fascicles during the primary CMPase treatment, and the protein dissolved during repeated incubation (No. 3) was also minimal in amount. These experiments served as control for the main experiment (No. 4), in the course of which the enzyme-treated fascicle was ground into powder and then incubated in buffer. In this case the same high-

TABLE 49

High-degree dissolution of collagen protein from the Achilles-tendon fibre fascicles on the effect of grinding into powder

Experiment No.	Collagen state	Treatment	Dissolution of protein (%)
1	Fibre fascicles	Incubation with buffer for 3 hours	0·5—1
2	Fibre fascicles	CMPase 0·1 mg/ml at 25 °C for 3 hours	2—6
3	Fibre fascicles	Same as 2, followed by washing and incubation with buffer for 30 min	1—2
4	Fibre fascicles	Same as 3, followed by grinding into powder and incubation in buffer for 30 min	25—30
5	Ground collagen	Incubation in buffer for 30 min	2—5
6	Ground collagen	CMPase 0·1 mg/ml at 25 °C for 30 min	25—30

192

degree solubilization of the protein occurred as in the case of the fibre (experiment No. 6) which had been ground into powder before being incubated with the enzyme. This experimental series has shown that the enzyme effect had been accomplished when the fibrillar structure was still intact. Only the diffusion of a greater amount of the collagen protein, strictly speaking, of the Hypro-containing polypeptide chains was inhibited. This inhibition was ceased by pulverization.

To study the question of reversibility, the pulverized substance was restituted into fibre fascicles as described below and the digestibility of the restituted fibres was examined. For the restitution experiment collagen was converted into gel by dissolving it in acetic acid, and from this gel it was precipitated by neutralization and adding NaCl or alcohol (the excess salt was removed by washing). The substance so obtained was fibrillar collagen, from which fine fibres can be separated by hand. In another series of experiments collagen gel was prepared by dissolving collagen in 0·1 N NaOH. The gel was neutralized and NaCl or alcohol was added. The recovered collagen, after having been dried, formed fibres with large surfaces. As shown in Table 50, the restituted fibres, like the original fibre fascicles, were insoluble, or scarcely soluble when incubated with CMPase. Consequently, the high-degree disintegration due to pulverization is a prerequisite of the enzymatic solubilization of collagen. The protein dissolved from the powdered fibres was collagen as shown by its 10 to 12% Hypro content. It is of interest that the protein appearing in the supernatant after direct digestion of the powdered, native Achilles tendon contained 13 to 14% Hypro. On the other hand, dissolution of the powder in NaOH and a subsequent restitution reduced the Hypro content. The data in

TABLE 50

Solubilization by CMPase of fibrils reconstituted from pulverized Achilles tendon

Experiment No.	Starting collagen	Treatment	CMPase effect, dissolved protein (%)	Hypro content of dissolved protein (%)
1	Ground collagen	—	25—30	13—14
2	Ground collagen	Dissolution in acetic acid, neutralization and reconstitution of fibrils by 5% NaCl	4—7	12—13
3	Ground collagen	Same as 2. followed by fibril formation, by alcohol precipitation	4—7	12—13
4	Ground collagen	Dissolution in 0·1 N NaOH, neutralization and reconstitution by 5% NaCl	5—8	10—11
5	Ground collagen	Dissolution in 0·1 N NaOH, neutralization and reconstitution of fibrils by alcohol precipitation	5—8	10—11

Note: Enzyme incubation at 37 °C for 30 min, 0·1 mg/ml enzyme

193

Tables 49 and 50 each reflecting an average value of 40 experiments clearly prove that the accelerated diffusion from the collagen-containing powdered tissues accounts for the intensified dissolution of the collagen protein on the effect of CMPase. However, if the pulverized substance is reconverted into fibrils and these are exposed to CMPase, only a very slight solubilization ensues. These experiments clearly prove that the dehydration of the collagen with acetone or alcohol and its grinding in a hammer mill or its pulverization in any other way fail to result in a denaturation of the collagen. The only effect of the pulverization is a promoted diffusion of the Hypro-containing polypeptide chains after these have been liberated from the collagen. The enzyme is able to exert its effect on the fibrils to the same degree as on the powdered collagen.

CHAPTER XVII

COLLAGENMUCOPROTEINASE AND TRYPSIN ACTIVITY

IN CHAPTER XV (p. 170) our studies on the existence and the mechanism of action of the CMPase were discussed (Banga and Baló 1956, 1962; Banga 1959a, b, 1962a; Baló et al. 1959, 1960; Baló and Banga 1961; Banga et al. 1961a, b).

Here the experiments concerning the problem of the relationship between the activity of CMPase and that of the trypsin are reviewed. Many of our observations suggest that our CMPase preparations, even those separated by electrophoresis, besides being active on collagen, possess a general proteolytic activity, supposedly due to a contamination with elastase. Elastase, having a proteolytic activity 2·5 times greater than has trypsin, may exert a substantial proteolytic effect when present, up to 10 to 15% in a CMPase preparation. On the other hand, the trypsin preparations of several firms were also active against the powdered collagen. Considering these observations one might deny the existence of CMPase as a specific enzyme and attribute the "CMPase effect" to the contaminating trypsin. The observations of Hodge et al. (1960) provided particular interest to this problem. These authors were unable to obtain "segment-long-spacing" (SLS) fibrils on the effect of ATP from tropocollagen solutions after trypsin digestion. Instead the monomers of the individual segments appeared. As an explanation of this effect, it has been assumed (see Chapter X, p 117) that the collagen molecules are held together longitudinally by a tyrosine-containing polypeptide and this is dissolved by trypsin. The liberation of this polypeptide prevents the formation of normal fibrils. Since during our experiments the inhibition of fibril formation was also found to be characteristic of the CMPase effect, the question has arisen which of the trypsin and the specific CMPase accounts for this effect. The problem to be solved, therefore, was, whether there exists a collagen-specific enzyme (CMPase) or not. If not, one should assume that the trypsin would be able to liberate a polypeptide with high Hypro content. This would be acceptable as collagen protein just because of its high Hypro content.

To clarify this question, ten different trypsin preparations of high purity were collected, such as 1. Worthington trypsin, twice cryst., salt-free; 2. Worthington trypsin, twice cryst. + 50% $MgSO_4$; 3. Armour Tryptar; 4. Trypure Novo (3 × 28); 5. Choay trypsine dialysée lyophilisée; 6. Merck trypsin; 7. Light trypsin; 8. Richter trypsin; 9. trypsin supplied by Dr. J. A. Northrop; 10. Boehringer trypsin. These preparations were subjected to various tests (Banga 1963a). We examined their homogeneity by paper electrophoresis at pH 6·5 as well as at pH 8·6. Definitely separating protein spots were obtained at both pH, and no alteration in trypsin was observed at alkaline pH. This is in contrast to the observations of Lewis et al. (1959) who found trypsin to be labile in alkaline media and for this reason did not apply alkaline pH in the separation procedure of either elastase, trypsin or chymotrypsin. Figure 70 shows the electrophoretic patterns of the trypsin preparations tested. For a comparison the pattern of a homogeneous elastase preparation is included in the figure. The different preparations were tested

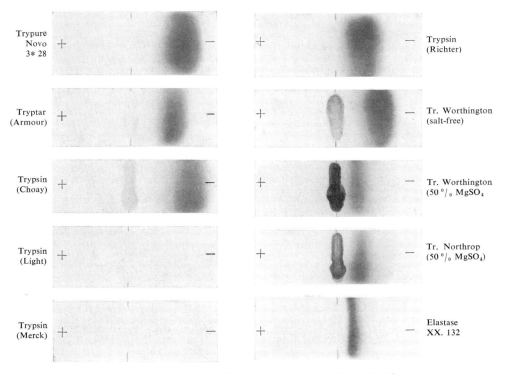

Fig. 70. Paper-electrophoresis of different trypsin preparations. Barbiturate buffer, pH 8·6, 300 V

under identical conditions. The bulk of each of the preparations migrated towards the negative pole, but their mobility was variable. In addition, certain preparations were inhomogeneous, especially those containing salt ($MgSO_4$). The salt-free preparations, namely the Worthington trypsin and the Choay (French) preparation, like the salt-containing preparations, also contained an immobile component. Such a protein component was also present in the crystalline trypsin (with 50% $MgSO_4$ content) kindly supplied by Prof. J. A. Northrop*. The Light and the Merck preparations and all the others showed no stainable protein component on the

* I am grateful to Prof. Northrop for the preparations.

196

paper strip when 2 mg was applied. An analysis of these preparations has shown that they contained 90% inorganic salts and only 10% protein. This composition explains why the protein component was not detectable. Both the mobility and the protein spot of the homogeneous elastase were different from those of the trypsin preparations, the mobility of the former being lower. This is in contrast to the data in the literature suggesting that its isoelectric point (I. P.) is about 9·5 (Lewis et al. 1956, 1959). According to these experiments the bulk of the crystalline trypsin preparations consists of a protein with an I. P. higher than that of the elastase.

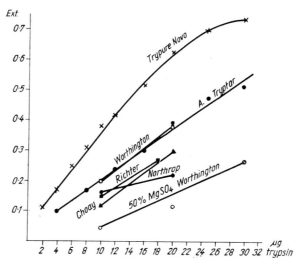

FIG. 71. The concentration curve on BANA substrate of trypsin preparations

Previously (Baló et al. 1959; 1960; Banga et al. 1961a, b) it was found that the mobility of the CMPase exceeds that of the elastase, and this difference made the separation of CMPase from elastase possible. Thus, a protein fraction displaying CMPase activity appears to be a component of most of the trypsin preparations.

In further experiments the activity of the trypsin preparations on the specific trypsin substrate BANA (N-benzoyl-DL-arginine-β-naphthylamide) was compared with that measured on the powdered Achilles tendon. First the enzyme activity curve of the preparations was established using the same BANA concentration under standard experimental conditions. Trypsin activity was assayed by the method of Blackwood and Mandl (1961). Figure 71 shows the concentration curve for seven trypsin preparations. The data for the Merck, Light and Boehringer preparations are not presented because the first two gave no measurable activity in the applied concentration, whereas the activity of the Boehringer trypsin was the same as that of the Choay firm. The elastase prepared either by starch-gel electrophoresis or Sephadex chromatography (Loeven 1963a) showed no activity on the BANA substrate when applied in a quantity of 20 μg. Table 51 presents the BANA activity of different elastase preparations compared with the activity of

14 S.F.E.C.

TABLE 51

Activity of elastase preparations as assayed on BANA preparations

	Elastase preparation	Quantity (μg)	Extinction at 550 mμ
1	No. 590530 (non-crystalline)	20	0·34
2	No. 213/F$_3$ (crystalline)	20	0·25
3	No. XX/132 elastase, homogeneous electrophoretically	20	0·01
4	Same as 3	50	0·10
5	Same as 3	100	0·25
6	Elastomucoproteinase, electrophoretically homogeneous	50	0·08
7	Same as 6	100	0·22
8	Control trypsin Trypure Novo (3 × 28)	20	0·61

the most active trypsin preparation, the Trypure Novo (3 × 28). It is seen that the pure preparations which have been found to be homogeneous when tested by electrophoresis showed a minimal activity even in a concentration of 100 μg. Accordingly, the elastase activity is easily separable from the trypsin activity by this method.

Each of the commercial trypsin preparations showed a collagenolytic activity on the powdered Achilles tendon. However, the degree of this activity varied (Table 52). For the sake of comparison 10, 20, 40 and 100 μg quantities were taken from each trypsin preparation and when by our method (Banga et al. 1961a) a substantial dissolution was demonstrable during 30 minutes, the gravimetrical assay was applied. In the case of low concentrations (10 and 20 μg) the protein dissolved in the supernatant was determined according to Lowry et al. (1951) with the Folin reagent; for this assay the standard curve was established on the basis of Kjeldahl values. The relationship between trypsin concentration and collagenolysis was linear only within narrow limits. The activities were calculated from these parts of the curves. The value

TABLE 52

CMPase activity of different trypsin preparations at 37 °C and 25 °C

Trypsin preparation	Collagenmucoproteinase unit/mg	
	37 °C	25 °C
Trypure Novo (3 × 28)	108	155
Armour Tryptar	220	75
Worthington (salt-free)	265	185
Northrop Trypsin	110	105
Choay Trypsin	65	77
Richter Trypsin	120	110
Merck Trypsin	10	15
Light Trypsin	10	10
Boehringer Trypsin	75	78

of the intersection of the prolonged straight line with the Y axis as zero value was substracted from the obtained values. Table 52 presents the activity of nine trypsin preparations at 25 °C and 37 °C expressed in CMPase units. Several preparations (Trypure Novo, Armour Tryptar and Worthington trypsin) showed different activities at the two different temperatures, the others (six preparations) gave equal values. These results fail to confirm the almost general opinion that the collagen protein would be denatured at 37 °C and the denaturation would make it more readily digestible by trypsin.

In the following the relative BANA activity of the trypsin preparations was compared with their relative CMPase activity determined on powdered Achilles tendon (Table 53). The highest activity measured on each of the substrates was taken as 100 and the relative activity of the other preparations was expressed in per cent. We assumed that a close agreement in the relative activities would indicate the identity of the mechanism of the specific trypsin activity (on the BANA) and of the collagenolytic activity. In the case of such an agreement both enzymes would belong to the same enzyme species. However, the data in Table 53 show that the relative activities measured on the two different substrates do not coincide. On the BANA substrate the Trypure Novo (3×28) preparation of the Danish firm Novo was the most active (100), whereas on the Achilles tendon the salt-free Worthington trypsin gave the highest activity. The activity of the latter preparation on the BANA substrate was as low as 58%. For the same substrate the activity of the CMPase preparation isolated by us was 30%, whereas on Achilles tendon as substrate this preparation was as active as the Worthington trypsin (100%).

These data indicate that the activity of the trypsin on BANA and the CMPase activity of the trypsin preparations cannot be attributed to the same enzyme function. For the independence of the latter from the former it would be a reasonable explanation to assume that the different trypsin preparations are contaminated with different amounts of CMPase. It might be assumed alternatively that the trypsin molecule has two active groups, one of which is responsible for the decomposition of the BANA, whereas the other for splitting off the heteropolysaccharide-containing mucoid$_2$. Since in the latter reaction mainly ester bonds are split, it would not be surprising if the ester-splitting effect of the trypsin played a part in this reaction.

TABLE 53

Relative activity of different trypsin preparations on BANA substrate and powdered Achilles tendon

Trypsin preparation	Relative activity (25 °C)	
	BANA	Achilles tendon
Trypure Novo (3×28)	100	88
Armour Tryptar	63	40
Worthington (salt-free)	58	100
Northrop Trypsin	46	40
Choay Trypsin	34	42
Richter Trypsin	41	54
Merck Trypsin	0	13
Light Trypsin	0	5
CMPase Trypsin	30	100

14*

According to Hodge et al. (1960) peptide tails with high tyrosine content are responsible for the longitudinal coupling of the collagen molecule and the corresponding linkages are attackable by trypsin. According to Kühn et al. (1961), on the other hand, the hexose and hexosamine content of the collagen diminishes during trypsin digestion. All these findings support our observations in connection with the mechanism of CMPase action. It is also possible that the CMPase effect is composed of two different enzyme activities, viz. a specific effect in the course of which mucoid$_2$ is liberated and the residual collagen molecule becomes labile and sensitive to the second effect, viz. the proteolytic activity of the trypsin.

EFFECT OF TRYPSIN INHIBITORS ON THE BANA ACTIVITY OF TRYPSIN
AND THE COLLAGENASE ACTIVITY OF CMPASE

The identity or distinctness of the activities of different trypsin preparations on the BANA and the powdered Achilles tendon can also be studied by a comparison of the effects displayed by different trypsin inhibitors on the two activities. If the two enzymatic effects are inhibited to the same degree under identical experimental conditions by a trypsin inhibitor, the two effects may be attributed to the same active group, viz. the group which is attacked by the inhibitor. If, however, the two activities are inhibited to different degrees, the active groups are probably different.

We examined the inhibitory effect of three well-defined trypsin inhibitors on both BANA and CMPase activities of two different trypsin preparations (Banga and Mayláth-Palágyi 1963). The following trypsin preparations were used: 1. Worthington trypsin, twice cryst., salt-free. This preparation showed the highest CMPase activity (100%) (Table 53). 2. Trypure Novo (3 × 28) which was the most active among the preparations on BANA. The inhibitors were: 1. highly-purified ovomucoid; 2. crystalline soy-bean inhibitor; 3. non crystalline soy-bean inhibitor.

TABLE 54

Inhibition of the activity of the Worthington Trypsin on BANA by trypsin inhibitors in McIlvaine buffer

Enzyme	Enzyme : inhibitor ratio	Percentage inhibition		
		Ovomucoid	Soy$^+$	Soy^{++}
Worthington Trypsin 20 μg	1 : 0·2	28	35	27
Worthington Trypsin 20 μg	1 : 0·4	56	47	33
Worthington Trypsin 20 μg	1 : 0·6	70	59	52
Worthington Trypsin 20 μg	1 : 0·8	78	67	75
Worthington Trypsin 20 μg	1 : 1·0	84	75	79

Note: + = crystalline; + + = non-crystalline

200

(We are grateful to Dr. I. Mandl, Columbia University, New York, for the trypsin preparations and the inhibitors).

In our experiments concentration curves were taken for the inhibitors in the presence of a standard enzyme concentration (20 μg). In the case of the highest

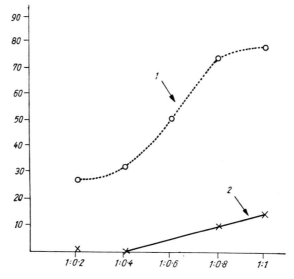

FIG. 72. Effect of the soy-bean inhibitor on the BANA (1) and CMPase (2) activity of the Worthington trypsin. Abscissa = enzyme inhibitor ratio; ordinate = percentage inhibition

concentration of each of the inhibitors the ratio of enzyme to inhibitor was 1 : 1. The activity-inhibition experiments on the BANA as substrate showed that the degree of inhibition by the three different inhibitors on the two trypsin preparations varied only slightly. The degree of inhibition increased together with the concentration of the inhibitor. At the 1 : 1 ratio of the enzyme to the inhibitor the values of the inhibition fluctuated between 75 and 84% (Table 54). In contrast to this, the enzyme activity on the Achilles tendon was slightly inhibited by the above inhibitors. At the 1 : 1 ratio the maximal inhibition was 15% (Table 55). In certain buffer systems, such as Tris and Na_2CO_3-HCl, the inhibition was of a higher degree, but even these values were lower than those measured on BANA as substrate. In Fig. 72 the inhibition of the two activities of the Worthington trypsin

TABLE 55

Inhibition of the CMPase activity of the Worthington Trypsin on Achilles tendon as substrate in McIlvaine buffer

Enzyme	Enzyme : inhibitor ratio	Percentage inhibition	
		Ovomucoid	Soy-bean
		Inhibitor	
	1 : 0·1	0	0
	1 : 0·2	0	0
Worthington Trypsin	1 : 0·4	0	0
	1 : 0·8	10	10
	1 : 1·0	15	15

201

by the soy-bean inhibitor is illustrated. These experiments supply further arguments supporting our theory proposing that the specific activity of the trypsin preparations is not identical with their CMPase activity. The two activities are bound either to two different enzyme-protein components or to two different active groups of the trypsin molecule. If the same active group were responsible for both activities, the relative inhibition values would have to be equal at a constant ratio of the enzyme to the inhibitor.

Collagenmucoproteinase and Metacollagenase

As it is clear from Chapter XIII. (p. 151) the term metacollagen covers the relaxed fibre prepared from the collagen fibre by chemical substances. In an earlier stage of our studies we obtained a collagen preparation by heating Achilles tendon for a short period (2 to 5 minutes); from such preparations only 5 to 8%, the so-called mucoid$_1$ (Banga and Baló 1954), passes into solution. At that time we thought that this preparation was also metacollagen. In the following experiments this preparation was used as metacollagen.

For this series of experiments the "metacollagen" prepared from the Achilles tendon was ground into powder and it was compared with a pulverized preparation obtained from untreated Achilles tendon. We assumed that in case the Achilles tendon is denatured while being ground, it must become as digestible with trypsin as metacollagen (Banga 1963b). The results in Table 56 clearly show that the activity of the same trypsin preparation on metacollagen as substrate (metacollagenase activity) is 3 to 10 times the activity measured on the pulverized collagen (CMPase activity). The specific enzyme activity is expressed in the unit used before,

TABLE 56

CMPase and metacollagenase activities of different trypsin preparations

Trypsin preparations	Specific enzyme activity		Trypsin preparations	Specific enzyme activity	
	CMPase	Meta-collagenase		CMPase	Meta-collagenase
Trypure Novo (3 × 28)	110	1150	Choay Trypsin	70	750
Armour Tryptar	220	600	Richter Trypsin	170	1100
Worthington Trypsin			Merck Trypsin	10	200
(salt-free)	270	750	Light Trypsin	5	50
Northrop Trypsin	110	460	Isolated CMPase*	270	1400

Note: Specific activity calculated from the enzyme-concentration curve for 1 mg enzyme

* = obtained from Decalso-purified elastase-enzyme complex by starch-gel electrophoresis.

202

i.e. mg collagen solubilized by 1 mg of the enzyme protein during a period of 30 minutes (Banga et al. 1961b).

The highest specific metacollagenase activity was shown by the CMPase preparation isolated in our laboratory by starch-gel electrophoresis. The value of this preparation was 1400 in contrast with the 270 measured on powdered Achilles tendon. Accordingly, CMPase is five times more active on the metacollagen than on the collagen. The activity of the different trypsin preparations measured on the powdered Achilles tendon as substrate were different from that of the same preparations measured on metacollagen as substrate. The relative activities do not cover each other (Table 57). Our CMPase was the only preparation that exerted

TABLE 57

Comparative data on the relative CMPase and metacollagenase activities of different trypsin preparations

Trypsin preparations	Relative activities		Trypsin preparations	Relative activities	
	CMPase	Meta-collagenase		CMPase	Meta-collagenase
Trypure Novo (3 × 28)	88	82	Choay Trypsin	42	54
Armour Tryptar	40	43	Richter Trypsin	54	79
Worthington Trypsin			Merck Trypsin	13	20
(salt-free)	100	54	Light Trypsin	5	5
Northrop Trypsin	40	33	Isolated CMPase	100	100

maximal activity on both substrates. It was of great interest and striking that the CMPase activity of the Worthington trypsin was equal to that of the CMPase isolated by us (100%), whereas its metacollagenase activity was as low as 54%. In metacollagenase activity the Trypure Novo preparation approximated the CMPase most closely. The same preparation was also highly active on the Achilles tendon and on BANA. It can be stated that the CMPase activity is not identical with the metacollagen activity. Consequently, the two substrates, viz. the pulverized Achilles tendon and the metacollagen prepared from the former are not identical "denatured" collagen proteins.

It is likely that a distinct active group is responsible for the metacollagenase activity of the CMPase, just like another for the activity of the same preparation on the Achilles tendon. As a result of the first effect the ester bonds of the collagen-bound $mucoid_2$ are split; the $mucoid_2$ content of the metacollagen is equal to that of the native tendon. The second effect results in splitting the peptide bonds which have become labile by the removal of $mucoid_2$. Obviously, in the metacollagen this secondary effect is more pronounced because from this substance the $mucoid_1$ passed into solution during the preceding thermal or chemical relaxation, whereas in the CMPase-treated Achilles tendon a polypeptide chain has been left behind which still contains mucoid$_1$. On an exposure to a thermal or chemical effect the latter will pass into solution rapidly and completely, indicating that complete solubilization of the insoluble collagen does not ensue unless both mucoid$_1$ and mucoid$_2$ have been split off. The order in which the two mucoids are removed is of no importance. If first mucoid$_1$ is liberated, the resulting metacollagen can be solubilized by CMPase which is active on mucoid$_2$, whereas if the mucoid$_2$ has been removed by CMPase every effect which leads to the formation of metacollagen will accomplish the solubilization.

SUMMARY

Whilst the verification of the complex morphological and chemical construction of the elastic fibre could not be recognized until the elastolytic enzymes were discovered, the complex structure of the collagen fibre was demonstrated by its special physicochemical and chemical characteristics. For the separation of soluble collagen from the insoluble one the classical physicochemical methods proved to be satisfactory and the existence of these components was evidenced without any enzyme.

While the electron-microscopic methods emphasize mainly the submicroscopic structure of the soluble collagens, we made efforts in this book to emphasize the functional role of these structures. According to our hypothesis, in the integrant collagen fibre which is capable of functioning the soluble and insoluble components and the mucoids playing a part in the stabilization of the former are of equal importance. In old age and in connection with the diseases of the connective tissue the physicochemical characteristics and the relative amounts of these components are altered.

The characteristics of the collagen which are manifested in its chemical contraction-relaxation in certain lyotropic substances are discussed in the light of polarization microscopy. A new morphological entity, the metacollagen, has been introduced. Besides the soluble collagens this is the most characteristic and, on the basis of its reactions, the best-defined form of the insoluble collagen. Whilst collastromin as an insoluble type of collagen can only be isolated from the skin, metacollagen can be prepared from isolated collagen fibres. It is a type of collagen fibre in which the fibrillar structure is held together by a mucoid substance identical with the mucoid$_2$. Mucoid$_1$, the substance which is released in the course of the thermal and chemical contraction has also been described. The existence of a new enzyme, the collagenmucoproteinase or CMPase which acts on the native collagen is assumed in our enzymological study. Polarization-optical studies connected with chemical contraction-relaxation have provided satisfactory evidence that this enzyme attacks the untreated collagen fibres and alters their submicroscopic composition. We succeeded in proving by biochemical experiments that the component solubilized by the enzyme in the initial phase is a mucoid substance. We have termed this substance mucoid$_2$. This is present in every type of connective tissue. In its composition mainly neutral mucopolysaccharides (MPS) play a part besides a little amount of acid MPS.

On the collagen fibres the CMPase exerts primarily a mucolytic effect, whereas on the powdered collagen-containing tissues it acts as a true collagenase. This property of the enzyme may be in relation with the fact that CMPase is present in every trypsin preparation and it has never been separated from trypsin. On the other hand, the CMPase effect is not identical with the effect of the trypsin on benzoyl-arginine-β-naphthylamide (BANA). We suppose that either the trypsin molecule has an active group that possesses also CMPase activity or the trypsin and the CMPase are so closely related to each other physicochemically that neither of them can be separated from the other completely. Anyhow, the effect exerted on the collagen powders should be considered a true collagenase effect. Consequently, we are convinced that in the animal (and human) pancreas an enzyme is produced which is capable of attacking the native collagen.

In our further studies the demonstration of the effect of this enzyme on the sub-microscopic structure of the collagen is considered to be the most significant step.

BIBLIOGRAPHY

ABDERHALDEN, E. and SCHITTENHELM, A. (1904): *Z. physiol. Chem.* **41** 293

ADAIR, G. S., DAVIS, H. F. and PARTRIDGE, S. M. (1951): *Nature (Lond.)* **167** 605

(ALEKSEYEVA) Алексеева, А. Щ. (1956): *Шезисы докладов к конференции по проблеме атеросклероз и коронарная недостаточность.* Москва, p. 17

— (1959): *Симпозиум по проблеме атеросклероза.* Ленинград, p. 4

AMATI, A. and CASTELLI, B. (1961): *Ital. J. Biochem.* **10** 292

AMBROSE, E. J. and ELLIOT, A. (1951): *Proc. roy. Soc. A* **208** 75

ANDREEWA, N. S., DEBABOV, V. A., MILLINOVA, M. I. SHIBNEV, V. A. and CHIRGADZE, Y. N. (1961): *Biofizika* (Moscow) **6** 244

ANITSCHKOW, N. (1925): *Ergebn. inn. Med. Kinderheilk.* **28** 1

— (1928): *Verh. dtsch. path. Ges.* **23** 473

— (1934): *C. R. 2nd Conf. Intern. Pathol. Geogr. Utrecht,* p. 44

ANITSCHKOW, N. and CHALATOW, S. (1913): *Zbl. allg. Path. path. Anat.* **24** 1

ASTBURY, W. T. (1938): *Kolloid Z.* **83** 130

— (1940): *J. Intern. Soc. Leather Trades Chemists* **24** 69

BAGDY, D. and BANGA, I. (1957): *Acta physiol. Acad. Sci. hung.* **11** 64

— (1958): *Experientia (Basel)* **14** 64

BAGDY, D., BANGA, I. and HORVÁTH, M. (1958): *Kísérl. Orvostud.* **10** 590

BAGDY, D., FALK, M. B. and TOLNAY, P. (1961): *Abstr. Papers 5th Intern. Congr. Biochem. Moscow,* p. 102

— (1962): *Acta physiol. Acad. Sci. hung.* **21** 123

BAGDY, D., TOLNAY, P., BORSY, J. and KOVÁCS, K. (1960): *Magy. Tud. Akad. Biol. Orv. Oszt. Közl.* **11** 277

BAHR, G. F. (1951): *Arch. Derm. Syph. (Chic.)* **193** 518

BALÓ, J. (1938): *Frankfurt. Z. Path.* **52** 205

— (1939a): *Beitr. path. Anat.* **102** 341

— (1939b): *Verh. d. Ges. Ungarischer Path.* **8** 133

— (1949): *Atti del 1° Convegno della Società Italiana di Anatomia Patologica Bologna* 137

— (1951): *Acta morph. Acad. Sci. hung.* **1** 255

— (1957): *Ciba Found. Colloqu. Aging* **3** 101

— (1958): *Magy. Tud. Akad. Biol. Orv. Oszt. Közl.* **9** 425

— (1963): *Intern. Rev. Conn.Tiss. Res.* Ed: Hall, D. A. Acad. Press, New York—London **1** 241

BALÓ, J. and BANGA, I. (1948): *Orv. Hetil.* **89** 465

— (1949a): *Orv. Hetil.* **90** 45

— (1949b): *Schweiz. Z. allg. Path.* **12** 350

— (1949c): *Nature (Lond.)* **164** 491

— (1950): *Biochem. J.* **46** 384

— (1953a): *Nature (Lond.)* **178** 310

— (1953b): *Acta physiol. Acad. Sci. hung.* **4** 187

— (1955): *Abstr. 3rd Intern. Congr. Biochem. Brussels.* 14—3

— (1962): *Medical and Clinical Aspects of Aging.* Ed: Blumenthal, H. T. Columbia Univ. Press, New York—London p. 357

Baló, J., Banga, I. and Bagdy, D. (1959): *Magyar Kémiai Folyóirat* **65** 89
Baló, J. Banga, I. and Schuler, D. (1954): *Acta morph. Acad. Sci. hung.* **4** 141
Baló, J. Banga, I. and Szabó, D. (1956): *Magy. Tud. Akad. Biol. Orv. Oszt. Közl.* **7** 385
Baló, J., Szabó, D. and Banga, I. (1960): *Acta histochem. (Jena)* **9** 69
Baló, J., Banga, I., Juhász, J., Szabó, D. and Szalay, E. (1957): *Gerontologia (Basel)* **1** 316
Banfield, W. G. (1952): *Anat. Rec.* **114** 157
— (1956): *J. Geront.* **11** 372
Banga, I. (1949a): *Kísérl. Orvostud.* **1** 143
— (1949b): *Intern. Congr. Biochem. Cambridge, Engl. Abstr. Commun.* 122 (1952): *Chem. Abstr.* **46** 7142
— (1951): *Z. Vitamin-, Hormon- u. Fermentforsch.* **4** 49
— (1952): *Acta physiol. Acad. Sci. hung.* **3** 317
— (1953): *Nature (Lond.)* **172** 1099
— (1954): *Acta morph. Acad. Sci. hung. Suppl.* **4** 2
— (1955): *Abstr. 3rd Intern. Congr. Biochem. Brussels* 4—8
— (1956a): *Thesis,* Budapest p. 62
— (1956b): *Schweiz. med. Wschr.* **86** 1045
— (1957): *Gerontologia (Basel)* **1** 325
— 1959a): *Acta morph. Acad. Sci. hung.* **8** 8
— (1959b): *Acta biol. Acad. Sci. hung. Suppl.* **3** 38
— (1960): *Acta physiol. Acad. Sci. hung. Suppl.* **18** 43
— (1962a): *Congress on Rheumatology in Piestany, Czechoslovakia.* Státni Zdravotnické Nakladatelstvi, p. 358
— (1962b): *Biochem. J.* **84** 116 P
— (1963a): *Acta physiol. Acad. Sci. hung.* **24** 1
— (1963b): *Acta physiol. Acad. Sci. hung.* **24** 137
— (1963c): *Abstr. I. Gen. Assembly of Hung. Ass. Biochem.* p. 25
— (1963d): *Expos. ann. Biochim. méd.* **24** 151
Banga, I. and Baló, J. (1950): *Kísérl. Orvostud.* **2** 271
— (1954): *Acta physiol. Acad. Sci. hung.* **6** 235
— (1956): *Nature (Lond.)* **178** 310
— (1957): *Connective Tissue Symposium of CIOMS.* Blackwell Scient. Publ., Oxford, p. 254
— (1959): *Acta physiol. Acad. Sci. hung.* **15** 127
— (1960a): *Biochem. J.* **74** 388
— (1960b): *Biochim. biophys. Acta (Amst.)* **40** 367
— (1961a): *Acta physiol. Acad. Sci. hung.* **20** 237
— (1961b): *Acta physiol. Acad. Sci. hung.* **20** 249
— (1961c): *Z. Vitamin-, Hormon- u. Fermentforsch.* **12** 59
— (1962): *Acta physiol. Acad. Sci. hung.* **21** 301
Banga, I. and Horváth, M. (1960): *Acta physiol. Acad. Sci. hung.* **17** 265
Banga, I. and Mayláth-Palágyi, J. (1963): *Acta physiol. Acad. Sci. hung.* **24** 151
Banga, I. and Schuler, D. (1953): *Acta physiol. Acad. Sci. hung.* **4** 13
Banga, I. and Szabó, D. (1965): *Acta morph. Acad. Sci. hung.* **13** 255
Banga, I., Bagdy, D. and Hegyeli, E. (1957): *Acta physiol. Acad. Sci. hung. Suppl.* **11** 36
Banga, I., Baló, J. and Horváth, M. (1959): *Biochem. J.* **71** 544
Banga, I., Baló, J. and Nowotny, A. (1949): *Z. Vitamin-, Hormon- u. Fermentforsch.* **2** 408
Banga, I., Baló, J. and Szabó, D. (1954 a): *Nature (Lond.)* **174** 788
— (1956a): *Acta physiol. Acad. Sci. hung.* **9** 61
— (1956b): *Acta morph. Acad. Sci. hung.* **6** 391
— (1956c): *J. Geront.* **11** 242
— (1956d): *Symposion über experimentelle Altersforschung. Experientia (Basel) Suppl.* **4** 28
— (1961a): *Seminar on Collagen.* Madras Intersci. Coll. 88032
— (1961b): *Acta physiol. Acad. Sci. hung.* **19** 19

BANGA, I., LOEVEN, W. A. and ROMHÁNYI, GY. *Acta morph. Acad. Sci. hung.* **13** 385
BANGA, I., MAYLÁTH-PALÁGYI, J. and JOBBÁGY, A. (1965): *Acta physiol. Acad. Sci. hung.* **26** 305
— (1966): *Kisérl. Orvostud.* **18** 189
BANGA, I., SCHULER, D. and LÁSZLÓ, J. (1954b): *Acta physiol. Acad. Sci. hung.* **5** 1
BEAR, R. S. (1942): *J. Amer. chem. Soc.* **64** 727
BECKER, A. (1962): *Abstr. Papers Pres. Collagen Symp. 2nd Intern. Cong. Sci. Soc. Leather Shoe and Allied Industr. in Hungary,* October 3—6
BERNFELD, P. (1958): In: *Lipoprotein Methods and their Clinical Significance.* Ed: Homburger, P. and Bernfeld, P. S. Karger, Basel—New York, p. 24
BERTELSEN, S. (1961a): *Acta path. microbiol. scand.* **51** 206
— (1961b): *Acta path. microbiol. scand.* **51** 229
BIHARI-VARGA, M. GERGELY, J. and GERŐ, S. (1963): *Orv. Hetil.* **104** 1401
BLACKWOOD, C. and MANDL, I. (1961): *Anal. Biochem.* **2** 370
BLIX, G. (1948): *Acta chem. scand.* **2** 467
BLOCK, R. J., DURRUM, E. L. and ZWEIG, G. (1956): *H. Manual of Paper Chromatography and Paper Electrophoresis.* Academic Press Inc., New York
BLOOR, W. R. (1943): *Biochemistry of the Fatty Acids.* Reinhold, New York, p. 45
BLUMENTHAL, H. T., LANSING, A. I. and WHEELER, P. A. (1944): *Amer. J. Path.* **20** 665
BOEDTKER, H. and DOTY, P. (1955): *J. Amer. chem. Soc.* **77** 248
BORSY, J., CSÁK, ZS. A., LÁZÁR, I. and BAGDY, D. (1959): *Acta physiol. Acad. Sci. hung.* **15** 345
BOUCEK, R. J. and NOBLE, N. L. (1959): In Lansing: *The Arterial Wall.* Williams, Wilkins Co., Baltimore p. 207
BOWES, J. H. and KENTEN, R. R. (1948): *Biochem. J.* **43** 358
— (1949): *Biochem. J.* **45** 281
BOWES, J. H. and MOSS, J. A. (1951): *Nature (Lond.)* **168** 514
— (1953): *Biochem. J.* **55** 735
BRAGDON, J. H. (1951): *J. biol. Chem.* **190** 513
BRESSLER, S. E., FILOGENOV, P. A. and FRENKEL, S. Y. (1950): *Dokl. Akad. Nauk SSSR* **72** 555
BUDDECKE, E. (1958a): *Z. physiol. Chem.* **310** 171
— (1958b): *Z. physiol. Chem.* **310** 182
— (1958c): *Z. physiol. Chem.* **310** 199
— (1960): *Z. physiol. Chem.* **318** 33
BURK, N. F. and GREENBERG, D. M. (1930): *J. biol. Chem.* **87** 197
BURTON, D., HALL, D. A., KEECH, M. K., REED, R., SAXL, H., TUNBRIDGE, R. E. and WOOD, M. J. (1955): *Nature (Lond.)* **176** 960
BUTTURINI, U. and GNUDI, A. (1959): *Boll. Soc. ital. Biol. sper.* **35** 28
BUTTURINI, U. and LANGER, M. (1962): *Klin. Wschr.* **40** 472
BUTTURINI, U., GIRO, C. and LANGER, M. (1959a): *Boll. Soc. ital. Biol. sper.* **35** 30
BUTTURINI, U., MAGNANI, B. and COCHERI, S. (1958): *Boll. Soc. ital. Biol. sper.* **34** 14
BUTTURINI, U. PRETOLANI, E. and GNUDI, A. (1959b): *Boll. Soc. ital. Biol. sper.* **35** 27
BUZÁGH, A. (1960): *Kolloid Z.* **169** 72

CAMPAGNARI, F. and GREGGIA, G. (1959): *Minerva med.* **50** 2899
CARTER, A. E. (1956): *Science* **123** 669
CHIBNAL, A. C. (1946): *Soc. Leather Trades Chem.* **30** 1
CHVAPIL, M. and ZAHRADNIK, R. (1960): *Biochim. biophys. Acta* **40** 329
CITI, S., LEONE, O., SALVINI, L., GRANDONICO, F. and VIOLA, S. (1960): *G. Geront.* **8** 581
CLAESSON, S. (1946): *Arh. Kemi. Min. Geol.* **23** A 1
COHEN, H., MEGEL, H. and KLEINBERG, W. (1958): *Proc. Soc. exp. Biol. (N. Y.)* **97** 8
COLVIN, J. R., SMITH, D. B. and COOK, W. A. (1954): *Chem. Rev.* **54** 687
COMPTE, P., BAZIN, S. and DELAUNAY, A. (1961): *Ann. Inst. Pasteur* **101** 185

COWAN, P. M. and McGAVIN, S. (1955): *Nature (Lond.)* **176** 264

COX, R. C. and LITTLE, K. (1961): *Proc. roy. Soc. B* **155** 232

CZERKAWSKI, J. W. (1958): *Abstr. Comm. 4th Int. Congr. Biochem. Vienna* **4**—45 43

— (1962): *Nature (Lond.)* **194** 869

CZERKAWSKI, J. W. and HALL, D. A. (1958): *Biochem. J.* **70** 6 P

DEASY, C. (1956): *J. Amer. Leather Chemists Ass.* **51** 584

DEES, M. B. (1923): *Anat. Rec.* **26** 169

DELAUNAY, A., BAZIN, S. and HENON, M. (1955): *C. R. Acad. Sci.* **241** 826

DELAUNAY, A., BAZIN, S., FAUVE, R. and HENON, M. (1956): *Rec. franç. Clin. Biol.* **1** 165

DEMPSEY, E. W., VIAL, J. D., LUCAS, R. V. and LANSING, A. I. (1952): *Anat. Rec.* **113** 197

DETTMER, N. (1952): *Z. Zellforsch.* **37** 89

— (1956): *Z. Zellforsch.* **45** 265

DETTMER, N., NECKEL, I. and RUSKA, H. H. (1951): *Z. Mikrosk.* **60** 290

DISCHE, Z. (1950): *J. biol. Chem.* **183** 489

DISCHE, Z., DANILCZENKO, A. G. and ZELMENIS, G. (1958): In: *Chemistry and Biology of Mucopolysaccharides.* Ciba Foundation Symp. London, p. 116

DOTY, P. and NISHIHARA, T. (1958): In: *Recent Advances in Gelatin and Glue Research.* Ed: Stainsby, G. Pergamon Press, New York, p. 92

DVONCH, W. and ALBURN, H. E. (1959): *Arch. Biochem.* **79** 146

DYRBYE, M. (1959): *J. Geront.* **14** 32

DYRBYE, M. and KIRK, J. E. (1957): *J. Geront.* **12** 20

DYRBYE, M., KIRK, J. E. and WANG, I. (1958): *J. Geront.* **13** 149

EASTOE, J. K. (1955): *Biochem. J.* **61** 589

EBNER, VON, (1894): *Sitzungsb. d. k. Akad. d. Wissensch. Math. Naturw. Cl. Wien* **103** 162

EIJKMAN, O. (1903): *Zbl. Bakt. I. Abt. Orig.* **35** 1

ELDEN, H. R. (1959): *Nature (Lond.)* **183** 332

ELDEN, H. R. and BOUCEK, R. J. (1959): *J. polym. Sci.* **41** 13

ELDEN, H. R. and CASSAC, B. (1962): *J. polym. Sci.* **59** 283

ELDEN, H. R. and WEBB, G. (1961): *Nature (Lond.)* **192** 742

ELSON, L. A. and MORGAN, W. T. J. (1935): *Biochem. J.* **27** 1824

EWALD, A. (1890): *Z. Biol.* **26** 1

EWALD, A. and KÜHNE, J. (1878): *Verh. Naturhist. Med. Vereins. Heidelberg* **1** 451

FINDLAY, G. H. (1954): *Brit. J. Derm.* **66** 16

FRANCHI, C. M. and DE ROBERTIS, E. (1951): *Proc. Soc. exp. Biol. (N. Y.)* **76** 515

FREY-WISSLING, A. (1953): *Submicroscopic Morphology of Protoplasm.* Elsevier Publ. Co., Amsterdam—Houston—London—New York

GALLOP, P. M., BLUMENFELD, O., FRANZBLAU, C. and SEIFTER, S. (1962): *Abstr. Spring Meeting Amer. chem. Soc.* March 21

GALLOP, P. M., SEIFTER, S. and MEILMAN, E. (1959): *Nature (Lond.)* **183** 1659

GERŐ, S. (1963): *Thesis*, Budapest

GERŐ, S., GERGELY, J., JAKAB, L. SZÉKELY, J. and VIRÁG, S. (1961a): *J. Atheroscler. Res.* **1** 88

— (1961b): *Orv. Hetil.* **102** 1165

GERŐ, S., GERGELY, G., DÉVÉNYI, T., JAKAB, L., SZÉKELY, J. and VIRÁG, S. (1960): *Nature (Lond.)* **187** 152

— (1961c): *J. Atheroscler. Res.* **1** 67

GERŐ, S., GERGELY, J., JAKAB, L., SZÉKELY, J., VIRÁG, S., FARKAS, K. and CUPPON, A. (1959): *Lancet* July 4 issue 6—7

GERŐ, S., GERGELY, J., FARKAS, K., DÉVÉNYI, T., KOCSAR, L., JAKAB, L., SZÉKELY, J. and VIRÁG, S. (1962): *J. Atheroscler. Res.* **2** 276

GILFILLAN, R. F., SBARRA, H. J. and BARDAWIL, W. A. (1960): *Fed. Proc.* **19** 144
— (1961): *Fed. Proc.* **20** 161
GOTTE, L., STERN, PENELOPE, ELSDEN, D. F. and PARTRIDGE, S. M. (1963): *Biochem. J.* **87** 344
GOTTSCHLICH, E. (1893): *Pflügers Arch. ges. Physiol.* **54** 109
GRAHAM, G. N. (1958): *Ph. D. Thesis*, University of Leeds
— (1960): *Biochem. J.* **75** 14 P
GRANDONICO, F., VIOLA, S., CITI, S., SALVINI, L. and LEONE, O. (1960): *G. Geront.* **8** 596
GRANT, N. H. and ROBBINS, K. C. (1955): *Proc. Soc. exp. Biol. (N. Y.)* **90** 264
— (1957): *Arch. Biochem. Biophys.* **66** 396
GRASSMANN, W. (1936): *Kolloid. Z.* **77** 1
— (1955): *Leder* **6** 241
GRASSMANN, W. and HÖRMANN, H. (1953): *Z. physiol. Chem.* **292** 24
GRASSMANN, W. and KÜHN, K. (1955): *Z. physiol. Chem.* **301** 1
GRASSMANN, W. and KUSCH, D. (1952): *Z. physiol. Chem.* **290** 216
GRASSMANN, W. and SCHLEICH, H. (1935): *Biochem. Z.* **277** 320
GRASSMANN, W., HANNIG, K. and ENGEL, J. (1961): *Z. physiol. Chem.* **324** 284
GRASSMANN, W., HANNIG, K. and SCHLEYER, M. (1960): *Z. physiol. Chem.* **322** 71
GRASSMANN, W., HÖRMANN, H. and ENDRES, H. (1953): *Chem. Ber.* **86** 1477
— (1955): *Chem. Ber.* **88** 102
GRASSMANN, W., NORDWIG, A. and HÖRMANN, H. (1961a): *Z. physiol. Chem.* **323** 48
GRASSMANN, W., HANNIG, K., ENDRES, H. and RIEDEL, A. (1956): *Z. physiol. Chem.* **306** 123
GRASSMANN, W., HOFMAN, U., KÜHN, K., HÖRMAN, H., ENDRES, H. and WOLF, K (1957): In: *Connective Tissues*. Ed: Tunbridge, R. E. Blackwell Scient. Publ., Oxford, p. 157
GROSS, J. (1949): *J. exp. Med.* **89** 699
— (1958): *J. exp. Med.* **108** 215
GROSS, J. and KIRK, D. (1958): *J. biol. Chem.* **233** 355
GROSS, J., HIGHBERGER, J. H. and SCHMITT, F. O. (1952): *Proc. Soc. exp. Biol. (N. Y.)* **80** 462
— (1954): *Proc. nat. Acad. Sci. (Wash.)* **40** 679
GUISEPPE, DE, L. and CASTELLI, B. (1957): *Boll. Soc. ital. Biol. sper.* **33** 1382
GUSTAVSON, K. H. (1926): *Colloid. Symposium Monograph.* **4** 79
— (1942): *Biochem. Z.* **311** 347
— (1956): *The Chemistry and Reactivity of Collagen*. Academic Press, New York
— (1958): In: *Recent Advances in Gelatin and Glue Research*. Ed: Stainsby, G. Pergamon Press, New York, p. 259

HALL, C. E., JAKUS, M. A. and SCHMITT, F. O. (1942): *J. Amer. chem. Soc.* **64** 1234
HALL, D. A. (1953): *Biochem. J.* **55** 35
— (1954): *Old Age in the Modern World*. (Report of the 3rd Congr. of intern. Ass. of Geront.) E. S. Livingstone Ltd., Edinburgh—London, p. 165
— (1955): *Arch. Biochem.* **59** 459
— (1957a): *Arch. Biochem. Biophys.* **67** 366
— (1957b): *Connect. Tiss. Symp. CIOMS*. Blackwell Scient. Publ., Oxford, p. 238
— (1958): *Biochem. J.* **70** 5 P
— (1961a): *J. Atheroscler. Res.* **1** 173
— (1961b): *Biochem. J.* **78** 49
— (1961c): *The Chemistry of Connective Tissue*. Charles C. Thomas, Springfield—Illinois
HALL, D. A. and CZERKAWSKI, J. W. (1959): *Biochem. J.* **73** 356
— (1961a): *Biochem. J.* **80** 121
— (1961b): *Biochem. J.* **80** 128
— (1961c): *Biochem. J.* **80** 134
HALL, D. A. and GARDINER, J. E. (1955): *Biochem. J.* **59** 465
HALL, D. A., REED, R. and TUNBRIDGE, R. E. (1952): *Nature (Lond.)* **170** 1264

HALL, D. A., TUNBRIDGE, R. E. and WOOD, G. C. (1953): *Nature (Lond.)* **172** 1100
HALL, D. A., LLOYD, P. E., HAPPEY, F., HORTON, W. C. and NAYLOR, A. (1957): *Nature (Lond.)* **179** 1078
HALL, D. A., KEECH, M. K., REED, R., SAXL, H., TUNBRIDGE, R. E. and WOOD, M. J. (1955): *J. Geront.* **10** 388
HARKNESS, R. D., MARKÓ, A. M., MUIR, H. M. and NEUBERGER, H. (1954): *Biochem. J.* **56** 558
HARTLEY, B. S., NAUGHTON, M. A. and SANGER, F. (1959): *Biochim. biophys. Acta (Amst.)* **34** 243
HASS, G. M. (1939): *Arch. Path.* **27** 334, 583
HEIM, V. and CSEH, I. (1933): *Gyógyászat* **73** 44
HIGHBERGER, J. H., GROSS, J. and SCHMITT, F. O. (1950): *J. Amer. chem. Soc.* **72** 3321
— (1951): *Proc. nat. Acad. Sci. (Wash.)* **37** 286
HODGE, A. J. and SCHMITT, F. O. (1958): *Proc. nat. Acad. Sci. (Wash.)* **44** 418
— (1960): *Proc. nat. Acad. Sci. (Wash.)* **46** 186
HODGE, A. J., HIGHBERGER, J. H., DEFFNER, G. G. J. and SCHMITT, F. O. (1960): *Proc. nat. Acad. Sci. (Wash.)* **46** 197
HORBACZEWSKI, J. (1882): *Z. physiol. Chem.* **6** 330
HÖRMANN, H. (1960): *Leder* **11** 173
— (1962): *Leder* **13** 79
HÖRMANN, H. and FRIES, G. (1958): *Z. physiol. Chem.* **311** 19
HOUCK, J. C. and PATCH, Y. M. (1959): *Proc. Soc. exp. Biol. (N. Y.)* **102** 421
HUECK, W. (1920): *Münch. med. Wschr.* **67** 535, 573, 606
HUGGINS, M. L. (1943): *Chem. Rev.* **32** 195
HUZELLA, T. (1941): *Die zwischenzellige Organisation auf der Grundlage der Interzellulartheorie und der Interzellularpathologie.* G. Fischer, Jena

JACKSON, D. S. (1957): *Biochem. J.* **65** 277
JACKSON, D. S. and FESSLER, J. (1955): *Nature (Lond.)* **176** 69
JAKUS, M. A. (1954): *Amer. J. Ophthal.* **38** 40
JOBST, K. (1954): *Acta morph. Acad. Sci. hung.* **6** 333
JOSUÉ, E. (1903): *Presse méd.* **11** 798

KÄRKELÄ, A. and KULONEN, E. (1957): *Acta chem. scand.* **11** 1434
— (1959): *Acta chem. scand.* **13** 814
KATZ, J. R., DERKSEN, J. C. and BON, W. F. (1931): *Rec. Trav. Chim.* **50** 725, 1138
KAYAHAN, S. (1959): *Lancet* **1** 223
KEECH, M. K. (1960): *Gerontologia (Basel)* **4** 1
KIRK, J. E. and DYRBYE, M. (1957): *J. Geront.* **12** 23
KISS, J. and MAJLÁTH, J. (1962): *Z. Kreislaufforsch.* **51** 235
KLEMPERER, P., POLLÁK, A. D. and BAEHR, G. (1942): *J. Amer. med. Ass.* **119** 331
KOKAS, E., FÖLDES, I. and BANGA, I. (1951): *Acta physiol. Acad. Sci. hung.* **2** 333
KOLPAK, H. (1935): *Kolloid. Z.* **73** 129
KONNO, K. and ALTMANN, K. I. (1958): *Nature (Lond.)* **181** 995
KOSSEL, A. and KUTSCHER, F. (1898): *Z. physiol. Chem.* **25** 551
KOVÁCS, K. and BAGDY, D. (1958a): *Orv. Hetil.* **99** 774
— (1958b): *Acta med. Acad. Sci. hung.* **12** 167
— (1959): *Ther. hung.* **7** 43
KOVÁCS, S. (Mrs) and ROMHÁNYI, GY. (1962): *Morph. igazságü. orv. Szle* **2** 191
KRAEMER, D. M. and MILLER, H. (1953): *Arch. Path.* **55** 70
KROMPECHER, S. (1928): *Z. Anat. Entwickl.-Gesch.* **85** 704
— (1930): *Beitr. path. Anat.* **85** 647
— (1940): *Z. Anat. Entwickl.-Gesch.* **110** 423
— (1960): *Nova Acta Leopold.* **22** 146

KRYLOV, D. (1916): *C. R. Soc. Biol. (Paris)* **79** 397

KÜHN, K. (1960): *Leder* **11** 110

— (1962): *Leder* **13** 73, 86

KÜHN, K. and ZIMMER, E. (1961): *Naturwissenschaften* **48** 220

KÜHN, K., HANNIG, K. and HÖRMANN, H. (1961): *Leder* **12** 237

KUNITZ, M. and NORTHROP, J. H. (1936): *J. gen. Physiol.* **19** 991

LABELLA, F. S. (1957): *Nature (Lond.)* **180** 1360

— (1958): *J. Histochem. Cytochem.* **6** 260

— (1961): *Arch. Biochem.* **93** 72

— (1962): *J. Geront.* **17** 8

— (1963): *J. Geront.* **18** 111

LAMY. F. and TAUBER, S. (1962): *J. biol. Chem.* **238** 939

LAMY, F., CRAIG, C. P. and TAUBER, S. (1961): *J. biol. Chem.* **236** 86

LANSING, A. I. (1954): *J. Geront.* **9** 362

— (1955): *Ciba Found. Colloqu. Aging.* **1** 88

— (1959): In: *The Arterial Wall.* Ed: Lansing, A. I. Williams and Wilkins, Baltimore, p. 136, 153

LANSING, A. I., ALEX, M. and ROSENTHAL, T. B. (1950): *J. Geront.* **5** 112

LANSING, A. I., BLUMENTHAL, H. T. and GRAY, S. H. (1948): *J. Geront.* **3** 87

LANSING, A. I., ROSENTHAL, T. B. and ALEX, M. (1953): *Proc. Soc. exp. Biol. (N. Y.)* **84** 689

LANSING, A. I., ROSENTHAL, T. B., ALEX, M. and DEMPSEY, E. W. (1952): *Anat. Rec.* **114** 555

LANSING, A. I., ROBERTS, E., RAMASARMA, G. B., ROSENTHAL, T. B. and ALEX, M. (1951): *Proc. Soc. exp. Biol. (N. Y.)* **76** 714

LAPICIRELLA, R., FERRARI, C., MARRAMA, P. and MORINI, C. (1960a): *G. Geront.* **8** 879

LAPICIRELLA, R., MARRAMA, P., DI MARCO, C., ALBERINI, B. and FERRARI, C. (1960b): *G. Geront.* **8** 605

LELKES, GY. and KARMAZSIN, L. (1955): *Acta morph. Acad. Sci. hung.* **5** 149

LEWIS, U. J. and THIELE, E. (1957): *J. Amer. chem. Soc.* **79** 755

LEWIS, U. J., WILLIAMS, D. E. and BRINK, N. G. (1956): *J. biol. Chem.* **222** 705

— (1959): *J. biol. Chem.* **234** 2304

LINDNER, J. (1961): *Histochemie der Atherosklerose.* (Dr. G. Schlettler) G. Thieme Verl. Stuttgart

LOEB, J. (1922): *Proteins and the Theory of Colloidal Behavior.* McGraw—Hill, New York

LOEB, J. and KUNITZ, M. J. (1923): *Gen. Physiol.* **5** 693

LOEVEN, W. A. (1960a): *Acta physiol. pharmacol. neerl.* **9** 44

— (1960b): *Acta physiol. pharmacol. neerl.* **9** 473

— (1962a): *Acta physiol. pharmacol. neerl.* **10** 228

— (1962b): *Acta physiol. pharmacol. neerl.* **11** 350

— (1963a): *Acta physiol. pharmacol. neerl.* **12** 57

— (1963b): *Intern. Rev. Tiss. Res. Vol. 1.* Ed: Hall, D. A. Acad. Press, New York—London, p. 183

— (1964a): *Proceedings Nato-Conference on the Structure and Function of Connective and Skeletal Tissue,* at St. Andrews, Scotland, June 15—25

— (1964b): *Acta physiol. pharmacol. neerl.* **12** 497

— (1964c): *Biochim. biophys. Acta (Amst.)* in the press

— (1964d): *Acta physiol. pharmacol. neerl.* in the press

— (1964e): *Colloque portant sur l'enzymologie et l'immunologie (plus spécialement sur l'élastase et corps derivés) dans l'atherosclerose.* Organized by the Faculty of Medicine, Bordeaux, October 23—24

LOOMEIJER, F. J. (1958): *Nature (Lond.)* **182** 182

— (1961): *J. Atheroscler. Res.* **1** 62

LOW, F. N. (1961a): *Anat. Rec.* **139** 105

— (1961b): *Anat. Rec.* **139** 250

Low, F. N. (1962): *Anat. Rec.* **142** 131

Lowry, O. H., Gilligan, D. R. and Katersky, E. M. (1941): *J. biol. Chem.* **139** 795

Lowry, O. H., Rosebrough, N. J., Farr, A. L. and Randall, R. J. (1951): *J. biol. Chem.* **193** 265

Mall, F. P. (1888): *Anat. Anz.* **3** 397

— (1896): *Johns Hopk. Hosp. Rep.* **1** 171

Malmgren, H. and Sylven, B. (1952): *Biochim. biophys. Acta (Amst.)* **9** 708

Manahan, J. and Mandl, I. (1961): *Biochem. biophys. Res. Commun.* **4** 268

Mandl, I. (1958): *Abstr. 4th Intern. Congr. Biochem. Vienna* 2—35

— (1961): *Advanc. Enzym.* Ed: Nord, F. F. Interscience Publ. **23** 221

Mandl, I. and Cohen, B. B. (1959): *Abstr. 13th Meeting Amer. chem. Soc.* 38 C

— (1960a): *Fed. Proc.* **19** 331

— (1960b): *Arch. Biochem. Biophys.* **91** 47

Mandl, I., Zipper, H. and Ferguson, L. T. (1958): *Arch. Biochem.* **74** 465

Mayláth-Palágyi, J., Banga, I. and Kiss, J. (1965): *Acta physiol. Acad. Sci. hung.* **27** 179

Meyer, A. and Verzár, F. (1959): *Gerontologia (Basel)* **3** 184

Meyer, K. (1953): In: *Some Conjugated Proteins.* Ed: Cole, W. A. Rudgers Univ. Press, p. 64

Meyer, K. H. and Ferri, C. (1936): *Arch. Physiol.* **238** 78

Mihályi, E. and Harrington, W. F. (1959): *Biochim. biophys. Acta (Amst.)* **36** 447

Miller, H., Haft, A. and Kraemer, D. M. (1952): *Proc. Soc. exp. Biol. (N. Y.)* **79** 411

Moret, V. and Gotte, L. (1956): *Boll. Soc. ital. Biol. sper.* **32** 231

Moretti, J., Boussier, G., and Jayle, M. F. (1957): *Bull. Soc. Chim. biol. (Paris)* **39** 593

Nageotte, J. (1927): *C. R. Acad. Sci.* **184** 115

Nagy, L. and Medgyesi, Gy. (1962): *Orv. Hetil.* **103** 1451

Narayanan, E. I., Devi, P. and Menon, P. S. (1953): *Indian J. med. Res.* **41** 295

Nasbeth, D. C., Martin, D. E., Rowe, M. I., Gottlieb, L. S. and Peterling, R. A. (1963): *J. cardiovasc. Surg. (Torino)* **4** 11

Naughton, M. A. and Sanger, F. (1958): *Biochem. J.* **70** 4 P

— (1961): *Biochem. J.* **78** 156

Naughton, M. A., Sanger, F., Hartley, B. S. and Shaw, D. C. (1960): *Biochem. J.* **77** 149

Németh-Csóka, M. (1960): *Acta histochem. (Jena)* **8** 282

— (1961): *Acta histochem. (Jena)* **12** 255

— (1963): *Acta histochem. (Jena)* **16** 70

Neumann, R. E. (1949): *Arch. Biochem.* **24** 289

Neumann, R. E. and Tytell, H. A. (1950): *Proc. Soc. exp. Biol. (N. Y.)* **73** 409

Neumark, T. (1964): *Acta morph. Acad. Sci. hung.* **12** 367

Nordwig, A. (1962): *Leder* **13** 10

Ogle, J. D., Arlinghouse, R. B. and Logan, M. A. (1961): *Arch. Biochem.* **94** 85

Orekhovich, V. N. (1952): *Prokollagena.*

Orekhovich, V. N. and Shpikiter, J. (1957): *Dokl. Akad. Nauk. SSSR* **115** 137

— (1958): In: *Recent Advances in Gelatin and Glue Research.* Ed: Stainsby, G. Pergamon Press, New York, p. 87

Orekhovich, V. N. and Tustanovsky, A. A. (1948): *Biokhimiya* (Moscow) **13** 58

Orekhovich, V. N., Tustanovsky, A. A., Orekhovich, K. D. and Plotnikova, N. E. (1948): *Biokhimiya* (Moscow) **13** 55

Oneson, I. and Zacharias, J. (1960): *Arch. Biochem.* **89** 271

Pahlke, G. (1954): *Z. Zellforsch.* **39** 421

Park, J. T. and Johnson, M. J. (1949): *J. biol. Chem.* **181** 149

Partridge, S. M. (1948): *Biochem. J.* **43** 387

Partridge, S. M. and Davis, H. F. (1955): *Biochem. J.* **61** 21

214

PARTRIDGE, S. M., DAVIS, H. F. and ADAIR, G. S. (1955): *Biochem. J.* **61** 11
PARTRIDGE, S. M., ELSDEN, D. F. and THOMAS, J. (1963): *Nature (Lond.)* **197** 1297
PAULING, L. and COREY, R. B. (1951a): *Series of papers in: Proc. nat. Acad. Sci. (Wash.)* **37**
— (1951b): *Proc. nat. Acad. Sci. (Wash.)* **37** 236
— (1951c): *Proc. nat. Acad. Sci. (Wash.)* **37** 272
— (1954): *Fortschr. Chem. Org. Naturstoffe* **11** 180
PEASE, D. C. (1961): *74th Meeting of Amer. Ass. Anat. Abstr. Anat. Rec.* **139** 332
PEPLER, W. J. and BRANDT, F. H. (1954): *Brit. J. exp. Path.* **35** 41
PRETOLANI, E. (1960a): *Bull. Soc. ital. Biol. sper.* **36** 571, 573
— (1960b): *G. Geront.* **8** 622

RAFFAY, I. and RICHTER, A. (1962): *Rheum. Balneol. Allerg. (Budap.)* **3** 53
RAMACHANDRAN, G. N. (1956): *Nature (Lond.)* **177** 710
— (1963): *Int. Rev. Conn. Tiss. Res. Vol. 1.* Acad. Press, New York—London, p. 127
RAMACHANDRAN, G. N. and KARTHA, G. (1954): *Nature (Lond.)* **174** 269
— (1955): *Nature (Lond.)* **176** 593
RAMACHANDRAN, G. N. and SANTHANAM, M. S. (1957): *Proc. Ind. Acad. Sci.* **45** 124
RAMACHANDRAN, G. N. and SASISEKHARAN, V. (1961): *Nature (Lond.)* **190** 1004
RAMACHANDRAN, L. K. (1962): *Biochem. biophys. Res. Commun.* **6** 443
RANDALL, J. T., FRASER, R. D. B. and NORTH, A. C. T. (1953): *Proc. roy. Soc. B* **141** 62
RANKE, O. (1925): *Beitr. path. Anat.* **73** 638
REDENZ, E. (1927): *Zieglers Beitr.* **76** 226
REUTERWALL, O. P. (1921): *Über die Elastizität der Gefässwände und die Methoden ihrer näheren Prüfung.* Stockholm
RICH, A. and CRICK, F. H. C. (1955): *Nature (Lond.)* **176** 915
— (1958): In: *Recent Advances in Gelatin and Glue Research.* Ed: Stainsby, G. Pergamon Press, New York, p. 20
— (1961): *J. molec. Biol.* **3** 483
RICHARDS, A. N. and GIES, W. J. (1902): *Amer. J. Physiol.* **7** 93
RICHTER, A. (1959): *Thesis,* Budapest
RIMINGTON, C. (1940): *Biochem. J.* **34** 931
RITTER, H. B. and OLESON, I. J. (1950): *Amer. J. Pathol.* **26** 639
ROBERT, L. and SAMUEL, P. (1957a): *Experientia (Basel)* **13** 167
— (1957b): *Ann. Biol. clin.* **15** 453
ROMHÁNYI, GY. (1955): *Acta morph. Acad. Sci. hung.* **5** 311
— (1958): *Nature (Lond.)* **182** 929
— (1959): *Acta histochem. (Jena)* **8** 340
— (1962): *Morph. igazságü. orv. Szle* **2** 161
ROY, C. S. (1880): *J. Physiol. (Lond.)* **3** 125
RYTER, A. and KELLENBERGER, E. (1958): *J. Ultrastruct. Res.* **2** 200

SACHAR, L., WINTER, K. K., SICHER, N. and FRANKEL, S. (1955): *Proc. Soc. exp. Biol. (N. Y.)* **90** 323
SAKAKIBARA, S., AKABORI, S., NAGAI, Y. and NODA, H. (1960): *Koso Kagaku Shipozium* **14** 267
SALVINI, L. (1960): *G. Geront.* **8** 551
SALVINI, L., GRANDONICO, F., VIOLA, S., CITI, S. and LEONE, O. (1960): *Gerontologia (Basel)* **8** 635
SAXL, H. (1957a): *Proc. 4th Congr. Intern. Ass. Gerontol. Merano* **2** 67
— (1957b): *Gerontologia (Basel)* **1** 142
— (1961): *J. roy. micr. Soc.* **79** 319
SCARCELLI, V. (1958): *Ital. J. Biochem.* **7** 19
— (1961): *Nature (Lond.)* **191** 710
SCARCELLI, V. and REPETTO, M. (1959): *Ital. J. Biochem.* **8** 169
SCHMITT, F. O., GROSS, J. and HIGHBERGER, J. H. (1953): *Proc. nat. Acad. Sci. (Wash.)* **39** 459

SCHMITT, F. O., GROSS, J. and HIGHBERGER, J. H. (1955): *Symp. Soc. exp. Biol.* **9** 148

SCHMITT, F. O., HALL, C. E. and JAKUS, M. A. (1942): *J. cell. comp. Physiol.* **20** 11

SCHNEIDER, F. (1949): *Angew. Chem.* **61** 259

— (1960): *Collegium* **97**

SCHNEIDER, I. J., WALFORD, R. I. and DIGNAM, W. J. (1960): *J. appl. Physiol.* **15** 992

SCHROHENLOHER, R. E., OGLE, J. D. and LOGAN, M. A. (1959): *J. biol. Chem.* **234** 58

SCHULDTZ-HAUDT, S. D. and EEG-LARSEN, N. (1961): *Biochim. biophys. Acta* **51** 560

SCHWALBE, G. (1877): *Z. Anat. Entwickl.-Gesch.* **2** 236

SCHWARZ, W. and DETTMER, N. (1953): *Virchows Arch. path. Anat.* **323** 243

SINEX, F. M. and FARIS, B. (1962): *Fed. Proc.* **21** 408

SMITHIES, D. (1955): *Biochem. J.* **61** 629

SOLS, A. (1947): *Nature (Lond.)* **160** 89

SØRENSEN, M. and HAUGAARD, G. (1933): *Biochem. Z.* **260** 247

SPERRY, W. M. (1955): *Meth. biochem. Anal.* **2** 83

STEIN, W. A. and MILLER, E. G. (1938): *J. biol. Chem.* **125** 599

STRAUMFJORD, J. V. and HUMMEL, J. P. (1957): *Proc. Soc. exp. Biol. (N. Y.)* **95** 141

SYLVEN, B. (1951): *Acta orthop. scand.* **20** 275

SYLVEN, B., PAULSON, S., HIRSCH, C. and SNELLMAN, O. (1951): *J. Bone Jt Surg.* **33** 333

SZABÓ, D. and BANGA, I. (1954): *Acta morph. Acad. Sci. hung. Suppl.* **4** 3

SZABÓ, I. K. and CSEH, G. (1962): *Naturwissenschaften* **49** 260

SZENT-GYÖRGYI, A. (1957): *Bioenergetics.* Acad. Press Inc., New York

TENNENT, D. M., ZANETTI, M. E., OTT, W. H., KURON, G. W. and SIEGEL, H. (1956): *Science* **124** 588

THOMAS, J. and PARTRIDGE, S. M. (1960): *Biochem. J.* **74** 600

THOMAS, J., ELSDEN, D. F. and PARTRIDGE, S. M. (1963): *Nature (Lond.)* **200** 651

TILAMUS, (1844): Cit: Mulder. *Vers. allg. Physiol. Chem.* **2** 595

TOLNAY, P. and BAGDY, D. (1959): *Biochim. biophys. Acta* **31** 566

— (1962): *Acta physiol. Acad. Sci. hung.* **21** 119

TOLNAY, P., SÓLYOM, A. and BORSY, J. (1962): *Naturwissenschaften* **49** 259

TÖRŐ, I. (1939): *Arch. exp. Zellforsch.* **22** 304

TRACY, R. E., MERCHANT, E. B. and KAO, V. C. (1961): *Circulat. Res.* **9** 472

TROITZKAJA-ANDREEWA, A. M. (1931): *Frankfurt. Z. Path.* **41** 120

TUSTANOVSKY, A. A. (1947): *Biokhimiya* (Moscow) **12** 285

TUSTANOVSKY, A. A., ZAIDES, A. L., BANGA, I. and ORLOVSKAJA, K. V. (1960): *Gerontologia (Basel)* **4** 198

TUSTANOVSKY, A. A., ZAIDES, A. L., ORLOVSKAJA, G. V. and MIHAJLOV, H. N. (1954): *Dokl. Akad. Nauk SSSR* **97** 191

USUKU, G. (1958): *Kumamoto med. J.* **11** 84

— (1959): *Kumamoto med. J.* **12** 12

VERES, J. (1961): *Kísérl. Orvostud.* **14** 73

VERES, J. and MAYLÁTH-PALÁGYI, J. (1964): *Kísérl. Orvostud.* **16** 52

VERZÁR, F. (1955a): *Experientia (Basel)* **11** 230

— (1955b): *Helv. physiol. pharmacol. Acta* **13** 64

— (1956): *Helv. physiol. pharmacol. Acta* **14** 207

VERZÁR, F. and HUBER, R. (1958): *Gerontologia (Basel)* **2** 81

WALFORD, R. I. and KICKHÖFEN, B. (1962): *Arch. Biochem. Biophys.* **98** 191

WALFORD, R. I. and SCHNEIDER, R. B. (1959): *Proc. Soc. exp. Biol. (N. Y.)* **101** 31

WALFORD, R. I., MOYER, D. L. and SCHNEIDER, R. B. (1961): *Arch. Path.* **72** 158

WINTER, K. K. and FRANKEL, S. (1956): *Fed. Proc.* **15** 539

WÖHLISCH, E. (1931): *Z. Biol.* **91** 137

WÖHLISCH, E. and ROCHEMONT, R. (1927): *Zieglers Beitr.* **76** 233
WÖHLISCH, R., WEITNAUER, H., GRÜNING, W. and ROHRBACH, R. (1943): *Kolloid Z.* **104** 14
WOLPERS, C. (1943): *Klin. Wschr.* **22** 624
— (1944): *Klin. Wschr.* **23** 169
WOOD, G. C. (1954): *Biochim. biophys. Acta (Amst.)* **15** 311
— (1958): *Biochem. J.* **69** 538
WU, F. C. and LASKOWSKI, M. (1960): *J. biol. Chem.* **235** 1680
WYCKOFF, R. W. G. and COREY, R. B. (1936): *Proc. Soc. exp. Biol. (N. Y.)* **34** 285

YOKOTA, H. (1957): *Kumamoto med. J.* **10** 25

ZACCHARIADES, P. A. (1900): *C. R. Soc. Biol. (Paris)* **52** 112, 182, 251, 1127
ZAHN, H. (1948): *Kolloid Z.* **111** 96
ZAIDES, A. L. (1956): *Biofizika* (MOSCOW) **1** 279
ZEMPLÉNYI, T. and GRAFNETTER, D. (1958): *Brit. J. exp. Path.* **39** 99
ZEMPLÉNYI, T., LOYDA, Z. and GRAFNETTER, D. (1959): *Circul. Res.* **7** 286
ZIFFREN, S. E. and HOSIE ,R. T. (1955): *Proc. Soc. exp. Biol. (N. Y.)* **90** 650

Subject Index

A

Accessory substance 189
Achilles tendon 45, 61, 178, 179, 200
Adenosine triphosphate (ATP) 111, 116
Adrenalin
  administration of 88
  sclerogenic effect of 88
Age factor 25, 26
  function of 24, 26
Albuminoid 95
Alloxan 31
Amino acid 7, 8, 21, 106
ε-amino group 143, 160
Amino-sugar 98
Aneurysm 83
Aniline-hydrogen-phtalate 184
Aniline reaction 11, 12, 71, 77, 78
Anisotropic staining 71, 73, 74, 75, 79
Anomalous colour 71
Anticlockwise bond 110
Antiparallel arrangement 116
Antiphlogistic effect 84
Antirheumatic drug 84
Aorta 3, 15, 19, 20, 21, 24, 42, 43, 44, 63 ff
  mucolipoprotein complex of 63, 64, 65, 66
Anthron-positive substance 63
Arteriosclerosis 82, 86, 88, 89, 92, 94, 95, 97
  index 85, 87
Aspartic acid 51, 94
Atelectasis 84
Atheroslerosis 82, 83, 86, 88, 98, 99, 100
Atropine 84
Attractive force 164
Auto-oxidated lipid 49

B

Backbone 109
BANA (N-bezoyl-DL-arginine-β-naphytyl-
  amide) 197, 200, 201, 206
Barrier system 189
Beaded fibril 15
Bifunctional enzyme 53

Bifunctional linkage 164
Birefringence 154
  formal 125, 141
  intrinsic 125
  molecular 151
  negative 75, 77, 171, 191
  positive 144, 145, 148, 149, 171, 191
  reduced 148
Borohydride 160
Branching fibres 158
Bridase 189
Bronchial asthma 85
Bronchiectasis 84
Bronchitis 84
Bronchopulmonary suppuration 85

C

Ca-atom
  role of 52
Calcification 88
Carbohydrate 160, 161, 162
Carboxypeptidase 160
Carragenin 120
Cartilage 5
Cationic chrome sulphate 140
  assumption of 140
Cementing substance 14, 23, 53, 73, 78
Central axis 109
  halo 16, 17
Cerebroside 63
Clockwise bond 110
Cholesterol 68, 83, 85
Chondroitin 97
Chondroitinase 32
Chondroitin sulphate 97, 98, 116, 182
  B 185
  C 184
Chrome chloride
  assumption of 140
Chylomicron 66
Chymotrypsin 30, 36, 38, 52, 196

219

Elastomucoproteinase (EMPase)
  thermolabile 40
  thermostable 40
Elastproteinase (E$_2$) 28, 39, 60, 61, 80, 81
Electron micrograph 158
Electrophoresis 37 ff
Electrostatical attractive force 118
Electrostatic charge 114
Electrostatical force 116
Electrostatical linkage 129, 130
Em-I Mucase of Loeven 80
Em-S Mucase of Loeven 80
End-to-end linkage 118
Envelope substance 152
Essential haemosiderosis 56
Essential lipaemia 86
Ester bond 161, 199, 203
Ester-like bond 160
Equatorial layer lines 16, 17
Extension 24, 26, 136
  excess 136, 137, 138
Euglobulin 34

F

Fatty acid
  non-esterified 100
Fatty liver 82, 83
Fibrillar disintegration 148
  internal structure 191
Fibril-long spacing (FLS) 111, 116
Fibrin 99, 171, 173
Fibrinogen 99
Fibroblast 3, 120
  activity 158
Filamenter structure 151
Flavobacterium 32
Fluorescent substance 49 ff
Folin-phenol reagent 182
Formaldehyde
  effect of 175
Fuchsin
  acid 186

G

Galactosamine 98
Galactose 160
Gamma-glutamyl peptide 161
Ganglia 171
Gelatin 168
Gelation-forming capacity 168

Globular protein 146
Globulin
  alpha$_1$ 57, 68
  alpha$_2$ 57
  beta 100
Glucagon 83
Glucosamine 98
Glucose 160
Glutamic acid 94
Gly-Asp-Ser-Gly sequence 52, 57
Glycoprotein 85, 97, 111, 160
Glycosidic bond 164, 181
N-glycosidic bond 162
O-glycosidic bond 162, 164
Glycopeptide
  alpha 118
Goitre 171
Granule 45

H

Haemorrhage 84
Heat-denaturation 121
Helical structure 108, 125, 173
Helix
  alpha 108
  triple 109, 112, 113
Heparin 66, 69, 111, 185
Heparin-sulphate 187
Heparitin-sulphate 185
Heteropolysaccharide 121, 187
  neutral 99, 182
Hexosamine 61, 98, 157, 167, 168, 179, 183,
  184, 185, 200
Hexuronic acid 167, 168, 179, 184, 185, 188
Histamine
  effect of 84, 131
Histidine 165
Hofmeister row 142
Hyaluronic acid 97, 182
Hyaluronidase 175, 177, 184, 185, 191
Hyase see Hyaluronidase
Hyase-like effect 175
Hydration capacity 130
Hydrogen bond 112, 139, 146, 149, 161
  interchain 109, 110
Hydrogen bridge 113, 191
Hydroxamic acid 161
Hydroxyproline 91, 94
  test 91
Hypercholesterolaemia 86, 88 ,100
Hypertension 88

222

Negative dichroism 131
Negative optical rotation 110
Network formation 163
Network-forming valence bond 165
Neuramic (neuraminic) acid 97, 168, 188
Neutral carbohydrate 162 ff
Neutral sugar 162, 164
Neutral swelling 126, 145

O

Objective table, heatable 147
Oedema formation 163
Oilred staining 66
Oligosaccharide 160
Orcein-elastin 55, 70, 80, 91
Orcein-stained aorta 91
Osazone 162
Ovomucoid 200
Oxidizing agent 135

P

Pancreas
  acinar tissue 31
  alpha cell 31
  glandular tissue 83
  islet tissue 31
  hypertrophy 83
  hyperplasia 83
  secrete 189
  secretion 31
Paper chromatography 32, 184
  electrophoresis 66, 68
PAS-reaction 63
PAS-positive mucopolysaccharide 40
Peracetic acid 15
Periodical arrangement 149
Permanent swelling 142
Peptide tail 200
Peptization 139, 147
Peptization effect 130, 141, 142, 144
Perpendicular position 123
Pepsin 30
Phenergan 84
Phenolelastoid 75, 76, 77
Phenol reaction 72, 144, 145, 151, 155, 156, 191
Phenylhydrazine 162
Picrofuchsin reaction 46
Pilocarpine 31

Placentar fibrinoid 171
Plaster of Paris 123
Pneumometer 85
Polar side group 16
Polarization-microscopic technique 71
Polyglycine 17
Polyproline 17
Polysaccharide 14, 60, 63, 71, 77, 92, 116, 158, 162, 187
Polyuronide 182, 187
Porocollagen 131
Post-heparin serum 69
Potassium permanganate 135
Precollagen 120
Procollagen 119, 120, 121, 126, 130, 132, 151, 152, 153, 157, 160, 161, 163, 165, 171, 177, 189, 191
Procollagen-free fibre 122, 126, 127, 128, 129, 130, 131, 151
Proelastase 35, 36
Proelastin 60
Proenzyme 34, 35
Protease 33, 38
  B 33
Pseudo-globulin 57
Pseudo-halide 142
Pseudomonas 32
Ps. pyocyanea 32
Puckered chain 108
Pulmonary oedema 84
Pulsating heart culture 3, 4

R

Radioactive isotop
  administration of 82, 83
Reactive serine 52
Reducing agents 135
  effect of 134
Reflection 16, 17
  equatorial 110
  meridional 110
Refraction index 125
Relaxation capacitiy 135
  chemical 128, 130
  kinetic of 143
Resorcin fuchsin staining 155
Reticular fibres 165
Ribonuclease 151
Ribonucleic acid (RNA) 111
Rheumatic zone 171
Restitution 193

Responsible for publication Gy. Bernát,
Director of the Publishing House of the
Hungarian Academy of Sciences and of the Academy Press
Responsible editor Julia North · Technical editor I. Csörgő
Jacket designed by J. Erdélyi
Set in Monotype New Times 10 on 11 pt
Printed in Hungary at the Academy Press